Mathematical Foundations for Social Analysis

MATHEMATICAL FOUNDATIONS

for SOCIAL ANALYSIS

ROBERT McGINNIS
Cornell University

THE BOBBS-MERRILL COMPANY, INC.
A Subsidiary of Howard W. Sams & Co., Inc.
Publishers INDIANAPOLIS · NEW YORK · KANSAS CITY

Preface

In reflecting on this book in its present form, I must confess that I am rather startled. As originally conceived, the book was to have been an introduction, a few chapters at most, to a work in probability theory and statistical inference for social scientists. It was to have comprised a brief, gentle, superficial survey of a few facets of contemporary mathematics. Virtually all that remains of this initial conception is the book's superficiality. Indeed, any attempt to describe within a few hundred pages today's currents in the tides of mathematical thought must remain superficial.

As it now stands, this book is intended to provide an introductory discussion of topics that are already ubiquitous in some branches of social science: sets, relations, real numbers, matrices, and convergence. At least as important as topical coverage is the attempt to impart an understanding of mathematical reasoning. I believe that this form of argument is a natural and necessary part of the scientific process with which social scientists should be intimately acquainted. It is for this reason that proofs of assertions are emphasized throughout this book. The serious reader should consider the deductive evidence offered in proof of a statement as carefully as he should the substance of the statement.

This book was written for the social scientist who finds himself frustrated by his inability to understand the growing segment of his professional literature that is written in the language of mathematics. It is also directed to the social scientist who is thwarted by his incompetence to work creatively—whether in the construction of theory or the design of research—in areas where his natural folk language is insufficient to the complex demands of the problem. This book alone, no matter how thoroughly mastered, is sufficient neither in scope nor in depth to eliminate these deficiencies. At best it provides a necessary first step toward an adequate grasp of mathematics as it is being used and as it can be used as a tool of social science.

v

If I were to be thorough about it, a complete list of acknowledgments to those who had a part in the shaping of this book would provide a companion volume of some length. However, there are some to whom I am so deeply indebted that I must pause here to offer them my thanks. R. D. Luce and Patrick Suppes read earlier versions of the manuscript with the unblinking eyes of true critics. Had it not been for their invaluable critical suggestions, a far less adequate version of the book might have appeared several years ago. Others, especially E. R. Borgatta, N. B. Ryder, M. Jones, L. F. Schnore, and G. C. Myers, have been extremely helpful in their discussions of the manuscript. To the elite corps of secretaries who struggled so patiently to transform my squiggles into a legible manuscript, Carol Mills, Leslie Armentrout, Linda Jones, Catharine Shull, and especially to The Greatest Secretary on Earth, Mrs. Alice Thompson, my deep appreciation. To the staff members of The Bobbs-Merrill Company who have been so consistently encouraging and to my friend William Hackett, Director of the College Division, I am indebted and grateful.

I wish to acknowledge the generous assistance of the Social Science Research Council in providing funds for the post-doctoral training in mathematics without which I should never have written this book. I am equally indebted to Robert F. Winch, Alvin Fend, Robert R. Bush, and Patrick Suppes for making mathematics such an exciting topic of study for a social scientist.

Finally, I should like to express my appreciation to Messrs. Kevin and Brian McGinnis, who patiently gave up more than one outing because of this book.

Needless to say, none of the above is responsible for any of the egregious errors that must inevitably creep into the book.

ROBERT McGINNIS

Ithaca, New York
August 1964

This book is dedicated to my dear friend,
Dorothy McGinnis,
my mother.

Foreword

In this volume the author emphasizes ". . . that the language of science must be universal, unmistakably clear, and concise." One can hardly argue with this point, but it is equally appropriate to remind those who strive for this objective that some scientific adventures occur in unscientific situations. Students are often encouraged to place emphasis on creativity, and this may in practice run counter to the need for precision. Possibly, there also is too much emphasis on language in a literary sense. Social scientists are often urged to make their articles more interesting to the reader, and even to find different ways to say things. In moving to the language of mathematics, *precision* is required, and this also implies parsimony. In mathematics, one is not rewarded for being able to express something by many different symbols, but by reducing the elements of a single language to the minimum necessary for expressing the idea. Some day, hopefully, editors of social-science journals will stop returning articles to authors with such comments as: "You ought to be more speculative." "Can't you make this more interesting?" Or: "This is as dry as a mathematical presentation."

The element of mathematics on which McGinnis focuses must be emphasized over and over again. There is nothing mystical about mathematics. It does, however, place a demand—even a responsibility—on the *reader* to be precise. The reader cannot absorb the language by casual familiarity and scanning. Note, for example, the threat to the nonmathematically trained that might be involved in passing over casually the initial definitions that occur on pages 4 and 5. "For the present, it is sufficient to think of a variable as a symbol for any element of any set of things among which some elements can be distinguished from others with respect to a stipulated property." How many students find it convenient to read this sentence and say: "Gobbledygook." And how many social scientists would encourage them to act this way? The statement is a clear and lucid one, but it requires slow reading and digestion. This requirement is one of the characteristics of mathematics—and of science implicitly. Without the careful reading, the cumulative task is made difficult, if not impossible.

The place of a book on mathematical foundations for social analysis is clear. The social sciences are evolving always in the direction of rigor. In the transitional period in which we operate, studying mathematics may not always be direct, but there is no question that, as time passes, a mathematical basis of training for social scientists will become as relevant as it is in the physical sciences. At the present stage there is certainly room for different types of training in the social sciences, but progressively it appears vital that more and more students should have mathematical training. Hopefully, one of the changes we may expect in the future is that mathematics will be introduced into the curriculum for social scientists early in training. Essentially, the mathematics that is learned by social scientists in crash programs after they have completed their Ph.D.'s is the same mathematics that a math major may have had in his sophomore year as an undergraduate. This volume by McGinnis could be used as easily and appropriately in an undergraduate curriculum today as in a graduate curriculum. It is clearly at a reasonable level for an undergraduate curriculum. When this volume is used as a graduate basis for instruction, graduate students should be encouraged to do at least as much work as would be expected of undergraduates. Graduate students will need to assume the humility implicit in careful reading, memorization, and acceptance of the fact that one cannot be a creative person without understanding the fundamentals.

The field of mathematics is an enormous one. It would be deceptive to any student to let him think that he is going to study the whole of the field. Mathematics has many specialties, and each has developed in great detail. It would be highly misleading to suggest that a book can be devised that is completely cumulative, that can be read from beginning to end going from simplicity to complexity. Yet, McGinnis appears to have molded some of this feeling of cumulative growth in his volume. The book is introduced by elementary considerations, essentially dealing with the primitive notions and definitional bases. From here, the language is developed; it proceeds to become a more complex language; and then it is placed in use. Finally, the topics of the calculus are introduced. This is a volume that can be *read*, because its order is appropriate. For the undergraduate student who is accustomed to assignments and expected to retain prior materials for subsequent use, the book should actually be easy.

It is clear, it is unencumbered, and it profits greatly from being written by a person who is a social scientist rather than a mathematician in initial training.

It is not appropriate to argue that every social scientist must have a commitment to mathematics in the future. It is appropriate to expect that every social scientist should be a scientist, however, and this does imply some commitment to knowledge about logic and the scientific method. Mathematics is closely related to these, and this book well demonstrates how such an introduction should serve to improve the language of the social scientist. It is conceivable that mathematical models are of only limited application in social science, but it can only turn out that mathematics as an introduction to language in science is useful.

Edgar F. Borgatta

Madison, Wisconsin
October 1964

Contents

Mathematical Foundations for Social Analysis

VARIABLES
AND
RELATIONS

I

The Language of Mathematics

The language of social science is today undergoing rapid and profound alterations. The essays that once characterized much of its literary output, although far from being relegated to the trash heap, are less in evidence today. In their place is writing that is methodologically meticulous, elaborately technical, sprinkled with mathematical formulas, and, in the eyes of some critics, plain and precise rather than elegantly literary.

This change represents a growing recognition among social scientists that the language of science must be universal, unmistakably clear, and concise. The language of science must indeed be all these things, yet it must still be rich enough in its vocabulary and grammar to permit the expression of ideas so complicated and abstract as to have been literally unthinkable a few years ago. For these reasons, one language more than any other is becoming the mother tongue of science. This is the language of mathematics.

The reader may find it odd to think of mathematics as a language rather than as, for instance, a scientific discipline. Certainly, mathematics can be seen from a variety of perspectives. It represents quite different things to different people, even to mathematicians of varying persuasions. A premise of this book is that, among the several views that can be taken of mathematics, one is paramountly useful in social science. In this view, mathematics is a branch of philosophy whose subject matter is a set of abstract entities, such as sets of elements and numbers; a vocabulary of symbols by which to label the objects; and, above all, a set of grammatical rules for using the vocabulary. The job of the mathematician is to use the vocabulary and grammatical rules to investigate the properties of the abstract entities.

It is the abstract nature of the mathematician's entities that makes mathematics potentially a quite powerful tool for social analysis. The subject matter of social science too is a set of abstract entities, such as the anthropologist's cultural complex or the economist's perfectly competitive market. To the extent that abstractions such as these can be identified with those of mathematics, much of the rich,

1

systematic body of knowledge that is mathematics can be exploited to the benefit of social science.

A major task of science is that of constructing general statements about some aspect of our world. These statements are declarative sentences. A collection of such sentences, when put together in a certain way, is called a theory. Once theoretical systems have been constructed, it remains to be determined whether they are true—that is, whether they adequately characterize certain states of nature. The determination requires empirical research, examining relevant facts systematically and evaluating those facts. This determination is the second major task of science, and it must be accomplished in accordance with an elaborate set of rules. As scientific theory becomes more complicated and abstract, and as the rules of verification become more rigid and complex, the language of mathematics becomes more clearly useful to the scientist.

None of the preceding statements, nor any of those to come, should be taken to mean that mathematics represents *the* salvation of social science. Certainly, there are many critical and vexing problems in social science to which mathematical applications would probably contribute nothing. Still, mathematics can be applied fruitfully to many areas in economics, psychology, sociology, and similar disciplines. It is the purpose of this book to introduce the reader to some of the more rudimentary aspects of mathematics as it is used in social science, in both the construction and the verification of theory.

1.1 Mathematics and Theory Construction

Fortunately, the interplay of mathematics and scientific theory can be discussed in essentially nonmathematical terms. Even the reader who has had only a brief introduction to one of the disciplines of social science should recognize that the theory of such fields is made up largely of two component parts, variables and relations. For the present, it is sufficient to think of a variable as a symbol for any element of any set of things among which some elements can be distinguished from others with respect to a stipulated property. In this sense, a variable represents an unspecified subset of a set. For instance, the symbol x may be used to represent any of the set of all real numbers on the numbers greater than six. For our present purposes, however, it is useful to think of a variable as the set represented by a symbol. In this sense, a variable is a set of entities among which some can be distinguished from others. A relationship is any rule by means of which subsets of one set are linked to subsets of another. Thus, the saying "the rich get richer, and the poor get children" is an informal assertion of a particular relation between the set of incomes and the set of reproductive patterns. Sets and relations will be considered in detail in later chapters.

If scientific knowledge is to be broadly encompassing, it must be concerned with large classes of phenomena rather than with more or less unique events. Accordingly, rather than being concerned, for example, with a particular person's reaction to being struck by a brick, a scientist must be concerned with broader classifications of phenomena, such as classes of stimuli and classes of pain reactions. The classification process is essential to the scientific process. It will be seen in Chapter 2 that a major effort of mathematicians has been devoted to the logic of classifications and their construction.

Once a scientist has constructed sets of abstract classifications, it remains for him to make assertions about the way in which they are related to one another. Now, the possible connection that might obtain between the scientific theorist's concern with relations among phenomena and the subject matter of mathematics may not be at all clear. As we shall see, however, any word that connotes a particular relationship between variables is indeed properly a mathematical term. In Chapter 3 and in later chapters, the idea of relations as studied by the mathematician is discussed in detail.

It is true that mathematics is an appropriate language for the theorist, but it is by no means the only one at his command. One may ask what makes the particular vocabulary of mathematics preferable to others. The paramount considerations—extreme economy and clarity—have been mentioned already. These two properties give us yet a third. Mathematically phrased theories sometimes permit one to recognize by means of logical deduction subtle consequences of an assertion that otherwise might be buried under layers of verbiage. The process of deducing consequences of an assertion or of a related set of assertions is familiar to most of us. Less familiar to many is the formalization of this process under the label of *axiomatic method*. Because this reasoning process is critically important to the construction of scientific theory, we shall take time to consider it before going on to examine the role of mathematics in the verification of theory.

1.2 The Axiomatic Method

Simply stated, the axiomatic method is the construction of a set of assertions and the deduction of a set of consequences from these assertions. In later chapters we shall encounter many applications of the process and learn something of its intricacies. For the present, a brief description of this logical process and a discussion of the way in which it is used by scientists is in order.

An *axiom* (synonymously called a *postulate*) is nothing more than a sentence, a declarative statement about sets of elements and relations among such sets. Usually, an axiom contains one or more words that we call *primitive notions*, ideas or concepts that remain undefined, such as the concepts of point or line in geometry. A system of axioms is a set of such statements about a common group of undefined terms. Reliance upon undefined terms may not appeal to a reader, but he should recognize that such reliance is necessary.

Historically, axioms were thought to be self-evident truths. For example, Euclid, in his monumental *Elements*, established a series of statements about such notions as point, line, and betweenness. He postulated, among other things, that a straight line can be drawn between any two points. In this view, the value of any system of axioms rested on the directness with which the system corresponded to current views of the real world. Today, the "self-evident" property of axioms is not held to be necessary. In fact, in mathematics, axioms need have no connection whatever with the real world; any attempt to establish such a connection is irrelevant. The only necessity in mathematics is that of determining that an axiom system has a certain property, to be described below. Then the consequences of the system may be deduced. Obviously, human beings are related to the world about them; therefore, one rather naturally takes a stronger interest in statements that can be seen to have some connection with this world. The establishment of such a connection, however, is not the job of the mathematician; it is, rather, a task for the scientist.

The question of empirical validity aside, an adequate axiom system must be *consistent*; two contradictory consequences cannot be implied by the same system. A second important condition is that the axioms be *independent*, which means that no one axiom in a given system should be derivable from others in the same system. A more detailed discussion of axiom systems, such as can be found in works listed in the Bibliography, would include certain other desirable properties. Consistency is the only necessary condition, however.

Once a satisfactory axiom system has been established, one might well ask, what good is such a set of statements? The answer, of course, is that the statements lead by the route of logical deduction to a series of consequent statements about the notions that make up the axioms. These consequent statements are usually called *theorems*. If a second statement follows directly from a theorem, it is called a *corollary*. Relatively trivial consequences of the axioms that are used mainly in the proof of theorems are sometimes called *lemmas*. Again, the correctness of a statement depends in no way on any correspondence it may have to the real world. A theorem is correct only if it follows from the axioms by appropriate steps of logic.

1.3 Mathematical Models

Once an axiom system has been constructed and a set of theorems has been derived from it, the scientist is in a position to use this system as a *model* of some facet of the world. The model is used to facilitate explanation, prediction, and, in some cases, control of the phenomena under investigation. It is important to understand how mathematical models are used for these purposes.

It must be clear that the view of models taken here is not necessarily that of all logicians. It is the one that seems most compatible with the purposes of this book. (See Suppes, *Introduction to Logic* [6], pages 253–254 and Suppes, "A Comparison" [7]* for a discussion of the term *model* as it is used in mathematics and in the physical and social sciences.) In this book the term refers to a collection of mathematically formulated axioms that express propositions about a phenomenon under consideration. Generally, the axioms of a model cannot be tested by direct observation. But the application of deductive reasoning to the model should yield theorems that can be so tested. A model, then, as the term is used here, is a mathematical representation of some aspect of nature.

The construction of theories, whether such theories take the form of mathematical models or less explicitly mathematical statements, is only one responsibility of the scientist. A responsibility of equal importance is that of assessment, of evaluation of the correctness of a particular theory. Both these responsibilities are anchored in the world as we know it. Model-building requires that sensate impressions be abstracted and identified with mathematical entities. Verification requires that other observational data be used to assess the consequences of the model. This twofold aspect of science was summarized by Coombs, Raiffa, and Thrall, ("Some Views" [3]). Their representation, slightly modified, is presented below as Figure 1.1.

* Complete references to works cited within each chapter may be found in the list of "Selected References" at the end of the chapter. Bracketed numbers indicate the order of each reference in the list.

As the sense of this diagram shows, the scientist's goal is that of making reasonable conclusions about some aspect of the real world. Two paths, that of experimentation or controlled observation and that of logical argumentation, are followed from initial observations to physical conclusions. The first path carries the investigator along the classical route of research. The objects under investigation are abstracted into an experimental design. A researcher selects from the endless mass of available facts a smaller collection of facts that seem pertinent to his problem. This collection is ordered in an experimental design, an arrangement that

Figure 1.1   TWO PATHS FROM OBSERVATION TO CONCLUSION

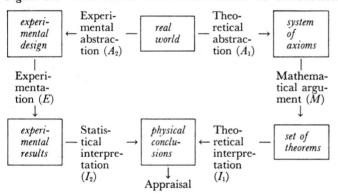

conduces to a more efficient analysis. The data are then manipulated, either by physical experimentation or by statistical means. Finally, conclusions are reached on the basis of statistical analysis of the data, which follows experimentation. This path, $A_2 - E - I_2$ in the diagram, is the classical pattern of empirical investigation. To some, it is the sum and substance of science. But, in itself, this path represents investigation without theory. At worst, it leads to the practice of "shotgunning," of investigating relationships at random, looking at more and more specific phenomena with little or no attempt at generalization. But science is considerably more than experimentation. A second path, that of theory construction, must be followed also.

The step A_1, theoretical abstraction, consists of establishing a chain of identification among properties of the objects under consideration and the axiomatic basis of the mathematical system. For instance, if one were considering some activity of a human group, the group might be identified with the notion of a set of elements as used in the axioms. Particular relationships within the group would be identified with mathematical operations and relations. These identities established, the axioms would be examined deductively for the theorems that they imply. This step is considered in greater detail in the next section.

Familiarity with mathematics is an indispensable asset to the theorist, especially at this point in the scientific process. The deduction of theorems from axioms is itself a mathematical operation. Moreover, the theorist can often embed his ideas in a system of axioms that mathematicians have already investigated thoroughly, such as axioms on real numbers or probability. By doing this he can take advantage of the investigations of others, using theorems that have been found to follow from the axioms. The theorist can, of course, do this only if he has a working knowledge of relevant aspects of mathematics. The purpose of this book is to provide a working knowledge of those parts of mathematics that are immediately useful to social scientists.

A second level of identification—this time, identification in reverse—is made at the step of theoretical interpretation, I_1. When the transition from axioms to theorems has been made by the process of mathematical argumentation, step M, the properties of the theorems must be identified with properties of the world. Finally, two sets of interpretations, one based on physical observation and the other, on formal mathematical reasoning, are constructed. One step remains: that of appraisal. If the two sets of interpretations are alike, it is concluded that the axioms of the mathematical system comprise a reasonably accurate theoretical description of the objects under consideration. If, on the other hand, the two sets of interpretations do not correspond, then one concludes either that some step in the observational process has backfired or that the mathematical model itself is an inadequate representation. In the latter case, the axioms should be re-examined and so modified as to yield theorems that are more consistent with subsequent experimental findings.

None of this discussion is intended to imply that the only theory in social science worth considering is that which is based on mathematical models and the axiomatic method. Certainly, a well-developed axiom system that accurately describes some aspect of the world does not spring full-blown from a factual vacuum. A long history of observing behavior, of constructing and testing small hypotheses, and of collating results is necessary before successful formalization, such as that described above, is feasible. The discussion and examples throughout this book should suggest, however, that mathematical models and the axiomatic method can serve as useful tools for theory construction in the social sciences.

1.4 The Logic of Implication

The words "prove," "deduce," and "derive" have occurred with considerable regularity in the preceding pages. It is time we decide precisely what these important terms mean. Each of them refers to the logical process of distilling necessary consequences from axiomatic systems. This process is sometimes called *if . . . then* reasoning. We say that *if* such and such is true (the axioms of a theory), *then* so and so is also true (the theorems). Notice that such a statement has no direct connection with any actual state of affairs in our world. In the deduction process a theorem is said to be correct only if the word *then* in the *if . . . then* statement is used correctly. The conditions following the *if* may be wildly ludicrous without invalidating the logical correctness of the complete statement. On the other hand, both the *if* and the *then* portions of the statement may correspond quite well with what is known to exist in the world about us, but the theorem may yet be incorrect. The *then* portions of the statement simply may not follow from the *if*. For instance, most people would agree with these four statements:

(1.4.1)   People eat bagels.
(1.4.2)   Bagels are food.
(1.4.3)   Rutabagas are food.
(1.4.4)   People eat rutabagas.

Nonetheless, it would be nonsensical to argue "If 1.4.1, 1.4.2, and 1.4.3, then (it is true that) 1.4.4." Although the statements are all true, a necessary connecting thread is lacking. That thread is known to logicians as the property of *implication*.

Consider any two propositions, A and B, on the order of those above. For both A and B we can say that the statement is either true or not true, according to some set of criteria. The falsity of A can be written as "not A is true." Then a connection can be established between the two propositions by the following definition:

(1.4.5) Let A and B be sentences. If whenever A is true B also is true, then it is said that A implies B.   **Definition**

This definition will be used throughout this book. It will be useful to adopt a shorthand notation commonly used in mathematics.

(1.4.6) Let the term *implies* be represented by the symbol $\rightarrow$. Thus, "$A \rightarrow B$" means "A implies B" or "If A, then B."   **Notation**

Now, definition 1.4.5 has an immediate consequence. If, whenever A is true, B is also true, then it must be the case that whenever B is false A is also false. This can be put much more briefly as follows:

(1.4.7) $(A \rightarrow B) \rightarrow ($not $B \rightarrow$ not $A)$.   **PROPOSITION**

The statement (not $B \rightarrow$ not A) is known as the *contrapositive* of the implication $(A \rightarrow B)$. For example, we know that all mammalian mothers are female, so the condition of motherhood implies that the subject is of the female sex. The contrapositive of this implication can be stated, "If a thing is not female, then it is not a mother."

An interesting question now arises. In the light of 1.4.7 it might seem sensible to think that the statement $(A \rightarrow B)$ implies the statement $(B \rightarrow A)$. The reader would do well to convince himself of the truth or falsity of this supposition before he proceeds. By the definition of implication, we know that $A \rightarrow B$ means that whenever A is true, B is also true. But this definition does not preclude the possibility of B being true even though A is false (look again at the definition of implication). It is entirely possible that one can find instances for which B is true and A is false, even though $A \rightarrow B$. For example, motherhood implies female sex, but the converse is not true because not all females are mothers.

There are special cases, of course, in which B implies A whenever A implies B. Such situations occur frequently enough to warrant a special name.

(1.4.8) The statement $B \rightarrow A$ (read "B implies A" or "if B, then A") is called the *converse* of the statement $A \rightarrow B$. If $A \rightarrow B$ *and* $B \rightarrow A$, we write $A \leftrightarrow B$ (read "A if and only if B").   **Definition**

For instance, the converse of the statement "If x is a man, then x is a mortal" is the (false) statement "If x is a mortal, then x is a man."

The ideas of implication, contrapositive, and converse are made a trifle clearer by a diagram. Suppose that we have a number of instances in which each of two propositions, A and B, is classed as being true or false (that is, as occurring or as failing to occur); for example, the proposition "x is a female" with respect to a set of objects. In every case, each proposition is classified as occurring or not occurring. Represent the classification "not A" by the symbol $\sim A$ and "not B" by $\sim B$. We can represent the total number of instances of classification by the letter n with various subscripts. For example, there is some number of instances in which both A and B occur, which can be labeled $n_{(A)(B)}$. The number of instances in which A occurs and B does not can be labeled $n_{(A)(\sim B)}$, and so on. The n pairs of classifications can be represented by Table 1.1. The reader should recognize intuitively that a table such as this has certain necessary arithmetic properties. Although we will be unable to prove the assertion for a time, it should be reasonably obvious that $n_{(A)(B)} + n_{(A)(\sim B)} = n_A$, that $n_{(A)(B)} + n_{(\sim A)(B)} = n_B$, and that $n_A + n_{\sim A} = n$. The reader should locate three additional equations that further characterize Table 1.1.

The statement $A \rightarrow B$ imposes one condition on such a table.

Table 1.1   SIMULTANEOUS CLASSIFICATION OF INSTANCES
OF PROPOSITIONS A AND B

	B	$\sim B$	
A	$n_{(A)(B)}$	$n_{(A)(\sim B)}$	n_A
$\sim A$	$n_{(\sim A)(B)}$	$n_{(\sim A)(\sim B)}$	$n_{\sim A}$
	n_B	$n_{\sim B}$	n

This condition is that $n_{(A)(\sim B)} = 0$. That is, there can be no instances in which A occurs and B does not, if the implication is true. The contrapositive requires that $n_{\sim B} = n_{(\sim A)(\sim B)}$. Does this agree with 1.4.7? The statement $B \rightarrow A$ requires that $n_{(\sim A)(B)} = 0$. Thus, if an implication and its converse are true, only two of the four simultaneous classifications can be observed. Only $n_{(A)(B)}$ and $n_{(\sim A)(\sim B)}$ can have values other than 0.

Exercises

1.1. In Table 1.1, suppose that proposition A represents the classification "was a smoker" and proposition B represents "died of lung cancer." Suppose that n represents a large number of observations of recently deceased persons.

(a) Interpret the numbers $n_{(A)(\sim B)}$, $n_{(\sim A)(B)}$, $n_{(\sim A)(\sim B)}$.
(b) Suppose it were found that $A \rightarrow B$. If you were a smoker, would you stop? Why?
(c) Suppose it were found that $B \rightarrow A$. If you were a smoker, would you stop? Why?
(d) Suppose it were found that $B \leftrightarrow A$. If you were a smoker, would you stop? Why?

1.2. Let $A \rightarrow B$ and $B \rightarrow \sim C$. List all consequences of these two axioms.

1.3. Suppose that $B \rightarrow A$. What else can be said?

1.4. List three attributes that either are possessed or are not possessed, such as living-dead, Republican-otherwise, from your own field of interest.

(a) How many implicative statements, such as $A \rightarrow B$, $C \rightarrow A$, can be written using these attributes?

(b) How many "if and only if" statements can be written?

(c) "Translate" each statement from Parts (a) and (b) into English. Do all these make sense? Why or why not?

1.5. An anthropologist doing fieldwork offers the following proposition: If (A): a woman is a member of tribe X, then (B): she wears a ring in her nose.

(a) On market day he observes ten women, all members of tribe X and each wearing a ring in her nose. Using numbers, make up a table similar to 1.1 showing what he observed. What does this table show us about the contrapositive?

(b) Let us now assume that the anthropologist sees seven women who are members of X wearing nose rings, and three women who are not members of X wearing earrings but not nose rings. Describe this situation in a table. What is now the logical status of the anthropologist's inference? What does this evidence suggest about the converse of the proposition?

(c) Now assume that the anthropologist sees five women who are from tribe X wearing nose rings, three women who are not from tribe X wearing earrings only, and two women who are not from tribe X wearing nose rings. Describe this situation in tabular form. What is the empirical status of the inference? What of the converse?

1.5 Forms of Proof

With the notion of implication in mind, we can now consider the way in which it is used to prove theorems. It was seen that a theorem is an assertion of the form "If A, then B," or $A \rightarrow B$. Proposition A is called the *hypothesis* of the theorem, and B is called the *conclusion* (or *consequent*). The hypothesis may be a single proposition, or it may be an entire system of axioms. The steps from hypothesis to conclusion constitute the proof. They are nothing more than crutches necessary for the human mind, which otherwise might be incapable of grasping the necessary relation between the two.

Proofs generally take one of two forms. The first of these is known as a *direct* proof. A direct proof establishes a series of steps by which it can be seen clearly that the hypothesis does in fact imply the conclusion. A typical direct proof would take the following form:

(1.5.1)   Axiom: A

Theorem: If A, then B.

(Hypothesis: Let A be true.)

(1) $A \to C$.
(2) $C \to D$.
(3) $D \to B$.
(4) Hence, $A \to B$.

The number of steps that a proof requires varies, depending largely upon the degree of sophistication the writer assumes in his audience. (The proof also depends upon something classed as "transitivity," which is discussed in Chapter 3.) What may be an obvious step to one reader may be completely incomprehensible to another. Regardless of the number of steps in a proof, it is either correct or false depending upon whether or not the rules of implication are used correctly.

As an example of the direct proof form, consider once again the assertion $(A \to B) \to (\sim B \to \sim A)$. Can the reader prove this? Before continuing in the text, it would be worthwhile to attempt a direct proof.

(1.5.2) $(A \to B) \to (\sim B \to \sim A)$.

(Hypothesis 1: Let $A \to B$. Hypothesis 2: Let $\sim B$ be true.)

(1) Whenever A is true, B is true.   (Hypothesis 1 and 1.4.5)
(2) But $\sim B$ is true.   (Hypothesis 2)
(3) $\sim A$ is true.   (Steps 1 and 2)
(4) $(\sim B) \to (\sim A)$ (Steps 2 and 3 and 1.4.5)
(5) Hence
     $(A \to B) \to (\sim B \to \sim A)$.   (Hypothesis and step 4)

Note that a parenthetic statement of justification is appended to each step in this proof. This will be the case in succeeding proofs whenever a particular step seems to be less than trivially obvious. No step in this proof should stagger the mind, but its original construction may jolt the reader. Ordinarily, a direct proof consists of granting an hypothesis and demonstrating clearly by proper use of implications that the consequence follows. In this case, however, the consequence itself involves an hypothesis. In words the theorem says: If A implies B, then it is true that [if not B is true], then not A is true, where the hypothesis of the consequent is bracketed. The theorem does *not* say that $(A \to B)$ $\to \sim B$. Thus, we must grant the hypothesis, $A \to B$, and, in addition, allow the special case, $\sim B$, covered by the consequent. These are done by Hypothesis 1 and Hypothesis 2 respectively. It is important to recognize that the proposition has a single hypothesis and that the consequent is true only in case not B is true.

In this proof it was necessary to admit two hypotheses or "if" statements. Hypothesis 2 yields nothing by itself, but, in combination with Hypothesis 1, gives the desired result. The proposition can be read "if A implies B, then if $\sim B$ is true, $\sim A$ is true." Step 3 makes the only real intellectual demand of the reader. Here he must recognize that, if B is true whenever A is true, it cannot be the case that A is true if B is false. Naturally, as axiom systems become richer, the derivation of true theorems becomes a more complicated process, demanding more of the reader who would follow the thread of the argument. Such a reader should lean heavily upon the parenthetic justifications. Moreover, he would do well to conceive of a proof as an intellectual game that is played almost as much for the fun of it as for obtaining desired results.

The second form of deductive proof is called *indirect*. In this process it is assumed that the hypothesis is correct *and* that the consequence is false. With these assumptions, it is then shown that a contradiction exists—that the assumptions cannot be correct if the consequence is false. An indirect proof takes the following form:

**Form of
Indirect Proof**

(1.5.3)   Axiom: A
            Theorem: If A, then B.

Proof

(Hypothesis 1: Let A be true.)
    (1) Assume $\sim B$.
    (2) $\sim B \to E$.

(3) $E \rightarrow F$.

(4) $F \rightarrow \sim A$ (contradicts the hypothesis).

(5) Hence, $A \rightarrow B$.

Intuitively, this is an unimpressive proof form. Unimpressive, that is, until it is thoroughly understood that the sole reason for uncovering a logical contradiction stems from the falsity of the assumption. If only the falsity of the assumption generates the contradiction, then the falsity itself must be false. But this says that the consequence (the theorem) is true. As an example, let us try to prove again that an implication implies a contrapositive, this time by means of an indirect form.

(1.5.4) $(A \rightarrow B) \rightarrow (\sim B \rightarrow \sim A)$.   **PROPOSITION**

(Hypothesis 1: Let $A \rightarrow B$. Hypothesis 2: Let $\sim B$ be   *Proof*
true. Hypothesis 3: Let A be true.)

(1) A is true.	(Hypothesis 3)
(2) B is true.	(Hypothesis 1 and 1.4.5)
(3) But $\sim B$ is true.	(Hypothesis 2)
(4) Assumption is contradic- tory, so $\sim B \rightarrow \sim A$ when- ever $A \rightarrow B$.	(Steps 1–3)

Exercises

1.6. Examine the following argument:

   Theorem: If an animal is a dog, then it does not lay eggs.

   Proof: (1) If an animal is a dog, then it has a coat of fur.

   (2) If it has a coat of fur, then it is warm-blooded.

   (3) If it is warm-blooded, then it bears live young.

   (4) If it bears live young, then it does not lay eggs.

   (5) Therefore, if an animal is a dog, then it does not lay eggs.

(a) Put the argument in symbolic form (i.e., let letters or other symbols stand for classes of phenomena). Is the proof direct or indirect?

(b) Is the argument logically correct?

(c) Is the argument correct in terms of the "real world?"

1.7. Examine the following argument:

   Theorem: If a group of persons is democratic, then it does not have a social structure.

Proof: (1) If a group is democratic, then it has no dictator.
   (2) If a group has no dictator, then any member can be in a position of authority.
   (3) If any member can be in a position of authority, then all members are equal.
   (4) If all members are equal, then the group does not have a social structure.

(a) Put the argument in symbolic form. Is the proof direct or indirect?
(b) Is the argument logically correct?
(c) Is the argument correct in terms of the "real world?"

1.8. Construct a system of at least three axioms using concepts from your field of interest. (HINT: Reference [8], Zetterberg, *On Theory and Verification*, provides a good illustration for sociologists.)

(a) Prove at least one theorem by the direct method.
(b) Prove at least one theorem by the indirect method.

Selected References

1. Allendoerfer, C. B., and Oakley, C. O. *Principles of Mathematics*. New York: McGraw-Hill Book Company, Inc., 1955. Chapter 1.
2. Braithwaite, R. B. *Scientific Explanation, A Study of the Function of Theory, Probability and Law in Science*. Cambridge, England: Cambridge University Press, 1955. Chapters 1 and 2.
3. Coombs, C. H., Raiffa, H., and Thrall, R. M. "Some Views on Mathematical Models and Measurement Theory," *Psychological Review*, 61 (March 1954), 132–144.
4. Kirshner, R. B., and Wilcox, L. R. *The Anatomy of Mathematics*. New York: The Ronald Press Company, 1950. Chapters 1 and 2.
5. Lazarsfeld, Paul F. "Evidence and Inference in Social Research," *Daedalus*, 87 (Fall 1958), 99–130.
6. Suppes, Patrick. *Introduction to Logic*. New York: D. Van Nostrand Co., Inc., 1957, Chapter 1.
7. Suppes, Patrick. "A Comparison of the Meaning and Uses of Models in Mathematics and the Empirical Sciences," *Synthese*, XII (September 1960), 287–301.
8. Zetterberg, Hans L. *On Theory and Verification in Sociology*. [A much revised edition.] New York: The Bedminster Press, 1963.

Elementary Theory of Sets

Psychologists, sociologists, and others are interested in the kind of events that either do or do not occur. Either the rat turns to the left in its maze or it does not; either the young lovers marry or they do not. Although these events seem quite different, they can be analyzed at both the theoretical and the research levels with similar or identical tools. The first section of this book describes the rudiments of these tools. This chapter and the next one may appear to the reader to deal more with logic than with mathematics. As a matter of fact, this is correct, because sets and relations are frequently described as the logical foundations of mathematics. As such, they are also building blocks for the development of mathematical and statistical tools of research that are used in the construction of social science theory. Thus, sets and relations are equally pertinent to the reader who views himself as a budding armchair theorist and to the one who is interested primarily in research.

Any logical system is based on one or more undefined terms, which are often called *primitive notions*. The terms *point* and *line*, for example, are used extensively in the development of definitions and theory in geometry, but are themselves never defined. They represent classical examples of the idea of primitive notions. The theory described in this chapter begins with two such undefined terms: *elements* and *sets*.

2

2.1 Elements

An *element* is virtually anything that we care to call an element. Any object, event, or state of nature may be called an element; a rat, the fact of the rat's turning left in a maze, the Eiffel Tower, bankruptcy, are all elements of some set. A notion this abstract may appear beyond all possibility of "practical" application, but it is precisely this abstraction that renders the idea so general and broadly useful. This becomes more apparent as we begin to work with sets of elements. It must be emphasized that this paragraph does not represent a definition, since we do not specify how to distinguish an object that is an element from one that is not. It is no more than an intuitive account of the way in which the noun *element* can be interpreted. In a strict mathematical sense, however, the word has neither definition nor substance.

2.2 Sets of Elements

A *set* is a collection or class of elements. Sometimes, it is said that the elements are *members* of a set. The collection may contain an uncountable number of elements, none, or any intermediate amount. A given set may be defined by a list of its elements. Thus, an enrollment sheet defines the set of all elements (students) enrolled in a given course. A set may also be defined *ontologically* by a description of some property that is common to every element in the set. The elements that have the property of being registered Democrats in the State of Vermont on a given date form a particular set. A property defines a set and, conversely, a set defines a property.

A definition by enumeration is sometimes called a definition by extension; one that gives a defining property is called a definition by intension. (See Russell, *Mathematical Philosophy* [7], pages 12–15, for a discussion of differences between the two forms.)

Throughout mathematics, symbols are introduced to represent notions, both defined and undefined. Elements are represented by lower-case letters, and sets of elements are represented by capital letters. When an element a and a set A are given, one of two situations must occur: Either a is an element of A or it is not. These situations will be symbolized as follows:

(2.2.1) If a is an element and A is a set of elements, then   **Notation**
(1) if a is a member of A, we write $a \in A$ (read "a in A" or "a is an element of A."
(2) if a is not a member of A, we write $a \notin A$ (read "a not in A" or "a is not an element of A.")

In this notation, the symbol ϵ is a script form of the lower-case Greek letter epsilon. Understand that no significance should be imputed to similarities or differences between letters assigned to elements and those assigned to sets. An element labeled x, for example, may or may not belong to a set labeled X, just as it may or may not belong to sets labeled A, B, or C. Labels alone are not intended to imply membership.

If element labels, say a and b, are introduced, it should be assumed that these *may* be different symbols for the same thing unless it is explicitly stated that they are not. Moreover, a label such as a need not represent a particular element, but could instead represent any of a large set. The context of the discussion, together with notational apparatus to be developed, should minimize any confusion over the use of such symbols.

At times, however, it will be convenient to distinguish among different elements. This can be accomplished by arbitrarily labeling the symbol for each different element with a subscript numeral, as a_1, a_2, a_3, $\cdots$, a_n. The letter n represents the largest number needed to assign a different number to each element. The three dots, $\cdots$, a "leader," indicate that the sequence continues as indicated. Thus, if A represents a set of students in a class and $a_4 \epsilon A$ and $a_9 \epsilon A$, then we know that a_4 and a_9 represent two different students in the same class. In other contexts, subscripts of this sort will be ignored.

2.3 Subsets

Certain elements in a set are sometimes distinguished, either ontologically or by listing them, as a set themselves. Such elements can be said to comprise a *subset* of the set. More specifically,

(2.3.1) A set B is said to be a *subset* of set A if and only if every element of B also is an element of A. If B is a subset of A, we write $B \subseteq A$ (read "B is contained in A" or "A includes B"). If B is not a subset of A, then we write $B \nsubseteq A$ (read "B is not contained in A").

Definition

Definition 2.3.1 is precise enough, but it can be stated yet more efficiently and with less possibility of confusion if more symbols are used. Hereafter, sets will be indicated by listing the elements within braces, "{ }." Thus, a set A containing n elements (where n stands for some arbitrary integer) may be represented by $\{a_1, a_2, \cdots, a_n\}$ or by $\{a, b, c, \cdots\}$.

A colon sometimes will be used within a pair of braces to mean "such that" or "which meet the conditions that." Thus:

(2.3.2) If A is the set of elements characterized by having some property, say P, then we write

$$A = \{a: a \text{ has property } P\},$$

which is read "the set, A, consists of elements, a, such that a has property P."

Notation

For example, if A is the set of all students enrolled in a university course, a subset B might be defined as

$$B = \{a: a \in A \text{ and } a \text{ is female}\}.$$

In this case, B is the set of all females enrolled in the course.

With these symbols the inclusion relation, $\subseteq$, can be defined as follows:

(2.3.3) $B \subseteq A \leftrightarrow B = \{b: b \in B \text{ and } b \in A\}.$

Definition

In a single line, this states that the set B is contained in the set A if and only if B consists of elements of the form b (which are in the set B) such that they are also in the set A.

An important subset of *any* defined set is the *empty set*, which contains no elements. The symbol ϕ, the Greek letter phi, is used to denote the empty set. The empty set is a basic mathematical concept and, as will be shown, an extremely useful one. In the meantime, an illustration of ϕ may be in order. Consider the set, A, of all American university professors. Let B be a subset of A subject to

$$B = \{a: a \in A \text{ and } a \text{ has three heads}\}.$$

An examination of this quite properly defined set should satisfy most readers that $B = \phi$.

Exercises

2.1. Let the set $A = \{$Clayton, Kenneth, Jeanette, Walter$\}$. List all possible subsets of this set without repeating any of the subsets in your list.

(HINT: ϕ is a subset of any set.)

(SECOND HINT: There should be 16 sets.)

2.2. List all sets constructed in Exercise 1 in which the set $\{$Kenneth, Walter$\}$ is con-contained.

2.4 Equality

The alert reader will have been dissatisfied with at least one symbol in the various definitions of inclusion. The term $=$ (equals) was used without having been previously defined. On the other hand, the meaning of the term may appear so intuitively obvious to the reader that it would be sheer pedantry to bother with a formal definition. It should be a firm rule for the development of a theoretical system, however, that any term introduced into the system must be preceded by a formal definition unless it is explicitly understood that the term is an element in the set of primitive notions. The relation of equality between sets is defined:

(2.4.1) $A = B \leftrightarrow A \subseteq B$ and $B \subseteq A$. If $A \nsubseteq B$ or $B \nsubseteq A$, then we write $A \neq B$. **Definition**

Two sets, then, are equal if and only if they have identical elements, that is, if they are in fact identical. From this it follows immediately that:

(2.4.2) For any set, A, $A = A$, **PROPOSITION**

since it is true that $A \subseteq A$, for any set A. The notion of equality can be extended with less formality to elements, that is, as a primitive notion. We say that $a = b$ whenever a and b are the same objects, that is, when the letters a and b are merely different labels for the same thing.

With definition 2.4.1 it is possible to distinguish between

two kinds of inclusion relation. First, it should be clear that the sentence "$A \subseteq B$" means one of two things—either A and B are equal or B contains all elements of A together with some that are not in A. To make explicit the second possibility, we have:

(2.4.3) If A and B are sets such that $A \subseteq B$ and $A \neq B$, then A is called a *proper* subset of B, and we write

$$A \subset B.$$

Definition

Exercises

2.3. Suppose that two sets, X and Y, are given by:

$$X = \{a;\ a \in Y\}.$$
$$Y = \{a;\ a \in X\}.$$

Then which of the following are true?

(a) $X \subseteq Y$
(b) $Y \subset X$
(c) $X \subset Y$
(d) $Y \subseteq X$

2.5 The Algebra of Sets

The words *operate* and *operation* occur frequently throughout this book. They are used here in much the same sense as that in which they appear in ordinary conversation. To operate on something is to bring about a change in it in a more or less orderly manner. An operation is just this process. In this book we shall require that every operation have a unique result.

The less common term *operator* is also used throughout the book. It refers to any mechanism that systematically effects a transformation. In this sense, marriage, graduation, and the draft are all operators on social status in that they bring about regular changes in status. The operators with which the present chapter is concerned are those that effect changes in sets. Among the most important of these are union and intersection of sets.

The operation *union of sets*, which is performed on two or more sets, yields a unique new set that contains all the elements in the sets upon which the operation was performed. We use the symbol "$\cup$" to indicate the operation. More precisely,

Definition

(2.5.1) If A and B are sets,

$$C = A \cup B \leftrightarrow C = \{c: c \in A \text{ or } c \in B\}.$$

In some works, the symbol "$+$" is used instead of $\cup$. Note that the conjunction *or* does not rule out the possibility of c belonging *both* to set A and to set B. Even cursory examination of 2.5.1 should convince the reader that:

PROPOSITION

(2.5.2) $A \cup B = B \cup A.$

Proof

Let A and B be sets. Then:
(1) $A \cup B = \{x: x \in A \text{ or } x \in B\}.$ (2.5.1)
(2) $B \cup A = \{x: x \in B \text{ or } x \in A\}.$ (2.5.1)
(3) But,

$$\{x: x \in A \text{ or } x \in B\} = \{x: x \in B \text{ or } x \in A\}. \quad (2.4.1)$$

(4) $A \cup B = B \cup A.$ (Steps 1–3)

The first two steps of the proof define the two sets under investigation by using the definition of set union, 2.5.1. Step 3 of the proof is the only one likely to require contemplation. In this step it is asserted that $A \cup B \subseteq B \cup A$ and that $B \cup A \subseteq A \cup B$. In his contemplation, the reader might ask himself what would be required to make this an incorrect step. For example, if one could locate a point in the first set but not in the second set of step 3, the assertion would necessarily be false because of 2.4.1, the definition of equality. Such a point would have to be a member of either A or B in the first place, and a member of neither A nor B in the second. Since these conditions are contradictory, such a point cannot be found. It is only consideration such as this that can satisfy one as to the logical status of an asserted proof. This apparently trivial proposition is called the *commutative law of set unions*. Thus, in general, any operation such as that of set union is called commutative if the order in which the operation is carried out does not affect the result. As will be seen below, not all set operations are commutative.

Many mathematical notions can be represented simply, in pictorial form. Graphic representations of sets are known as *Venn diagrams* or *Euler circles*. In such a representation, we identify the elements with points of the figure. Figure 2.1

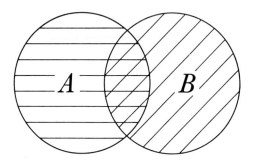

Figure 2.1

pictures two sets labeled A and B. Notice that some, but not all, of the points in A also are contained in B. If $C = A \cup B$, then C is represented by the entire lined area of Figure 2.1.

When more than two sets are being operated upon, it often becomes desirable to group some of the sets and operations together. This is accomplished by the use of parentheses, "( )," or brackets, "[ ]." The following provides our first formal encounter with such a device.

(2.5.3) If A and B are sets, then let $x \in (A$ or $B)$, or, equivalently, $x \in (A \cup B)$, mean $x \in A$ or $x \in B$ (or both $x \in A$ and $x \in B$).   **Notation**

The reader should be especially wary when he encounters such marks and squiggles as parentheses in an expression. They may give the expression an entirely different meaning from the meaning it would have without them.

Nevertheless, parentheses do not affect the operation of set union. To illustrate this fact, let A be a set of school students in the first six grades, let B be a set of students in grades 7–9 inclusive, and let C be a set of students in grades 10–12. Then $(A \cup B)$ is the set of students in the first nine grades and $(B \cup C)$ is the set of students in grades 7–12. The operation $(A \cup B) \cup C$ is the union of the set of students in the first nine grades with the set of those in grades 10–12. The operation $A \cup (B \cup C)$ is the union of the set of students in the first six grades with the set of those in grades 7–12. But both unions give the set of students in the first twelve grades. In general, then,

$(2.5.4)$ $A \cup (B \cup C) = (A \cup B) \cup C.$ **PROPOSITION**

Let A, B, and C be sets.   *Proof*

(1) $A \cup (B \cup C)$
 $\qquad = x: \{x \in A \text{ or } x \in (B \text{ or } C)\},$ (2.5.1)
(2) $\qquad = x: \{x \in A \text{ or } x \in B \text{ or } x \in C\}.$ (2.5.3)
(3) $(A \cup B) \cup C$
 $\qquad = x: \{x \in (A \text{ or } B) \text{ or } x \in C\},$ (2.5.1)
(4) $\qquad = x: \{x \in A \text{ or } x \in B \text{ or } x \in C\},$ (2.5.3)
(5) $\qquad = A \cup (B \cup C).$ (Steps 2 and 4)

This identity is called the *associative law of set unions*. In general, an operation is associative if the manner of grouping the elements does not affect the outcome. It will be seen shortly that the union is not the only associative set operation and that not all set operations are associative.

The definition of set union, 2.5.1, can be made much more general. As it stands, the definition deals only with the union of two sets. To make it sufficiently general, still another notational form is needed. Let $\times$ be any operator; that is, any rule for the manipulation of elements. Let us assign a different positive integer to each of a sequence of sets. Let the numbers range from 1 to n, where n is the number of sets in the sequence. Finally, let the letter i represent *each number in succession* from 1 to n. This notation may be stated as $(i = 1, 2, \cdots, n)$.

Notation*

(2.5.5) Let $\times$ represent any set operator and A_i represent the ith set in a class of sets $(i = 1, 2, \cdots, n)$. Then $\overset{n}{\underset{i=1}{\times}} (A_i)$ indicates that the operation is performed on A_1, then on $A_2, \cdots$, and finally on A_n.

With such notation, it is possible to generalize definition 2.5.1 as follows:

Definition

(2.56.)

$$B = \overset{n}{\underset{i=1}{\cup}} (A_i) \leftrightarrow B = \{b: b \in A_1 \text{ or } b \in A_2 \text{ or}, \cdots, \text{ or } b \in A_n\}.$$

This says that the set B consists of the union of all sets A_i, $(i = 1, 2, \cdots, n)$, if and only if every element b in B also is in *at least* one set A_i.

The operation of *intersection* is noted $\cap$ and is defined by

Definition

(2.5.7) If A and B are sets, then the intersection of A and B, noted $A \cap B$, is given by

$$A \cap B = \{x: x \in A \text{ and } x \in B\}.$$

In some works the symbol "$\cdot$" is used in place of "$\cap$." Notice that in Figure 2.1 the set $A \cap B$ is represented by crosshatched lines.

As an illustration of the notions of union and intersection, consider the set A of all students enrolled in our hypothetical university class. Let B, C, and D be subsets of A such that

$$B = \{a \in A: a \text{ is male}\},$$
$$C = \{a \in A: a \text{ is female}\},$$
$$D = \{a \in A: a \text{ receives a final grade of F}\}.$$

Now, if it is assumed that there are two and only two sexes represented in the class, it follows that $B \cup C = A$ and $C \cup D = \{a: a \in A, a \text{ is a female or an F student or both}\}$.

---

* This notation provides for the definition of *iterative* or repeated operators. Iterative operators will be employed throughout this book. To prove propositions involving them, however, requires a special form of direct proof, called mathematical induction, that is not introduced until Chapter 5. For this reason, proof of theorems such as 2.6.6 below cannot be given for the present (see Exercise 5.29).

$C \cap D = \{a: a \in A, a \text{ is both female and an F student}\}.$
$B \cap C = \{A: a \in A, a \text{ is both male and female}\}.$

The last equation illustrates what is meant by *mutually exclusive* or *disjoint* sets. That is,

(2.5.8) Two sets A and B are said to be disjoint or mutually exclusive $\leftrightarrow A \cap B = \phi$. **Definition**

In Figure 2.1 the sets A and B are not mutually exclusive, but they would be if the two curves did not cross or if the crosshatched subset represented the empty set.

It follows from definition 2.5.7 that $B \cap A = \{x: x \in B \text{ and } x \in A\}$. But this is the same set as $A \cap B$, which is sufficient to prove that

(2.5.9) $\qquad A \cap B = B \cap A,$ **PROPOSITION**

which tells us that the operation of set intersection is *commutative*, as is the set union.

Since the $(A \cap B)$ is just a set, we are perfectly free to examine its intersection with another set, C. The set $(A \cap B) \cap C$ is just the set of elements in $(A$ and in $B)$ and in C, where the parentheses clearly do not alter the meaning of this sentence. Similarly, the set $A \cap (B \cap C)$ is the set of elements in A and $(B$ and $C)$, where once again the parentheses can be removed without changing the meaning of the sentence. This should be sufficient to convince one that the following is true:

(2.5.10) $\quad (A \cap B) \cap C = A \cap (B \cap C).$ **PROPOSITION**

Either side of the identity can be written unambiguously as $A \cap B \cap C$. As was the case with the set union, once a binary operator can be extended from two to three sets, it can immediately be extended to any finite number, n. The binary definition of intersection is just the special case, $n = 2$, of the following:

(2.5.11) $\bigcap\limits_{i=1}^{n} (A_i) = \{x: x \in A_1 \text{ and } x \in A_2 \text{ and } \cdots \text{ and } x \in A_n\}.$ **Definition**

Exercises

2.4. In which of the following true statements is the set B necessarily a subset of A?

(a) $A \subseteq B$
(b) $B \subset A$
(c) $A = B$
(d) $B = \{x: x \in A$ and $x \in C\}$
(e) $B = \{x: x \in A$ or $x \in C\}$
(f) $A \subset (B \cap C)$
(g) $(B \cap C) \subseteq A$

2.5. If A is the set of sociologists in the U. S., and if B is the set of demographers in the U. S., define in words what a new set C is, given each statement below.

(a) $C = \{x: x \in A$ and $x \in B\}$
(b) $C = \{x: x \in A$ and $x \notin B\}$
(c) $C = \{x: x \in A$ or $x \in B\}$
(d) $C = \{x: x$ is a U. S. citizen$\}$

2.6. Let A_1 represent the set of adults who are judged clinically to be psychologically normal, A_2 the set of those diagnosed as neurotic, and A_3 the set of those diagnosed as psychotic. Let B_1 represent the set of noninstitutionalized persons and B_2 the set of those in mental institutions. Define in words each of the sets below.

(a) $A_3 \cap B_2$
(b) $\bigcup\limits_{i=2}^{3} A_i$
(c) $A_1 \cap B_2$
(d) $\bigcup\limits_{i=1}^{2} B_i$
(e) $A_3 \cap B_1$
(f) $\left(\bigcup\limits_{i=2}^{3} A_i \right) \cap B_2$

2.7. It has been hypothesized in sociology that marital stability is related in a "U-shaped" fashion to socioeconomic status. That is, the middle-classes stay married; the upper classes and the lower classes are more likely to say "the devil with it." Represent this hypothesis set-theoretically. Use the notation P_{ij} to represent the probability of observing the intersectional set A_iB_j, where A_i represents socioeconomic status set i and B_j represents marital status j.

2.8. Suppose that members of the House of Representatives could be partitioned into the subsets $A_1 = \{x:x$ is a liberal Democrat$\}$; $A_2 = \{x:x$ is a conservative Democrat$\}$; $A_3 = \{x:x$ is a liberal Republican$\}$; $A_4 = \{x:x$ is a conservative Republican$\}$. Then let the same parent set be partitioned into sets $B_1 = \{y:y$ represents the Deep South$\}$; $B_2 = \{y:y$ represents the North Atlantic or Middle Atlantic region$\}$; $B_3 = \{y:y$ represents any other area$\}$.

(a) For each i and j, interpret $A_i \cap B_j$.

(b) Explain what must characterize and provide a contemporary example of an element in the set $A_2 \cap B_2$.

(c) What can you say about the set $A_2 \cup A_4$?

(d) What is represented by $\{A_1 \cup A_3\} \cap B_1$?

2.9. Let the set

$$A = \{a, b, c, d, e, f, g, h, i, j, k, l\}$$

with subsets:

$$A_1 = \{a, b, c\} \qquad A_2 = \{g, h, i\}$$
$$A_3 = \{c, e, f\} \qquad A_4 = \{c, f, k\}$$
$$A_5 = \{a, c, j\} \qquad A_6 = \{b, e, l\}$$

(a) Define the set $A_1 \cup A_2$.

(b) Define the set $A_3 \cup (A_6 \cup A_1)$.

(c) Define the set $\overset{4}{\underset{i=1}{\cup}} (A_i)$.

(d) Show that $A_5 \cup A_4 = A_4 \cup A_5$. (Note that this is *not* a general proof.)

(e) Define the set $\{a: a \in A_1 \text{ and } a \in A_5 \text{ and } a \in A_4\}$.

(f) Define the set $\overset{3}{\underset{i=1}{\cap}} (A_{(2i-1)})$. (HINT: When $i = 1$, $2i - 1 = 1$. When $i = 2$, $2i - 1 = 3$.)

(g) List the disjoint pairs of sets above.

(h) Show that $(A_1 \cap A_5) \cap A_4 = A_1 \cap (A_4 \cap A_5)$.

2.6 Further Properties of Set Operations

In the preceding section, it was seen that set intersections are commutative and associative. The associative property of set intersections is illustrated in Figure 2.2. Here A_1 is represented by the shaded area and A_2 and A_3 by the horizontal and vertical lines, respectively. The set $(A_1 \cap A_2)$ is represented by horizontal lines and shading. The set $(A_2 \cap A_3)$ is shown by crosshatched lines. Notice that the intersection of $(A_1 \cap A_2)$ with A_3 is represented by cross-

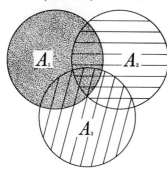

Figure 2.2

hatching over shading. Now consider the set $(A_2 \cap A_3)$ and the portion of that set which is also in A_1. This once again is shown as a crosshatched area over shading.

Since $(A_2 \cup A_3)$ is the set of all points that are either in A_2 or in A_3, $A_1 \cap (A_2 \cup A_3)$ is the set of all elements that are in A_1 and that are either in A_2 or in A_3; that is, the elements that are in A_1 and A_2 or in A_1 and A_3. Thus,

(2.6.1) $A_1 \cap (A_2 \cup A_3) = (A_1 \cap A_2) \cup (A_1 \cap A_3).$ **PROPOSITION**

This is called the *first distributive law of sets*. The reader would do well to construct a Venn diagram to illustrate this law.

The *second distributive law* is obtained by similar reasoning. The set formed by $A_1 \cup (A_2 \cap A_3)$ consists of all elements that are in A_1 or that are in the intersection of the sets A_2 and A_3. If, for example, A_1 were the set of all registered Republicans, A_2 the set of all university professors, and A_3 the set of all males, the set $A_1 \cup (A_2 \cap A_3)$ would consist of all persons who were either Republicans or male university professors, or both. The set $(A_1 \cup A_2)$ would consist of all who were Republicans or professors (or both), and $(A_1 \cup A_3)$ would consist of all who were either Republicans or males (or both). The set $(A_1 \cup A_2) \cap (A_1 \cup A_3)$, then, would be that set consisting of all who were either Republicans or professors and who were either Republicans or males. Four subsets, then, are indicated by the set $(A_1 \cup A_2) \cap (A_1 \cup A_3)$: (1) Republicans (of either sex and regardless of occupation); (2) Republican males (a subset of the Republicans); (3) Republican university professors (also a subset of Republicans); and (4) male university professors. But this is precisely the set of all those who are either Republicans or male university professors (or both). Thus, it has been illustrated that:

(2.6.4) $A_1 \cup (A_2 \cap A_3) = (A_1 \cup A_2) \cap (A_1 \cup A_3).$ **PROPOSITION**

This is the *second distributive law of sets*.

Hereafter, it will be convenient to assign a symbol to the set of all elements in the domain of discourse. The symbol Ω, the Greek letter omega, will be used to represent this set.

In the illustration that dealt with sets of students, the set A could have been represented by Ω if by definition the domain of discourse had been restricted to students in the single class. By a different definition, A could have been made a subset of Ω, say the set of all students in the university, or in the United States. Whenever a set noted by a capital letter is introduced, it should be understood that it is a subset of some set Ω. It is profoundly important that the parent set, Ω, be carefully specified in any scientific generalization.

The complement of set A is the set of all elements that are *not* in A and is denoted $c(A)$. More formally,

$$(2.6.5) \qquad c(A) = [a : a \,\epsilon\, \Omega \text{ and } a \,\epsilon\!\!\!/\, A].$$ **Definition**

In using this definition the membership of A in Ω usually will be made implicit.

It should be immediately apparent that $c(\Omega) = \phi$ and, conversely, that $c(\phi) = \Omega$. The fact that $c(c(A)) = A$ is called the *rule of involution*. Moreover, $A \cup c(A) = \Omega$ and $A \cap c(A) = \phi$. These two equations make up the *law of complementarity of sets*. It may be less readily apparent, but it is equally true that:

$$(2.6.6) \qquad c\left(\bigcup_{i=1}^{n} (A_i)\right) = \bigcap_{i=1}^{n} (c(A_i)).$$ **THEOREM**

To avoid confusion, it would be wise to examine 2.6.6 closely. A diagrammatic representation may help.

In Figure 2.3, $c(A_1)$ is represented by horizontal lines, $c(A_2)$ by vertical lines, and $c(A_3)$ by diagonal lines. Now, the intersection of these complements is represented by that space in which cross-hatching runs in all three directions. Notice that none of the three sets is contained in this area. Thus, to be in the intersection of the complements, an element can be in none of the sets. If it is in none of the sets, it must be in the complement of their union.

The left term of 2.6.6 simply represents the complement of the union of the n sets. Now, each of the sets A_i has a complement set that is not necessarily identical with any other complement set. If an element is a member of no set, then it must be a member of the complement of every set; that is, it must be in the intersection of $c(A_i)$. This, of course, is represented by the right term of 2.6.6.

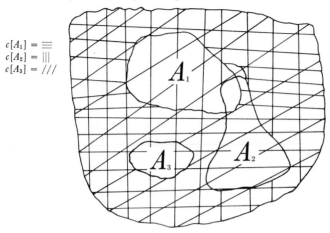

$$c[A_1] = \equiv$$
$$c[A_2] = |||$$
$$c[A_3] = ///$$

Figure 2.3

Definition 2.5.4 states that the union of n sets, A_i, is the set of all elements belonging to *at least one* of the n sets. The complement of this set then must be the set of elements that belong to *none* of the n sets.

The preceding discussion should make clear to the reader that terms containing parentheses or brackets must be read with extreme care. In each of the following statements, for example, the set on the left is quite different from the one on the right.

(2.6.7)   **PROPOSITION**

$$(1)\quad \bigcup_{i=1}^{n} (c(A_i)) \neq c\left(\bigcup_{i=1}^{n}(A_i)\right).$$

$$(2)\quad \bigcap_{i=1}^{n} (c(A_i)) \neq c\left(\bigcap_{i=1}^{n}(A_i)\right).$$

$$(3)\quad (A \cup B) \cap C \neq A \cap (B \cup C).$$

In 2.6.7 and similar propositions, "$\neq$" should be interpreted to mean that at least some classes of sets satisfy the inequality not that it can be satisfied by any class of sets. (Can the reader construct three sets, A, B, C, for which the two sets of 2.6.7.3 are equal?)

In 2.6.6 it was seen that an element that is a member of

no set, A_i, is a member of the complement of every such set. Now consider elements that are *not* in every one of the n sets. Such elements then are in the set that is the complement of $\bigcap_{i=1}^{n} A_i$. At the same time, the union of n sets of complements must contain every element that is not in the intersection of the n sets. Thus,

(2.6.8) $$c\left(\bigcap_{i=1}^{n} (A_i)\right) = \bigcup_{i=1}^{n} (c(A_i)).$$ **THEOREM**

2.6.6 and 2.6.8 are known as the *two laws of dualization* (or De Morgan's laws).

The operation of set *difference* is defined by:

(2.6.9) $B - A = \{b: b \in B \text{ and } b \notin A\}$.   **Definition**

In the illustration that followed 2.5.7, then,

$C - D = \{a \in A: a \text{ is a female who did not receive a final grade of F}\}$.

$D - C = \{a \in A: a \text{ is a male who received a grade of F}\}$.

$A - B \cup C = \phi$.

These examples should make clear the truth of the statement

(2.6.10)   **PROPOSITION**
(1) $A - B = B - A \leftrightarrow A = B$.
(2) $A - B = A - (A \cap B)$.
(3) $A - B = A \cap c(B)$.

Exercises

2.10. Use the set A and subsets A_i, as defined in exercise 2.7, letting $A = \Omega$, then

(a) Define the set $c(A_1 \cup A_6)$ by enumerating the elements.

(b) Show that $c\left(\bigcup_{i=1}^{4} (A_i)\right) = \bigcap_{i=1}^{4} (cA_i)$ by enumerating the elements.

(c) Define the set $(A_1 \cup A_4) - A_5$ by enumerating the elements.

(d) Define the set $c[(A_1 \cap A_5) - A_4] \cup A_6$ by enumerating the elements.

2.11. In a tabulation of 100 college students, it was found that 20 students were enrolled in an anthropology course; 45 students were enrolled in a psychology course, 30 students, in a sociology course; 10 were in both sociology and anthropology; 7, in psychology and anthropology; 5, in sociology and psychology; and 5, in a course in all three subjects. How many students were

(a) not taking courses in the social sciences?
(b) studying only sociology?
(c) working only in anthropology?
(d) studying either sociology or anthropology?
(e) doing work in psychology or anthropology but not in sociology?

2.12.

(a) By the use of Venn diagrams, show the second distributive law of sets 2.6.4 for three sets:
$$A_1 \cup (A_2 \cap A_3) = (A_1 \cup A_2) \cap (A_1 \cup A_3).$$
Note again that the use of such diagrams is an aid to visualization and in no way constitutes a proof.
(b) Using a Venn diagram different from 2.3, show that the second law of dualization (2.6.8) is true for the case $n = 3$.
(c) If $A \cup B = \Omega$, show that $A - B = c(B)$ by use of such a diagram.

2.13. It was seen in Section 1.4 that A implies B if whenever A is true, B also is true. If A and B are sets, represent the following by Venn diagrams:

(a) $A \rightarrow B$
(b) $(A \rightarrow B) \rightarrow (C(B) \rightarrow C(A))$
(c) $B \rightarrow A$
(d) $A \leftrightarrow B$

2.14. Prove formally:

(a) $A \cap c(A) = \phi$
(b) $A \cup c(A) = \Omega$
(c) $A - B = A \cap c(B)$

2.15. Suppose that two mental tesst are uncorrelated if and only if $T_1 \cap T_2 = \phi$, where T_1 is the "something" in the mind involved in the performance of the first test and T_2 is the "something" in the mind involved in the performance of the second test. Without making any assumptions about the correlation of T_1 and T_2, show that in this case, if another test is constructed such that
$$T_3 = T_1 - (T_1 \cap T_2),$$
then the third test is uncorrelated with the second.
(HINT: show that $T_3 \cap T_2 = \phi$.)

2.16. Interpret the second distributive law of sets, 2.6.4, by letting $A_1 = \{x : x$ is an American household with female head$\}$, $A_2 = \{x : x$ is an American household with retired household head$\}$, $A_3 = \{x : x$ is an American household in which the male head and his wife are living$\}$.

2.17. Suppose that a community contains three distinct ethnic minority groups and that each community resident can be identified as to membership or non-membership in one of these groups. Let $A_i = \{x : x$ is a member of minority group $i\}$.

(a) Interpret $A_1 \cap A_2$. Could this set be nonempty?

(b) What is the set $c(A_1 \cup A_3)$?

(c) Interpret 2.6.6 in this case. That is, explain what $c \left(\bigcup_{i=1}^{3} (A_i) \right)$ and $\bigcap_{i=1}^{3} (c(A_i))$

would represent in this case.

(d) Repeat part (c) of this exercise in the case of the second law of dualization, 2.6.8.

2.7 Summary of Terms

In a relatively brief space, the reader has encountered a large set of concepts. Before making use of these, it would be wise to review the work to this point. The basic terms introduced thus far have been the following:

element: undefined, but thought of as an abstract entity (synonym: point).

set: undefined, but thought of as a collection of elements such that, for every element a, either a is a member of the set or it is not. The set is defined either by listing its elements or by defining some property (synonyms: collection, class).

subset: a set, all of whose elements are contained in another set.

Ω: the set of all elements in the domain of discourse.

The operations defined on elements and sets of elements are the following:

union of sets: the operation of forming the set whose elements belong to at least one of a class of sets, denoted

$$\bigcup_{i=1}^{n} (A_i).$$

intersection of sets: forming the set whose elements belong to each of a class of sets, denoted $\bigcap_{i=1}^{n} (A_i)$.

complement of a set A: forming the set consisting of all elements in Ω that are not in A, denoted $c(A)$.

difference of a set B from a set A: the operation of forming the set consisting of all points in A that are not in B, denoted $A - B$.

Beyond this, the following relations have been encountered on sets and on elements of sets:

membership of an element in a set: undefined, denoted $a \in A$ (read "a is an element of A").

nonmembership of an element in a set: denoted $a \notin A$ (read "a is not a member of A").

inclusion of a set in another set: noted $A \subseteq B$ or (A is a subset of B). If $A \subset B$, then $A \subseteq B$ and $A \neq B$.

exclusion of a set from a set: noted $A \nsubseteq B$ (A is not a subset of B).

equality of sets: a relation between sets A and B such that every element of A is an element of B and every element of B is an element of A, denoted $A = B$.

2.8 Summary of Rules for Operations on Sets

Title

Commutative	I	$A_1 \cup A_2 = A_2 \cup A_1$.
	II	$A_1 \cap A_2 = A_2 \cap A_1$.
		$A - B = B - A \leftrightarrow A = B$.
Associative	I	$A_1 \cup (A_2 \cup A_3) = (A_1 \cup A_2) \cup A_3$.
	II	$A_1 \cap (A_2 \cap A_3) = (A_1 \cap A_2) \cap A_3$.
Distributive	I	$A_1 \cap (A_2 \cup A_3)$
		$\quad = (A_1 \cap A_2) \cup (A_1 \cap A_3)$.
	II	$A_1 \cup (A_2 \cap A_3)$
		$\quad = (A_1 \cup A_2) \cap (A_1 \cup A_3)$.
Complementarity	I	$A \cap c(A) = \phi$.
	II	$A \cup c(A) = \Omega$.
Dualization	I	$c(A_1 \cup A_2) = c(A_1) \cap c(A_2)$, in general, $c\left(\bigcup_{i=1}^{n} A_i\right) = \bigcap_{i=1}^{n} (c(A_i))$.
	II	$c(A_1 \cap A_2) = c(A_1) \cup c(A_2)$, in general, $c\left(\bigcap_{i=1}^{n} A_i\right) = \bigcup_{i=1}^{n} (c(A_i))$.
Involution		$c(c(A)) = A$.

Exercises

2.18. Some of the following are true. Locate each true statement and prove it.

(a) $A \subseteq B \to A \subset B$
(b) $A \subset B \to A \subseteq B$
(c) $\{\phi\} \cup \{\phi, \{\phi\}\} = \{\phi\}$
(d) $\{\phi\} \cap \{\phi, \{\phi\}\} = \{\phi\}$
(e) $\{\phi, \{\phi, \{\phi\}\}\} - \{\phi\} = \{\phi, \{\phi\}\}$

2.19. Translate each of the following into English sentences and decide which, if any, are true:

(a) $c(c(A)) = c(c(c(c(A))))$
(b) $A = c(c(c(A)))$
(c) $c(A \cup B) = c(B \cup A)$
(d) $B \cup C = C \cup B$
(e) $c(A \cup B \cup C) = c(A) \cap c(B) \cap c(C)$
(f) $c(A \cap B \cap C) = c(A) \cup c(B) \cup c(C)$

2.20. Translate the commutative and associative laws of set union and intersection into English sentences.

2.21. Prove that the commutative and distributive laws do not apply to set differences.

2.22. Draw Venn diagrams of *four* sets to illustrate each of the following rules of set algebra:

(a) $A \cup B \cup C \cup D = C \cup B \cup D \cup A$
(b) $A \cap (B \cap C) \cap D = (A \cap B) \cap (C \cap D)$
(c) $C(A \cup B \cup C \cup D) = C(A) \cap c(B) \cap c(C) \cap c(D)$

2.23. Prove each of the following:

(a) $A \cup B = (A \cap B) \cup (A \cap c(B)) \cup (c(A) \cap B)$
(b) $(A \cap c(B)) \cup B = A \cup B$
(c) $(A \cup B) \cap B = B$
(d) $A \cap (\Omega - A) = \phi$
(e) $A \cup (\phi) = A$

2.24. For sets A, B, C, D, let all the following be true:
  (1) $B - C = C - B$
  (2) $A \cap D = D$
  (3) $C \cap D = C$
Then, which of the following statements are true?

(a) $A = D$
(b) $A = C$
(c) $B = C$
(d) $C \subseteq A$
(e) $A \subseteq D$
(f) $B \cup D = D$

(g) $A \cup D = A$
(h) $B \cup D = C \cup D$
(i) $B \cap C = B$
(j) $C - B = \phi$

2.25. Prove 2.6.6:

(a) for the case $n = 3$
(b) for the case $n = 5$

2.26. Prove 2.6.8:

(a) for the case $n = 4$
(b) for the case $n = 6$

Selected References

1. Allendoerfer, C. B., and Oakley, C. O. *Principles of Mathematics.* New York: McGraw-Hill Book Company, Inc., 1955. Chapter V.
2. Birkhoff, Garrett, and MacLane, Saunders. *A Survey of Modern Algebra* (Revised Edition). New York: The Macmillan Company, 1953. Chapter XI.
3. Halmos, Paul. *Naive Set Theory.* Princeton, New Jersey: D. Van Nostrand Co., Inc., 1960.
4. Kemeny, John G., Merkil, H., Snell, J. L., and Thompson, G. L. *Finite Mathematical Structures.* Englewood Cliffs, New Jersey: Prentice-Hall, Inc., 1959. Chapter 2, pages 51–70.
5. Kemeny, John G., Snell, J. L., and Thompson, G. L. *Introduction to Finite Mathematics.* Englewood Cliffs, New Jersey: Prentice-Hall, Inc., 1957. Chapter 2.
6. Kirshner, R. B., and Wilcox, L. R. *The Anatomy of Mathematics.* New York: The Ronald Press Company, 1950. Chapter 4.
7. Russell, Bertrand. *Introduction to Mathematical Philosophy.* London: George Allen and Unwin, Ltd., 1919. Chapter 2.
8. Suppes, Patrick. *Axiomatic Set Theory.* Princeton, New Jersey: D. Van Nostrand Co., Inc., 1960. Pages 1–32.
9. Tarski, Alfred. *Introduction to Logic* (Second Revised Edition). New York: Oxford University Press, 1946. Chapter 4.

Relations on Sets

A remarkably brief list of primitive notions was required to develop the algebra of sets: *set*, *subset*, and certain terms from logic (*and*, *or*, *if* ··· *then*, *in*, *only*, *not*). If one new notion, that of *ordered pair*, is added to this list, the system of Chapter 2 can be expanded to embrace a concept that is among the most important in mathematics: the concept of relations. The importance of this idea, which will *not* be included among the primitive notions, was indicated in the discussion of science and the scientific method in Chapter 1.

3.1 The Ordered Pair

From the definition of equality in 2.4.1, it should be clear that the two sets $\{a_1, a_2\}$ and $\{a_2, a_1\}$ are equal. The order in which the elements of a set are listed is completely arbitrary. The notion of order, however, is indispensable to us in studying relations. Consider, for example, two persons related by the statement "is younger than." It is clear that, if Mr. A is younger than Mr. B, Mr. B is *not* younger than Mr. A. The relationship "is younger than" can be made meaningful for this pair only if the two members of the pair are ordered.

A set consisting of two elements, a_1 and a_2, in which the order is specified, will be called an *ordered pair* and will be noted $\langle a_1, a_2 \rangle$. The reader must understand that sets and ordered pairs are distinguished from one another by the following:

$$\{a_1, a_2\} = \{a_2, a_1\}.$$
$$\langle a_1, a_2 \rangle \neq \langle a_2, a_1 \rangle.$$

Two sets, then, are equal if they contain the same elements, regardless of the order in which the elements are listed; but two ordered pairs are said to be equal only if they contain identical elements *and* only if the elements are listed in identical order. None of this constitutes a definition, of course. Rather, it is an intuitive explanation of what is represented by the primitive notion of ordered pair.

3

The ordered pair idea provides a means for constructing a mathematical representation of the idea of relationships. Without this concept, there could be no such thing as science. In the ensuing discussion, two similar but quite distinct terms will be used, and it is important that the reader understand clearly the ways in which they differ. The terms are *relationship* and *relation*. By a relationship we mean a *property* that defines a relation. *Relation* means a set of ordered pairs generated by a relationship. Thus, the predicate phrase ". . . is the husband of . . ." defines a relationship, so long as the word husband is specified adequately. The relation generated by this relationship is a set of ordered pairs. One element of a typical ordered pair, say the first, is a married male. The second element is his wife.

3.2 The Cartesian Product

In the next section, a relation will be defined as a pairing of certain elements in one set with elements in another. As a first step toward the analysis of relations, it is reasonable to examine the set of all possible ordered pairs that can be constructed between two sets. This set is called the *Cartesian product*, or, sometimes, the *product set*. It is defined as follows:

(3.2.1) If A and B are sets, then the Cartesian product set defined on A to B, denoted $A \times B$, is: **Definition**

$$A \times B = \{\langle a, b \rangle : a \in A \text{ and } b \in B\}.$$

Because the multiplication sign (cross) is used to denote the Cartesian product, $A \times B$ is sometimes called the *cross-product* of A and B.

Each element $a \in A$ is contained in as many ordered pairs as there are elements $b \in B$. Notice in particular that the definition says nothing that would prevent one from forming the Cartesian product of a set with itself, that is, a set of the form $A \times A$.

If $A = \{a_1, a_2, a_3\}$ and $B = \{b_1, b_2\}$, then the Cartesian product $A \times B$ contains six elements (ordered pairs) and can be represented as follows:

$A \times B = \{\langle a_1, b_1 \rangle, \langle a_1, b_2 \rangle, \langle a_2, b_1 \rangle, \langle a_2, b_2 \rangle, \langle a_3, b_1 \rangle, \langle a_3, b_2 \rangle\}.$

The reader must recognize that a Cartesian product set is just a set and, hence, is subject to all rules of set operations that were developed in Chapter 2. Thus, for example, the order in which the elements are listed is unimportant. But since the elements themselves are ordered pairs, the order of the two elements making up each pair is quite important.

It must be perfectly clear that we are now dealing with elements of two kinds: those which might be called *irreducible* and those which are made up of ordered pairs of irreducible elements. Despite this difference, both types are treated identically in set theoretic analysis.

Exercises

3.1. Where $A = \{a_1, a_2, a_3, a_4\}$ and $B = \{b_1, b_2\}$ construct:

(a) $A \times B$
(b) $B \times A$
(c) $A \times A$
(d) $B \times B$

3.2. Where $A_1 = \{a_1, a_2\}$ and $A_2 = \{a_2, a_1\}$, construct:

(a) $A_1 \times A_2$
(b) $A_2 \times A_1$
(c) Compare and contrast 3.2 (a) and (b) with 3.1 (a) and (b). What can you say about Cartesian products when the two crossed sets are equal?

3.3. Where $A = \{1, 2, 3\}$ and $B = \{4, 5\}$, construct:

(a) $A \times B$
(b) $B \times A$
(c) $A \times A$

3.4. Suppose that a fraternity has four active members and three pledge members. As part of "Hell Week" activities, the fraternity decides to have one of the pledges dress as a coed and go to a dance with one of the active members. How many choices for pledge-active couples are available for the fraternity to choose among? Represent this in the form of a cartesian product set.

3.3 Relations

Rather than attempting to discuss specific relations, it will be far more efficient at first to think in terms of the set of all relations. Call a relation on the sets A and B the set R. Then R, itself, is the set of ordered pairs that satisfies the conditions of some relationship. That is,

(3.3.1) A relation on a set, A, to a set, B, is any subset of $A \times B$, and will be denoted by a capital letter, as with any set.   **Definition**

This defines what is known as a *binary* relation and is a special case of *n*-ary relations. A *ternary* relation is a set whose elements are ordered triples of the form $\langle a_1, a_2, a_3 \rangle$. An *n*-ary relation, then, is a set whose elements are ordered *n*-tuples of the form $\langle a_1, a_2, \cdots, a_n \rangle$. In this book, we shall be concerned primarily with binary relations. Whenever the word relation is encountered, the word binary is implied unless otherwise noted.

From 2.4.2, which stated that $A \subseteq A$ for all sets A, it follows that $A \times B$ is itself a relation. The Cartesian product of sets is called the *universal* relation. The notion that a is related to b by R will be expressed aRb. Thus, if R is the relationship "is the husband of," and if a, a male, is married to b, a female, then aRb. That is,

(3.3.2) For an ordered pair, $\langle a, b \rangle$, and a relation, R, if $\langle a, b \rangle \in R$, then we write aRb.   **Notation**

The symbol R is used in two different ways in this notation, but it defines the same set in both cases. The sentence "$\langle a, b \rangle \in R$" is read "the ordered pair $\langle a, b \rangle$ is an element of R." The sentence "aRb" is read "element a is paired to element b by the relationship R." It is clear that the *set* R is uniquely defined by aRb.

Exercises

3.5. Let A be the set {George, Abraham, Lunt}, and let B be the set {Sarah, Martha, Fontaine}.
(a) Construct $A \times B$.
(b) Construct the set defined by aQb where Q is given by the relationship "is the husband of."

3.6. Consider sets A and B in which $A = \{$John, Sally, Peter, Kay$\}$ and $B = \{$Paul, George, Casey, Judy$\}$. Let S be given by the relationship "is of the sex opposite to that of." Construct S on:

(a) $A \times A$
(b) $A \times B$
(c) $B \times A$
(d) $B \times B$

3.7. Consider the sets A and B, in which

$A = \{1, 2, 3, 4, 5, 6, 9, 12\}$
$B = \{1, 3, 4, 5, 6\}$

Construct the set defined by aRb in which R represents the relationship:

(a) is twice
(b) is half
(c) is three times
(d) equals
(e) is less than
(f) is less than or equal to

3.8. Let $A = \{$San Juan, New York, Philadelphia, Chicago$\}$. Interpet $A \times A$ demographically as a migration network. In particular, what would be represented by $\langle a_i, a_i \rangle$, where a_i is the ith city in the set?

3.9. Let S be a set of four persons in interaction. Construct relations representing communication on $S \times S$ such that:

(a) one person is snubbed;
(b) no communication is reciprocated;
(c) the set S degenerates into two two-person groups.

3.4 Illustrations of Relations

Consider the chicken. In a peer group he manifests a remarkable phenomenon that is generally called the pecking order. Each element in a set of chickens appears to abide by a set of rules whereby, if a pecks b, then b proceeds to his own scapegoat (or scapechicken, if one prefers), which is never a, and delivers it a peck in retaliation. The current victim then seeks out *his* assigned peckee, and the chain of retribution continues in a regular fashion. All this is interesting not merely because it is so alien to the altruistic behavior of human groups, whether in Lidice, Warsaw, or Birmingham, but also because it can be represented efficiently as a set-theoretic relation.

Let $P \subset A \times A$, where A is a set of chickens. Then if P is a pecking relation, certain properties must be true of it. For instance, if we assume that chickens are not masochistic, $\langle a, a \rangle \notin P$. Further, $\langle a, b \rangle \in P \rightarrow \langle b, a \rangle \notin P$. Finally, if each chicken is assigned exactly one victim, then it follows that $\langle a, b \rangle \in P$ and $\langle a, c \rangle \in P \leftrightarrow b = c$. It will be seen later that these are basic properties of many important relations. If P were a dominance relation on a set of people to the same set, might it have properties different from or in addition to those of P?

Other examples of relations can be obtained by examining subsets of $A \times B$ where A is the set of all human males and B is the set of all human females. Certain subsets of this Cartesian product define the following relationships:

(3.4.2)   is a relative of
(3.4.3)   is the son of
(3.4.4)   is married to
(3.4.5)   knows
(3.4.6)   likes

Moreover, each of these examples, except for 3.4.4, illustrates another point, briefly mentioned above. A perfectly acceptable and frequently useful universal relation is the cross product of a set, A, with itself—that is, $A \times A$. If A were the set of all human males, as above, then the relationships 3.4.2, 3.4.3, 3.4.5, and 3.4.6 also could be defined on $A \times A$ as well as $A \times B$.

Exercises

3.10. Let the relations generated by the relationships of 3.4.2–3.4.6 be designated by R_2, R_3, R_4, R_5, and R_6 respectively. Assume that these relations are on $A \times A$, where A is the set of humans. Determine for which of these five relations, R_i, the following are true for all elements $x \in A$, $y \in A$, and $z \in A$:

(a) $\langle x, y \rangle \in R_i \leftrightarrow \langle y, x \rangle \in R_i$
(b) $\langle x, y \rangle \in R_i \rightarrow \langle y, x \rangle \notin R_i$
(c) $\langle x, y \rangle \in R_i$ and $\langle y, z \rangle \in R_i \rightarrow \langle x, z \rangle \in R_i$
(d) $\langle x, x \rangle \in R_i$

3.11. List the properties of the relations $=$ ("equals") and $<$ ("is less than") on $A \times A$, where A is the set of numbers.

3.5 Algebra of Relations

Since it is a set, a relation is subject to all operations defined on sets. Thus:

Definition

(3.5.1) If R and S are relations on $A_1 \times A_2$,

(1) $R \cup S = \{\langle a_1, a_2 \rangle \, \epsilon \, A_1 \times A_2 : a_1 R a_2 \text{ or } a_1 S a_2 \}$.

(2) $R \cap S = \{\langle a_1, a_2 \rangle \, \epsilon \, A_1 \times A_2 : a_1 R a_2 \text{ and } a_1 S a_2 \}$.

(3) $S - R = \{\langle a_1, a_2 \rangle \, \epsilon \, A_1 \times A_2 : a_1 S a_2 \text{ and not } a_1 R a_2 \}$.

(4) $c(S) = \{\langle a_1, a_2 \rangle \, \epsilon \, A_1 \times A_2 : a_1 S / a_2 \}$.

To illustrate these operations, let A_1 be the set of all human females and A_2 be the set of all human males. Let R be the relation given by the relationship "is the wife of," and let S be the relation given by "is the mother of." Then Part 1 of 3.5.1 comprises the set of all opposite-sexed couples who are either mother and son or wife and husband. Part 2 singles out the considerably smaller set of couples who are both mother and son *and* wife and husband (Jocasta and Oedipus are an ordered pair in this set). Part 3 consists of all mother-son pairs who are not married to one another. Part 4 consists of all pairs of females and males who are not mother and son respectively. These four operations can be combined according to the rules summarized in Section 2.8.

From the notion of an ordered pair, $\langle a_1, a_2 \rangle$, and of a relation on $A_1 \times A_2$, it is clear that the sets A_1 and A_2 must be distinguished even if they are identical. To do this, it is necessary to introduce the logician's idea of a *quantifier*. A quantifier is a phrase used to qualify the status of a variable in a sentence. Each of the following three phrases is a quantifier: (a) there exists one and only one; (b) there exists (one or more); (c) for all (or for each). These will be seen in sentences such as "For each a there exists one and only one b such that . . . ," or "For each a there exists b such that . . . ," or "For each a it is true that for all b. . . ." Notice how quantifiers are used in the following definition, which distinguishes between the two sets on which a relation is defined.

(3.5.2) If R is a relation defined on set A to set B, then the   **Definition**
domain and range of R are given by:

(1) Domain of $R = \{a: a \in A,$ and there exists $b \in B$ such

that $\langle a, b \rangle \in R\}$.

(2)   Range of $R = \{b: b \in B,$ and there exists $a \in A$ such

that $\langle a, b \rangle \in R\}$.

In the illustration used with definition 3.5.1, the domain of S is the set of all women who had sons. The range of S is the set, A_2, consisting of all males, since it is presumed that every male had a mother. Where A is the domain and B the range of R, the relation is said to exist "on A to B."

The *transpose*, $t(R)$, *of a relation on* $A \times B$ is a subset of $B \times A$ and is defined as follows:

(3.5.3) If $R \subseteq A \times B$, then the transpose of R, noted   **Definition**
$t(R)$ is given by:

$$t(R) = \{\langle b, a \rangle \in B \times A: \langle a, b \rangle \in R\}.$$

That is, if the ordered pair $\langle a, b \rangle$ is in the set defined by R, then the ordered pair $\langle b, a \rangle$ is in the set defined by $t(R)$. In many cases, the transpose of a "sensible" relation is itself a sensible relation. The relation "is a parent of" is the transpose of the relation "is the offspring of."

Exercises

3.12. A useful tool in describing relations is a diagram of the following sort: a dot at the intersection of a particular column and row stands for the existence of a pair. Conventionally, the column position represents the first member of the pair, called the *domain* member (see 3.5.2), and the row position represents the second element, called the *range* member. Thus, if $A = \{a_1, a_2, a_3\}$ and $B = \{b_1, b_2, b_3\}$ and $R = \{\langle a_1, b_2 \rangle, \langle a_3, b_1 \rangle, \langle a_3, b_2 \rangle\}$ R would be shown as:

$$
\begin{array}{c|ccc}
b_3 & & & \\
b_2 & \cdot & & \cdot \\
b_1 & & & \cdot \\
\hline
& a_1 & a_2 & a_3
\end{array}
$$

(a) Show $A \times B$ in this example.

(b) Show $B \times A$. (Note that the elements of the form b_i now represent the columns and a_i the rows.)

(c) Show $c(R)$.

(d) Show $c(c(R))$.

(e) Show $(A \times B) - R$. Compare this with $c(R)$.

(f) Show $t(R)$.

3.13. Consider:

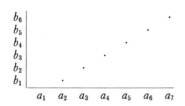

Where the elements of the form a_i are from a set, A, of gross prices of wheat in dollars, and the elements of the form b_i are from the set B, which is a set of bushels of wheat purchased:

(a) Write out R.

(b) What could R mean in words?

3.14. Let A be the set of all students and B the set of all Ivy League universities. Let R be the relation given by "is a female student at" and S be the relation given by "is a student at," with $R, S, \subseteq A \times B$. Describe in words the following subsets:

(a) $R \cap S$

(b) $R \cup S$

(c) $S - R$

(d) $c(R \cup S)$

3.15. Let A be the set $\{a_1, a_2, a_3, a_4, a_5\}$ and B be the set $\{b_1, b_2, b_3, b_4, b_5, b_6\}$.

Also, let R_1 be the set $\{\langle a_1, b_2 \rangle, \langle a_1, b_1 \rangle, \langle a_1, b_3 \rangle\}$.

let R_2 be the set $\{\langle a_1, b_1 \rangle, \langle a_2, b_2 \rangle, \langle a_3, b_3 \rangle, \langle a_4, b_4 \rangle\}$.

let R_3 be the set $\{\langle a_1, b_2 \rangle, \langle a_3, b_2 \rangle, \langle a_4, b_5 \rangle, \langle a_5, b_6 \rangle\}$.

(a) List $R_1 \cup R_2$.

(b) List $R_1 \cap R_2$; $R_1 \cap R_3$.

(c) List $R_1 - (R_2 \cup R_3)$.

(d) List the domain and range of R_1, R_2, and R_3.

(e) List $t(R_1), t(R_2), t(R_3)$.

(f) Show $t(R_1), t(R_2), t(R_3)$ using the tool introduced in Exercise 3.13.

(g) Show R_1, R_2, R_3 as in (f). Compare (f) and (g).

3.16. If $A = \{1, 2, 4, 10\}$, $B = \{4, 5, 6, 9, 12, 16\}$, R_1 is the relationship "is twice," R_2 is the relationship "is greater than," and R_3 is the relationship "is half," with $R_1, R_2, R_3 \subseteq A \times B$, list the subsets given by:

(a) $R_1 \cup R_2$

(b) $R_1 \cap R_2$

(c) $R_1 \cap R_3$
(d) $t(R_2)$
(e) $t(R_1)$
(f) $t(R_3)$

3.17. Prove that $R \subseteq A \times B \to R \cup c(R) = A \times B$.

3.18. If R and S are relations such that $R, S \subseteq A \times B$, prove that:

(a) $R \cup S = S \cup R$.
(b) $R \cap S = S \cap R$.
(c) $S - R \neq R - S$ unless $S = R$.

3.19. A relation, I, on $A \times A$, called the *identity relation*, is given by $I = \{\langle a, b \rangle : a, b \in A$ and $a = b\}$. Some examples of elements in identity relation sets are $\langle a, a \rangle$, $\langle b_j, b_j \rangle$, $\langle 3, 3 \rangle$. In Exercise 3.12,

(a) show I on $A \times A$, on $B \times B$.
(b) show $c(I)$ on $A \times A$.

3.6 Properties of Relations

The illustrative relationships, 3.4.2–3.4.6, differ from one another in more than the fact that they do not all define identical relations. "Is a relative of" and "is the son of" are certainly similar, the latter being a subset of the former. The two differ, however, in certain very important respects. Call the former relation R_1 and the latter, R_2. If we say that all members of the same family are related, it is obvious that every man is related to himself. No man is his own father, however. Thus, for any element, a, in the set of all people, aR_1a, but $a\not{R_2}a$ where $\not{R}$ (read "not R") means that the set R does not contain an ordered pair of the form $\langle a, a \rangle$. R_1 is said to be *reflexive* and R_2 to be *irreflexive*. Formally,

(3.6.1) A relation, R, on $A \times A$ is reflexive $\leftrightarrow aRa$ for every $a \in A$.   **Definition**

(3.6.2) A relation, R, on $A \times A$ is irreflexive $\leftrightarrow a\not{R}a$ for every $a \in A$, where $a\not{R}a$ means $\langle a, a \rangle \notin R$.   **Definition**

Two relations already encountered are reflexive. These are given by the relationships of equality and inclusion (of subsets in sets). Their negations, $\neq$ and $\not\subseteq$, are clearly irreflexive.

Consider the relation given by "likes." This relation is not reflexive; we all know people who do not like themselves. On the other hand, this certainly is not an irreflexive relation, because most of us do like ourselves. It seems, then, that we must recognize a third classification of relations. Relations that are neither reflexive nor irreflexive are called *non-reflexive*.

(3.6.3) A relation, R, on $A \times A$ is non-reflexive $\leftrightarrow$ there exists a_1, and $a_2 \in A$ such that $a_1 R a_1$ and $a_2 \not\!R a_2$.   **Definition**

The two relationships, R_1, "is a relative of" and R_2, "is the son of," differ in another respect. (Here consider R_1, and R_2 defined on the cross product of the set of males to the set of males.) For every ordered pair $\langle a, b \rangle \in R_1$, it is also true that $\langle b, a \rangle \in R_1$. That is, if a is a relative of b, then b certainly is a relative of a. Whenever $a R_2 b$, however, it must be the case that $b \not\!R_2 a$. This says simply enough that if a is the son of b, then it is never the case that b is the son of a. R_1 is said to be *symmetric*, and R_2 is said to be *asymmetric*. That is,

(3.6.4) A relation, R, is symmetric on $A \times A \leftrightarrow$ for every ordered pair, $\langle a, b \rangle \in A \times A$ such that $a R b$, then $b \not\!R a$.   **Definition**

(3.6.5) A relation, R, is asymmetric $\leftrightarrow$ for every ordered pair, $\langle a, b \rangle \in A \times A$ such that $a R b$, then $b R a$.   **Definition**

These two definitions do not take into consideration an extremely important class of relations. The *inclusion relation*, for example, certainly is not symmetric, as the following counterexample will show. Let $A = \{a_1, a_2\}$ and $B = \{a_1, a_2, a_3\}$. Then $A \subseteq B$, but $B \not\subseteq A$. There are, however, situations in which, for two sets A and B, $A \subseteq B$ and $B \subseteq A$. Definition 2.4.1, the definition of set equality, tells us that this situation obtains only when $A = B$. There are, then, cases in which relations are symmetric *only* with respect to equal elements. This class of relations is important enough to be given a label of its own. It is called the *anti-symmetric* class of relations and is defined:

Definition

(3.6.6) A relation, R, is *antisymmetric* on $A \times A \leftrightarrow$ for every $\langle a, b \rangle \in A \times A$ such that aRb and bRa, then $a = b$.

The antisymmetric property may be thought of as a combination of two others, namely, asymmetry and reflexiveness. That is, if any two elements, a and b, in an antisymmetric relation are distinct, then they are asymmetric in the sense that $aRb \rightarrow b\not{R}a$. On the other hand, if aRb and $b\not{R}a$ then $a = b$, but this is the reflexive property. A relationship that generates an antisymmetric relation usually contains the phrase "at least as . . . as . . . ," or the equivalent. For example, the relationships "is at least as tall as," "is no smarter than," and "has at least as much influence as" all generate antisymmetric relations. Notice that antisymmetric relations include the equality relation. Equality is unique in that it is both symmetric and antisymmetric (for simplicity, equality will be called a symmetric relation).

Life would indeed be less complicated if all relations were either symmetric, asymmetric, or antisymmetric. Consider the relationship "loves." If, whenever a loves b, b loves a, our world would be a considerably less difficult, if somewhat duller, place in which to live. But sometimes a loves b and b does not love a. That such is the case indicates that we have not exhausted the symmetry properties of relations. The addition of one more class, however, will accomplish this. A relation is said to be nonsymmetric on a set of ordered pairs if it is neither symmetric nor asymmetric. That is,

Definition

(3.6.7) A relation, R, on a set $A \times A$, is nonsymmetric $\leftrightarrow$ there exist $\langle a_1, b_1 \rangle$, $\langle a_2, b_2 \rangle \in R$ such that b_1Ra_1 and $b_2\not{R}a_2$.

The symmetry property of relations is particularly important to social scientists. To understand this, one need only consider such relationships as "loves," "hates," "communicates with," "chooses" (in a sociometric choice situation), and "is willing to negotiate with." The entire complexion of interpersonal relationships hinges on whether or not they generate symmetric relations.

Still another property of some relations is known as

transitivity. To get an idea of the significance of this property, consider again the two illustrative relationships, R_1, "is a relative of," and R_2, "is the son of." Suppose that the two ordered pairs $\langle a_1, b_1 \rangle$ and $\langle b_1, c_1 \rangle$ are in R_1. Similarly, suppose that $\langle a_2, b_2 \rangle$ and $\langle b_2, c_2 \rangle$ are in R_2. Note carefully that an element, b_1, "links" the two pairs in R_1, and that b_2 "links" the two pairs in R_2. Because of these linkages, it should be possible to say something about the *new* ordered pairs, $\langle a_1, c_1 \rangle$ and $\langle a_2, c_2 \rangle$. The ordered pair $\langle a_1, c_1 \rangle$ is in R_1 by the definition of this relation. That is, if a_1 is related to b_1, and if b_1 is related to c_1, then a_1 must be related to c_1, at least if R_1 is restricted to "blood" relationships. The ordered pair $\langle a_2, c_2 \rangle$, on the other hand, cannot be in R_2. That is, $a_2 R_2 b_2$ means that a_2 is the son of b_2, and $b_2 R_2 c_2$ means that b_2 is the son of c_2, from which it can be concluded that a_2 is the *grandson* of c_2. If kinship situations of the "I'm my own grandpa" sort are disregarded and it is agreed that the grandson of a person is never the son of that same person, then it follows that $a_2 \not{R}_2 c_2$ or, equivalently, $\langle a_2, c_2 \rangle \notin R_2$. The relation R_1 is called *transitive*; R_2 is called *intransitive*. More generally:

(3.6.8) A relation, R, is said to be transitive in the set $A \times A \leftrightarrow$ for every $a_1 \in A$, $a_2 \in A$, $a_3 \in A$, if $a_1 R a_2$ and $a_2 R a_3$, then $a_1 R a_3$.   **Definition**

(3.6.9) A relation, R, is said to be *intransitive* in the set $A \times A \leftrightarrow$ for every $a_1 \in A$, $a_2 \in A$, $a_3 \in A$, if $a_1 R a_2$ and $a_2 R a_3$, then $a_1 \not{R} a_3$.   **Definition**

Once again, a bit of reflection leads to the conclusion that transitivity and intransitivity are not exhaustive classes. The relationship "likes," or even "knows," for that matter, certainly is not transitive on the set of all people. A common problem in the area of friendships, jealousy, frequently stems from the fact that a likes (or loves, if one prefers to be more dramatic) b, that b likes c, but that a does not like c at all. In some mutual admiration societies, however, there are members x, y, and z, all of whom like one another, thus making the relation transitive in this particular subset of people. A relation that is neither transitive nor intransitive is said to be *nontransitive*.

(3.6.10) A relation, R, is nontransitive on $A \times A$ if there exist elements in $A \times A$ $\langle a_1, a_2 \rangle$, $\langle a_2, a_3 \rangle$ and $\langle a_1, a_3 \rangle \; \epsilon \; R$ and if there exist elements $\langle a_4, a_5 \rangle$ and $\langle a_5, a_6 \rangle \; \epsilon \; R$ but $\langle a_4, a_6 \rangle \; \notin \; R$.

Definition

Much of what is called orderliness in nature is nothing more than transitivity. Economists and other social scientists have long been excited about the transitivity property of relations in connection with the search for a useful definition of rationality. Among the most important of aspects of human behavior studied by social scientists is decision-making, which sometimes appears to be intuitively rational and at other times appears to be decidedly nonrational. Why do some people decide to vote for candidate A rather than candidate B? Why do some consumers decide to purchase Brand X rather than some other brand of the same product? Questions similar to these have led social scientists to investigate preference relations that people have on sets of commodities. Some have asserted that the rational man is the one whose preference patterns are uniformly transitive. Most social scientists, however, would say that this is an inadequate definition, but that transitivity must play a necessarily important role in any satisfactory definition.

3.7 Properties of ϵ, $\subset$ and $=$.

The reader may still harbor doubts as to the importance for social science of the preceding subject matter. One cannot contest the fact that every preceding definition could have been offered in ordinary English rather than in the cryptic symbols of mathematics. While the language of sets and relations is important to social scientists for several reasons, one reason overwhelms the others. Mathematical symbolism is far more precise than garden-variety English. Because of this precision, statements and their consequences can be expressed in set symbols with less possibility of misunderstanding or distortion than would obtain if another language were used. To illustrate this, and at the same time to point out the distinctive properties of three important relations, consider the following statements:

(3.7.1)   Roger is a mouse.
(3.7.2)   Roger is my favorite mouse.
(3.7.3)   Mice are rodents.

Now these are statements of relationship, and all appear to be completely unambiguous. Notice, however, that in each case the relationship is expressed as a form of the verb *to be*. In this sense, the relationships are indistinguishable. In set-theoretic terminology, however, the relations that they generate not only are distinguishable but also have quite different properties. Let us translate the statements into the language of sets and set-theoretic relations. Let r stand for Roger, M for the set of mice, and R for the set of rodents. Then the three statements become the following:

(3.7.4) $r \in M$.
(3.7.5) $r =$ the mouse that is my favorite.
(3.7.6) $M \subseteq R$.

Consider first the relationship "is an element of," $\in$. Membership is irreflexive because an element is never a member of itself. An element is always a member of a set, never of an element. Furthermore, membership is asymmetric because a set is never an element of one of its own elements, although it may be an element of another set. That is, even if $a \in A$, $A \notin a$. Finally, membership is non-transitive. For example, the element a is in the set $\{a, b\}$, and the set $\{a, b\}$ is in the set $B = \{\pi,$ Stravinski, $\{a, b\}$, Astabula$\}$, but the element a is not in the latter set. The reader may still feel that the relationship $\in$ is transitive, that if $a \in \{a, b\}$ and $\{a, b\} \in B$, the element a is lodged in the set B. But this is not the case, because $\{a, b\}$ is itself an *element* in a set and is distinct from the element a. In fact, $a \neq \{a\}$; that is, an element a and a *set* consisting of the element a are themselves two different things.

The relationship of equality obviously generates different properties. From 2.4.1 it should be clear that equality is reflexive and symmetric. It is certainly true that $A = A$ and that, if $A = B$, then $B = A$. It is also immediately evident that if $A = B$ and $B = C$, then $A = C$. Thus, equality is also transitive.

Finally, the relation of inclusion is distinct both from that of membership and from that of equality. From 2.4.1 we see that inclusion is reflexive, that is, $A \subseteq A$ for every set A. This relation, however, is antisymmetric, for the only case in which $A \subseteq B$ and $B \subseteq A$ is the case in which $A = B$. The inclusion relation, as with equality, is transitive, for if $A \subseteq B$ and $B \subseteq C$, then clearly, $A \subseteq C$. The distinctive properties of these three relations are summarized in Table 3.7.1.

Table 3.7.1   PROPERTIES OF THE RELATIONS MEMBERSHIP, INCLUSION AND EQUALITY

Property	Relation		
	ϵ	$\subseteq$	$=$
Reflexivity	Irreflexive	Reflexive	Reflexive
Symmetry	Asymmetric	Antisymmetric	Symmetric
Transitivity	Nontransitive	Transitive	Transitive

This certainly shows that, although the verbs in statements 3.7.1–3.7.3 are indistinguishable when stated as relationships in English, they imply quite different things and have different relational properties.

Exercises

3.20. Let $A = \{a, b\}$. Using both diagram (see Exercise 12) and enumeration of the specific sets, show:

(a) all elements in the Cartesian product, $A \times A$,
(b) three reflexive relations contained in $A \times A$,
(c) all symmetric relations contained in $A \times A$.

3.21. What properties of relations are illustrated by the following relationships?

(a) older than
(b) not equal to

(c) angry at
(d) similar to

3.22. In his book *Models of Man*, Herbert A. Simon suggests that the word "cause" should be used carefully when describing a relationship between two or more variables. He suggests that the term "interdependence" would be a better choice in many instances. However, he makes clear that whenever "cause" is an appropriate term, the relation between two variables must have one of the properties of relations discussed in this section of the book. Can the reader guess the property? What property should a relation have to be termed one of "interdependence"?

3.23. In an attempt to describe communication in small groups, Bavelas, in his article, Mathematical Model for Group Structures, uses the notion of *cell* and a relation he calls "touching." Two of the five basic assumptions he lists are:

(1) If cell A_1 is touching another cell, A_2, then A_2 is said to be touching cell A_1.
(2) A cell cannot touch itself.

(a) Denote the relation "touching" by R. Restate assumptions 1 and 2 in set-theoretic language.
(b) What kind of relation is R under assumption 1? Assumption 2?

3.24. Many scholars are interested in what constitutes "rational" economic behavior. Consider a person's relation of preference, P, among a set of commodities, so that xPy means x is preferred to y.

(a) If one's economic behavior is rational, what properties of relations should P possess?
(b) Construct a commodity set, A, and construct a rational relation on $A \times A$.
(c) Construct a nonrational relation on $A \times A$.
(d) Which property of a rational relation might be expected to be violated by choice-makers?

3.25. Formally prove that:

(a) $\subseteq$ is transitive.
(b) $\subseteq$ is antisymmetric.
(c) $=$ is transitive. (HINT: Use part (a) of this exercise and 2.4.1 the definition of equality.)

3.26. On what cross-product sets would each of the following relations be defined?

(a) Has been at war with at least once in the twentieth century.
(b) Is diagnosed as being psychologically. . . .
(c) Casts his presidential election ballot for. . . .
(d) Has assessed corporate value of. . . .

3.27. Let $A = \{a, b, c, d\}$. By means of relational diagrams (see Exercise 3.12), show a (nonempty) relation on $A \times A$ that is:

(a) reflexive
(b) symmetric
(c) transitive
(d) symmetric and transitive
(e) irreflexive and transitive

3.28. Suppose that four relations, R, S, T, and U, are contained in $A \times A$ and have these properties:

R	S	T	U
reflexive	irreflexive	reflexive	irreflexive
symmetric	asymmetric	antisymmetric	asymmetric
transitive	transitive	nontransitive	intransitive

(a) Define a relationship that generates each relation.
(b) In English, contrast relations R and U.
(c) In English, contrast relations S and T.

3.29. What can be said about the following relations if R, S, T, and U are as in Exercise 3.27?

(a) $R \cup S$
(b) $R \cap T$
(c) $(R \cap S) \cup (S \cap U)$.
(d) $(S - R)$
(e) $c(U)$

3.30. Some of the following statements are false. Decide which statements are true and give a counterexample for each of the ones that are not.

(a) The complement of a symmetric relation is an asymmetric relation.
(b) The complement of a reflexive relation is an irreflexive relation.
(c) The union of two transitive relations is a transitive relation.
(d) The intersection of a transitive and an intransitive relation is the empty set.
(e) The union of an asymmetric and a reflexive relation is an antisymmetric relation.

3.8 Connectedness

To this point several properties of relations have been classified by examining individual ordered pairs in R. A new dimension can be added to this analysis by examining the entire domain and range of a relation. To show that this will in fact add something new, consider two similar relations: Let R_1 stand for the relationship "is younger than," and R_2, the relationship "is the younger brother of." Define both relations on $A \times A$ where A is the set of all males, and assume that no two males are exactly identical in age. The reader should verify that, in terms of the properties defined to this point, the relations are alike. Both are irreflexive, asymmetric, and transitive. However, when all pairs of distinct elements, a_1 and a_2, in the set A are examined, it becomes clear that the relations are quite different in one respect. In the case of R_1, for every pair of distinct elements in A either xR_1y or yR_1x; that is, either x is younger than y, or y is younger than x, for all x, y in A. This definitely is not the case for R_2, however, since there exist elements, say a and b, in A such that a and b are not brothers, hence $a\cancel{R}_2b$ and $b\cancel{R}_2a$. The relation R_1 is said to be *connected* in A, and R_2 is said to be non-connected.

(3.8.1) A relation, R, defined on $A \times A$, is connected in $A \leftrightarrow$ for every $x \in A$ and $y \in A$, $x \neq y$, either xRy or yRx.   **Definition**

Relationships such as "is older than," "is taller than," "is balder than" are connected in a set of persons if it is assumed that no two people are absolutely indistinguishable in these respects. Kinship relationships, such as "is a second cousin of," on the other hand, seldom are connected in sets of persons.

It is sometimes useful to distinguish between relations that are connected and those that are *strongly connected*. In 3.8.1 connectedness was defined by considering every pair of *distinct* elements. A relation R is said to be strongly connected in a set A if, for every pair of elements, whether or not they are distinct, either xRy or yRx. That is,

(3.8.2) A relation R, defined on $A \times A$, is strongly connected in $A \leftrightarrow$ for every $x \in A$ and $y \in A$, either xRy or yRx.   **Definition**

Clearly, every relation that is strongly connected is connected in A, but not all connected relations are strongly connected. The relation "is younger than," for instance, is connected, but it is not strongly connected. The relation "is at least as old as," however, is strongly connected, since everyone is at least as old as himself. All this leads to the following simple theorem:

(3.8.3) R is strongly connected $\leftrightarrow$ R is connected and reflexive.   **THEOREM**

The proof is left as an exercise.

The property of connectedness can be especially useful

for sociologists. An important sociological concept is that of a secondary group, which is sometimes defined as "a group of people with impersonalized, segmentalized relations among its members."* How much less ambiguous this definition might be if the properties of the relations, especially the connectedness property, were specified clearly. Need each member be connected by means of each relation to every other member? Need the relations be transitive in order to make them relevant to the determination of a secondary group? Are the symmetry properties of the secondary-group relations different from those that are found among primary groups? If sociological theorists paid more attention to questions such as these, the field might develop a considerably more fruitful body of theory than has been the case to date.

Exercises

3.31. Let A be the set of human beings. Indicate which of the following are connected, strongly connected, or nonconnected relations if $R_i \subseteq A \times A$ ($i = 1, 2, 3, 4$) and

(a) R_1 is the relationship "is at least as tall as."
(b) R_2 is the relationship "is heavier than."
(c) R_3 is the relationship "knows."
(d) R_4 is the relationship "is no more heavy than."

3.32. Are the following implications true or false? Explain your answers.

(a) Let R be a relation that is connected; let X be the statement "all elements in the Cartesian cross-product are present in R," hence $R \rightarrow X$.
(b) Let R_0 be a relation that is strongly connected; let X be the same as above, hence $R_0 \rightarrow X$.

3.33. Prove 3.8.3, both implication and converse.

3.34. In what Cartesian cross-product set is each of the following relations contained, and what is the connectedness property of each:

(a) Communicates with (in a small group interactional experiment)
(b) Is at least as intelligent as
(c) Has greater social distance from the referent than

3.35. Determine whether a relation can satisfy the following conditions. If the conditions are not contradictory, then select a relationship from any field of social science that satisfies them:

* Arnold Rose, *Sociology: The Study of Human Relations* (New York: Alfred A. Knopf, 1956), page 562.

(a) Connected, asymmetric, transitive
(b) Strongly connected, irreflexive, nonsymmetric, intransitive
(c) Strongly connected, asymmetric, intransitive
(d) Nonconnected, symmetric, reflexive, transitive

Selected References

1. Allendoerfer, C. B., and Oakley, C. O. *Principles of Mathematics.* New York: McGraw-Hill Book Company, Inc., 1955. Pages 104–123.
2. Bavelas, A. A Mathematical Model for Group Structures. *Applied Anthropology*, 1948, Vol. 7, No. 3, 16–30.
3. Kirshner, R. B., and Wilcox, L. R. *The Anatomy of Mathematics.* New York: The Ronald Press Company, 1950. Chapter 5.
4. Rose, Arnold. *Sociology: The Study of Human Relations.* New York: Alfred A. Knopf, 1956.
5. Suppes, Patrick. *Axiomatic Set Theory.* Princeton, New Jersey: D. Van Nostrand Co., Inc., 1960.
6. Suppes, Patrick. *Introduction to Logic.* Princeton, New Jersey: D. Van Nostrand Co., Inc., 1957. Chapter 10.
7. Tarski, Alfred. *Introduction to Logic* (Second Revised Edition). New York: Oxford University Press, 1946. Chapter 4.

Functions and Correspondences

The word *function* is one of the most abused terms in the vocabulary of social science. Sociologists, to cite one of the more extreme groups of offenders, are prone to use this term at the slightest provocation. In the sociological literature one constantly comes across such terms as functional analysis, functional significance, functional interdependence, latent and manifest functions, and dysfunction.

Those who use these terms usually do so in an attempt to convey one of two ideas. The part that an element plays in a system is often called the *function* of that element in the system; for example, one speaks of the function of organized religion in society or of the liver in the body. In other contexts, the word *function* evidently refers to some sort of relationship between elements in a system; for example, in sociology texts one may read about the functional interdependence of social stratification and occupational specialization. It is not difficult to see that such varied, ill-defined use of a single term can hinder the development of a rigorous body of theory.

Despite the loose fashion in which many social scientists use it, the term *function* has a single, routine, and almost totally unambiguous meaning for one group of theorists. Among mathematicians, the word *function* almost universally refers to a specific subset of the class of relations. This usage is so well established and so important for social theorists that it will be adopted here.

4

4.1 Functions

Consider the two relationships "is the son of" and "is the father of," which are clearly similar. Both are irreflexive, asymmetric, and intransitive. Moreover, neither is connected in the set of all males. The two differ, however, in one extremely important respect. Let R_1 be the relation given by "is the father of," and let R_2 be that given by "is the son of." Note that, for every element in the domain of R_1, there may be one, two, a score, or more than one hundred elements in the range. No man is necessarily restricted to being the father of just one son. On the other hand, every man is restricted to having exactly one (biological) father. Thus, for every element in the domain of R_2, there is exactly one corresponding element in the range. It is this property that distinguishes the two relations and it is because of this distinction that relation R_2 is said to be a function, while R_1 is not.

(4.1.1) A relation, R, on a set A to a set B, is a function $\leftrightarrow$ for every element $a \in A$ there is exactly one element $b \in B$ such that $\langle a, b \rangle \in R$.

Definition

The reader should note that this definition does not require that each element in the range of the relation be unique. For example, the set

$$A = \{\langle a_1, b_1 \rangle, \langle a_2, b_1 \rangle, \langle a_3, b_1 \rangle\}$$

is a function, despite the fact that there are three elements in the domain and only one in the range. In distinction to this, the set

$$B = \{\langle a_1, b_1 \rangle, \langle a_1, b_2 \rangle, \langle a_1, b_3 \rangle\}$$

is not a function, because the three different elements in the range all correspond to the single element, a_1, in the domain.

It is often convenient to represent relations pictorially, a device that may make clearer the notion of function. Figures 4.1.a–4.1.d represent relations. Each of these figures represents four-element sets whose elements are ordered pairs of the form $\langle a, b \rangle$. Each figure, then, represents a relation on $A \times B$, but only three of them represent functions. Before proceeding to the next paragraph, the reader may glance at the figures and decide for himself which of the four is not a function. The figures are to be interpreted as follows: Each dot represents an ordered pair whose members are found by imagining two lines that intersect at the dot; one parallel to the horizontal axis, and the other parallel to the vertical axis. The imagined lines have been drawn in for the dot on the far right of Figure 4.1.a. This dot then represents the ordered pair $\langle a_1, b_1 \rangle$. Throughout this book, whenever a relation is represented by a figure, the domain will appear on the horizontal baseline and the range on the vertical axis.

Figures 4.1.a and 4.1.d are functions since, for every element in the domain, A, there is just one element in the range, B. Moreover, in these two relations, each element $b \in B$ is paired with an element $a \in A$ just once. Figure 4.1.b is a function also, because no element in the domain is

Figure 4.1

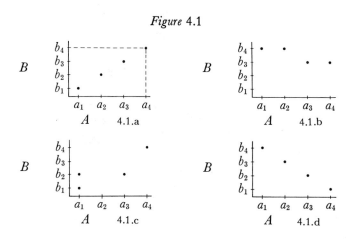

paired with more than one element in the range, even though two elements, b_3 and b_4, in the range are each paired with two elements in the domain. Figure 4.1.c represents a relation that is not a function because $\langle a_1, b_1 \rangle$ and $\langle a_1, b_2 \rangle$ are in the relation depicted by this figure.

These figures suggest an alternate definition of function:

(4.1.2) R is a function on A to $B \leftrightarrow \langle a_1, b_1 \rangle \langle a_1, b_2 \rangle \in R$ implies $b_1 = b_2$.   **Definition**

The reader should verify that this is completely equivalent to definition 4.1.1.

Functions are sometimes referred to as *mappings* of a domain into a range. If F is a function on A to B, F is said to be a mapping of A into B, or the set A is said to be mapped into B by F. This is sometimes noted by $F \colon A \to B$ or $b = F(a)$, which says that an element $b \in B$ is the *F-cor-*

respondent of an element $a \epsilon A$, or, alternatively, that b is the *image* of a under F. The reader would do well to make himself familiar with these phrases; each of the various alternates may be employed in this or in other texts, in an attempt to impart some literary flavor to an extremely basic language.

In many cases, functions can be represented by equations that relate the elements in the domain to their correspondents in the range. As an example, the equation

$$y = 3x + 5$$

represents a function if $x \epsilon X$ and $y \epsilon Y$ on $X \times Y$ where the domain and the range consist of sets of numbers.* For every element, x, in the domain, the corresponding element, y, in the range is that number which equals three times the value of x plus five. If this is represented in the form $f(x) = 3x + 5$, then, for example, $f(3) = 14$ and $f(0) = 5$.

It is perfectly consistent with the definition of function for the range to contain only a very small number of elements, regardless of the number of elements in the domain of definition. Suppose A is the domain consisting of all positive integers (the numbers 1, 2, 3, $\cdots$) and f is a function on $A \times A$ such that for every number less than ten in the domain the f-correspondent is the number two, and that, for every number equal to or greater than ten in the domain, the f-correspondent is twice the value of the number. This function is the following set of ordered pairs:

$$f = \{\langle 1, 2 \rangle, \langle 2, 2 \rangle, \cdots, \langle 9, 2 \rangle, \langle 10, 20 \rangle, \langle 11, 22 \rangle, \cdots\}.$$

A function of this type is sometimes represented as follows:

$$f(x) = \begin{cases} 2 & \text{if } x < 10 \\ 2x & \text{if } x \geq 10 \end{cases} \qquad x = 1, 2, 3, \cdots,$$

where $<$ means "less than" and $\geq$ means "equal to or greater than."

When the domain and range of a function are subsets of the set of real numbers, the function is often denoted f and the f-correspondent $f(x)$. For example, if the domain of f, say X, is the set of all integers, $x \epsilon X$, then the following functions, among many others, can be defined:

---

* See Chapters 5–7 for a discussion of different kinds of numbers.

$$f_1(x) = x^2$$
$$f_2(x) = 3 + 2x.$$
$$f_3(x) = \eta$$

The range of f_1 is a set of nonnegative integers; the range of f_2 is the set of all integers; and the range of f_3 is the single number η, called a *constant*, where η may represent any given number. From these three equations it follows that:

$$f_1 = \{\cdots, \langle -2, 4\rangle, \langle -1, 1\rangle, \langle 0, 0\rangle, \langle 1, 1\rangle, \langle 2, 4\rangle, \cdots\}$$
$$f_2 = \{\cdots, \langle -2, -1\rangle, \langle -1, 1\rangle, \langle 0, 3\rangle, \langle 1, 5\rangle, \langle 2, 7\rangle, \cdots\}$$
$$f_3 = \{\cdots, \langle -2, \eta\rangle, \langle -1, \eta\rangle, \langle 0, \eta\rangle, \langle 1, \eta\rangle, \langle 2, \eta\rangle, \cdots\}.$$

Exercises

4.1. Consider the following sets of ordered pairs:

$$A = \{\langle a_1, b_1\rangle, \langle a_2, b_2\rangle, \langle a_3, b_1\rangle\}$$
$$B = \{\langle a_1, b_2\rangle, \langle a_2, b_2\rangle, \langle a_3, b_3\rangle\}$$
$$C = \{\langle a_1, b_1\rangle, \langle a_1, b_2\rangle, \langle a_1, b_3\rangle\}$$
$$D = \{\langle a_1, b_1\rangle, \langle a_2, b_2\rangle, \langle a_3, b_3\rangle\}$$
$$E = \{\langle b_1, a_1\rangle, \langle b_2, a_1\rangle, \langle b_3, a_3\rangle\}$$

(a) Represent each of the above sets by means of a dot diagram.
(b) Which of the above sets of ordered pairs are functions?

4.2. Let $A \,; \{m, n\}$ and $B = \{p, q\}$. Show all possible nonempty relations that are functions on $A \times B$. (HINT: There are eight.)

4.3. Let a relation, F, on a set, A, be given by $F(a) = a$ for all $a \in A$ (this is called the identity relation). Does $F(a)$ define a function?

4.4. If F and G are two functions such that $F = G$, what can one say about the domain and range of F and G?

4.5. If the domain of two functions, F and G, are equal, does it follow that their ranges are equal? Why?

4.6. If F is a function defined by the Sewell Scale of Socio-Economic Status for rural families, and the domain of F is the set of rural families in the U. S., what is the range of F?

4.7. A constant function is a function defined in such a way that there exists only one element in the range. Consider the function $f(x) = 2$ for all real x. Illustrate by means of a diagram why this relation is a function.

4.8. The word coding sometimes denotes a research procedure by which a symbol is attached to a response in order to identify the response. Does this coding procedure define a function?

4.9. An anthropologist has said: "A change in any of the elements of the culture of a given group of people is functionally related to all other elements." How is this use of the notion of a function related to the definition of a function proposed in this chapter?

4.2 The Inverse of a Function, f^{-1}

Definition 3.5.3 introduced the transpose of a relation, noted $t(R)$, as a new relation constructed by inverting domain and range. That is, if R is a relation and if $\langle a, b \rangle \in R$, then $\langle b, a \rangle \in t(R)$. Since a function is a relation, it should be clear that every function has a transpose. From Definitions 3.5.3 and 4.1.1, we have the following:

(4.2.1) If f is a function on a set A to a set B, then   **Definition**
$t(f) = \{\langle b, a \rangle : a \in A, b \in B \text{ and } \langle a, b \rangle \in f\}$.

It is true that $t(f)$ is a relation, but it is not necessarily the case that it is a function. Consider the relations R_1 and R_2 defined by "is the father of" and "is the son of," respectively. It is clear that $R_1 = t(R_2)$ and that R_2 is a function. However, R_1 is not necessarily a function, since a man may have more than one son. These two relations serve to illustrate the fact that not all functions have transposes that also are functions. At various points in this book it will be convenient to give a special notation to the transpose of a function that is also a function. The usual notation in mathematics is f^{-1}, ("f inverse").

(4.2.2) For any function, f, if $t(f)$ is a function, then $t(f)$ **Definition**
is called the inverse of t, and denoted f^{-1}.

The reader should verify that, in the preceding section, $t(f_1)$ and $t(f_3)$ are not functions, whereas $t(f_2)$ is a function. Thus, f_2^{-1} has meaning, but f_1^{-1} and f_3^{-1} are undefined.

Exercises

4.10.

(a) Construct the transposes of the relations and functions in Exercise 4.1.

(b) Which of these transposes are functions?

4.11. Let $f(x) = x^2$. Then $t(f)$ is not a function. Why? (HINT: What is $f(-2)$? $f(2)$?) Is $g(x) = x^3$ a function? What about $t(g)$?

4.12. Construct the transposes of the following relationships:

(a) "is the wife of"
(b) "is a sibling of"
(c) "was defeated by"
(d) "is the f-correspondent of"

4.13. Construct a relation that has only one element in the range for each element in the domain and that also has only one element in the domain for each element in the range.

(a) Is a relation constructed by the above necessarily a function?

(b) Is the transpose of such a relation necessarily a function?

4.14. Let $f_1 = \{\langle a_1, b_1 \rangle, \langle a_2, b_3 \rangle, \langle a_3, b_2 \rangle\}$
$f_2 = \{\langle a_1, b_1 \rangle, \langle a_2, b_3 \rangle, \langle a_3, b_3 \rangle\}$

(a) What is $f_1(a_2)$?
(b) What is $f_2(a_1)$?
(c) What is $f_1^{-1}(b_2)$?
(d) What is $f_2^{-1}(b_3)$?
(Careful.)

4.3 One-to-One Correspondences

A function f for which $t(f)$ is also a function, is called a *one-to-one correspondence*, or simply a 1-1 correspondence. That is,

(4.3.1) If f is a function such that f^{-1} is defined, then f is called a one-to-one correspondence.   **Definition**

Distinctions between relations, functions, and correspondences can be of great value to social scientists in sharpening their definitions. Consider, for example, the anthropological classification of marriage forms. The terms monogamy, polygyny, polyandry, and group marriage usually require a great amount of space for adequate definition. Typically, the space of course, is filled with words in the author's language, and at least some of these words are subject to several interpretations. In the language of relations, functions, and correspondences, however, the terms could be defined with a minimum of space and confusion. To illustrate, let A be the set of all men; B, the set of all women; and R, a relation on A to B. Say R is given by the relationship "is the husband of." Then,

Illustrative
Definitions

(4.3.2)

(1) R is monogamy if R is a function whose inverse is defined (if R is a 1-1 correspondence).
(2) R is polyandry if R is a function whose inverse is not defined.
(3) R is polygyny if R is a relation (not a function) whose transpose is a function.
(4) R is group marriage if R is a relation (not a function) whose transpose is not a function.

The reader may object that this is all a mirage. After all, the term "is the husband of" was introduced, and this surely is fraught with definitional confusion. Is a man who has lived with a woman for several years "the husband of" the woman even though they have not been legally married? What about civil ceremonies, which are not recognized in certain countries? Is a man "the husband of" a woman if they were not wed in a religious ceremony and if they subsequently reside in a country that recognizes no marriage other than a religious one?

To eliminate these objections, recall that not only does a property define a set, but a set also defines a property. The relationship defined by "is the husband of" may also be defined simply by listing the elements in the set that comprise the relation. The fact that a set is an artifact, constructed by man rather than by nature, is irrelevant. All definitions are man-made. A major advantage of definitions based on sets and relations, as has already been pointed out, is that they eliminate much of the imprecision inherent in most language.

Exercises

4.15. Let $A = \{x_1, x_2, x_3\}$. Show all three-element correspondences on $A \times A$. Graph each. (HINT: There are six.)

4.16. Let I be the set of integers, positive and negative. Which of the functions defined by the following phrases are one-to-one on $A \times A$?

(a) "is half"
(b) "is at least twice"
(c) "is the square of"
(d) "is greater than"
(e) "is the cube of"

4.17. Does the issuing of a serial number to a man in the armed forces define a one-to-one correspondence? Specify the range, the domain.

4.18. Let f be a one-to-one correspondence on $A \times A$ and assume $f(x) = y$. Then for x, $y \in A$, prove:

(a) $f^{-1}(f(x)) = x$.
(b) $f(f^{-1}(y)) = y$.

4.19. Sociometric techniques are often used in the determination of leadership within a social group. For example, members of a group might be asked with whom they would like to engage in a given activity.

(a) Define a relation on a five-person group where leadership exists. Define a second relation on the same group in which leadership does not exist. Is either relation a one-to-one correspondence?
(b) Under what conditions could the relation as defined in (a) be a constant function?

4.4 The Algebra of Functions

In Section 3.5, it was seen that certain operations can be performed on relations. Since functions are special cases of relations, they ought to be subject to these same operations. Certain restrictions are needed, however, if the operations are to make any sense when applied to functions. It is fairly evident that, if f is a function on A to B, $c(f)$ is the set of all ordered pairs in $A \times B$ which are not in f. If f and g are two functions, it is necessary to be somewhat more careful in deciding just what $f \cup g$ and $f \cap g$ amount to. Since f and g are sets of ordered pairs, the union, $f \cup g$, must be a set of ordered pairs whose elements are either in f or in g. Functions f and g may be defined on different domains and different ranges. A union of two or more functions usually will appear rather bizarre, however, unless the functions are defined on a single domain and a single range. The set $\{\langle \text{Mr. } a, \text{ Mrs. } a \rangle, \langle \text{Mr. } b, \text{ Mrs. } b \rangle, \langle 1, 2 \rangle, \langle 3, 4 \rangle, \cdots \}$ may comprise the union of two perfectly sensible functions without itself making much sense. The reader should verify the following by constructing a counterexample to the statement that the union of two functions is also a function.

PROPOSITION

(4.4.1) The union of two functions is not necessarily a function.

The intersection of two or more functions is necessarily the empty set if their respective domains or their ranges are disjoint. Even if the intersections of the domains and the ranges are not empty, it does not necessarily follow that the intersections of the functions are not empty. But if $f \cap g$ is not empty, then the intersection necessarily comprises a function. That is,

THEOREM

(4.4.2) If f and g are functions such that $f \cap g \neq \phi$, then $f \cap g$ is a function.

Proof

(By indirection). Let f and g be functions such that $f \cap g \neq \phi$, and assume that $f \cap g$ is not a function.

(1) There exist two elements $\langle a, b \rangle$ and $\langle a, c \rangle$ in $f \cap g$ such that $b \neq c$. (Hypothesis and 4.1.1)

(2) But $\langle a, b \rangle$ and $\langle a, c \rangle$ are in f and in g. (2.5.7)

(3) Neither f nor g is a function; this fact contradicts the hypothesis. (Step 2 and 4.1.1)

Exercises

4.20. Let $f_1 = \{\langle a_1, b_2 \rangle, \langle a_2, b_2 \rangle, \langle a_3, b_3 \rangle, \langle a_4, b_1 \rangle\}$
$f_2 = \{\langle a_3, b_3 \rangle, \langle a_4, b_4 \rangle, \langle a_5, b_5 \rangle\}$

(a) Is $f_1 \cup f_2$ a function? Show this by means of a diagram.
(b) Is $f_1 \cap f_2$ a function? Show this by means of a diagram.
(c) Is $f_1 - f_2$ a function? Show this by means of a diagram.

4.21. Construct two relations on any subset of $A \times A$, $A = \{a, b, c\}$ that are functions such that $f_1 \cup f_2$ is a function and $f_1 \cap f_2 = \phi$. Is it generally true that if $f_1 \cup f_2$ is a function, then $f_1 \cap f_2$ is empty? If not, provide a counterexample.

4.22. Let A and B be, respectively, the set of females and males in the United States. Let f be a function given by "is the son of the female parent," and let g be the function given by "is the husband of." Is $f \cup g$ a function? What is $f \cap g$?

4.5 Composition of Functions

A uniquely interesting and useful property of functions is that they may sometimes be combined, by a process known as *composition*, into a new function. Composition of functions may be thought of as the operation of constructing the function of a function. The composition of two functions is defined only under the condition that the range of one function is contained in the domain of the other. Suppose, for example, that f is a function on A to B and that g is a function on C to A. Then we may say that for every a, b, c such that $\langle a, b \rangle \in f$ and $\langle c, a \rangle \in g$, $b = f(a)$ and $a = g(c)$. The composition of these functions is written $f(g(c))$ and is itself a function on C to B. Before proceeding to a formal definition, an example or two will help to unravel the skein of words just encountered.

Let Ω consist of a set of humans, with set $A = \{a: a$ is the father of an eldest daughter who is married$\}$, $B = \{b: b$ is a married eldest daughter$\}$, $C = \{c: c$ is a husband$\}$. Then let f be a function on A to B given by the relationship "is the father of," and let g be a function on B to C given by "is the wife of." Then we have $f = \{\langle a, b \rangle: a$ is the father of $b\}$ and $g\{\langle b, c \rangle: b$ is the wife of $c\}$. Now consider a new function, h, given by $h = g(f)$, which could be written $h(a) = g(f(a))$. The term $g(f(a))$ instructs "take the g-correspondent of the element b that is the f-correspondent of the element a." By considering all this carefully, the reader should see that $g(f(a))$ is a linking of two elements into the pair $\langle a, c \rangle$, in which both are males who, furthermore, are related. The element $g(f(a))$ could be written as $g(b)$ if it is understood that this particular element, b, is selected under f by the selection of a particular element, a. But $g(b)$ gives a man, c, who is the husband of the married eldest daughter, b. Then the identity $h(a) = g(f(a))$ gives a particular connection between elements a and c in which a is the father of a particular eldest daughter and c is the husband of the daughter. Thus, $h = \{\langle a, c \rangle \colon a$ is the father-in-law of c, the husband of an eldest daughter$\}$. The function h could be called the father-in-law function. From this discussion, h is seen to be constructable from two simple functions: "is the father" and "is the wife." This is the idea of composition.

As a second example, suppose that a research worker is given the task of obtaining the exact age of a set of subjects. Clearly, the researcher is constructing a function on A, the set of subjects, to B, the set of ages. Call this function, which consists of ordered pairs of people and ages, f. The f-correspondent of an A is some single number $b \, \epsilon \, B$, that is, $b = f(a)$. Now suppose that the researcher completes his task only to learn that the precise age of the subjects was not needed at all. Instead, it was necessary to know only whether the subject was or was not older than 20 years. The researcher must then go over the list of subjects and ages again and reorder them. At this stage he will be constructing a function on the set B to a set C, where C consists of the two elements older than 20 years and not older than 20 years. Call these elements c_1 and c_2, respectively. Let the function g consist of all ordered pairs with the first element from the set of ages and the second from the set C. To complete his task, the worker must take the function of a function, that is, he must construct a composition of the two functions, f and g. In order to be systematic, he may write down the expression $g(f(a))$. Note that this is indeed what he needs, namely, ordered pairs in $A \times C$. In practice, he would proceed as follows: For the f-correspondent of each $a \, \epsilon \, A$, he would obtain the g-correspondent, which is an element in C. He would then pair each a with the g-correspondent obtained. Note that the result is a function consisting of ordered pairs $\langle a, c \rangle$. Once this set is obtained, the job is completed.

Still another example of the composition of functions is provided by the area in which this operation is probably most useful, the composition of functions of real numbers. Consider the following three functions, defined on the cross-product of the set of real numbers with itself.

$$f(x) = x - 2$$
$$g(x) = 2x + 4.$$
$$h(x) = \tfrac{1}{2}x$$

Then,

$$
\begin{aligned}
g(f(x)) &= g(x - 2), && \text{(since } f(x) = x - 2) \\
&= 2(x - 2) + 4, && \text{(since } g(x) = 2x + 4) \\
&= 2x, && \text{(since } 2(x - 2) = 2x - 4)
\end{aligned}
$$

and

$$
\begin{aligned}
h(g(f(x))) &= h(2x), && \text{(since } g(f(x)) = 2x) \\
&= x. && \text{(since } h(x) = \tfrac{1}{2}(x) \text{ so that} \\
&&& h(2x) = \tfrac{1}{2}(2x) = x)
\end{aligned}
$$

Now we may ask whether $f(g(h(x)))$ also is equal to x. To answer this question, simply construct the composition:

$$
\begin{aligned}
g(h(x)) &= 2(h(x)) + 4, \\
&= 2(\tfrac{1}{2}x) + 4, \\
&= x + 4,
\end{aligned}
$$

and, finally,

$$
\begin{aligned}
f(g(h(x))) &= (x + 4) - 2, && \text{(since } g(h(x)) = x + 4) \\
&= x + 2.
\end{aligned}
$$

Thus, the order of composition is important. This is analagous to saying that the operation of composition of functions is not commutative. With these examples, the reader should understand a formal definition of composition.

(4.5.1) If f is a function from A to B' and g is a function **Definition** from B to C, and if $B' \subseteq B$, then the composition of f and g, noted $g(f)$, is a function, h, on A to C such that $\langle a, c \rangle \in h \leftrightarrow$ there exists an element $b \in B'$ such that $\langle a, b \rangle \in f$ and $\langle b, c \rangle \in g$.

Thus, whenever these conditions are satisfied, the two sentences $c = h(a)$ and $c = g(f(a))$ are equivalent. The reader should recognize that the two sentences $c_1 = g(f(a))$ and

$c_2 = f(g(a))$ are not equivalent in general. No generality was lost by restricting the preceding definition to the composition of two functions. The definition of composition can be extended quite simply to any arbitrary number of functions because the composition of two functions is a single function that may then be composed with a third function. This operation again yields a single function, which may be composed with a fourth function so long as the conditions of the definition are satisfied. The process could be continued indefinitely.

Exercises

4.23. Let $f_1 = \{\langle a_1, b_1 \rangle, \langle a_2, b_2 \rangle, \langle a_3, b_3 \rangle\}$, $f_2 = \{\langle c_1, a_1 \rangle, \langle c_2, a_2 \rangle, \langle c_3, a_3 \rangle\}$.
Show both with a diagram and by listing the elements the function f_3 given by $f_3 = f_1(f_2(c))$.

4.24. If $f(x) = 3 + 2x$ and $g(x) = x + 1$, what is $f(g(x))$? $g(f(x))$?

4.25. If $F(x) = x - 1$ and $G(x) = x + 1$, what is $F(G(x))$? $G(F(x))$?

4.26. If $f(x) = 2x + 1$, $g(x) = 2x - 1$ and $h(x) = 2x$, construct:

(a) $g(h(f(x)))$.
(b) $h(g(f(x)))$.
(c) $f(h(g(x)))$.

4.6 The Binary Operation, o

A special case of functions is so extremely important for mathematical work that it has been given the special label *binary operation* and the generic notation **o**. The domain of any function is an arbitrary set of elements. The reader should recall (from 3.1) that an ordered pair is considered to be an element. Thus, it is entirely consistent to define a function in which the elements of the domain set are *ordered pairs*. Any such function is denoted **o** and is called a binary operation. As with any functions, the elements of **o** are ordered pairs, but in this case the first member of the pair is itself an ordered pair. A typical element of a binary operation on $A \times B$ to C could be noted $\langle \langle a, b \rangle, c \rangle$.

Returning again to kinship for an example, if A is the set of all males and B is the set of all females, then the relation "is the husband of" is a function on A to B with elements of the form $\langle a, b \rangle$. Call this relation h. Let B be the set of all only children. Then the relation g, "are the parents of," is a binary operation on h to B.

(4.6.1) If R is any relation on A to B, and C is any set, then a binary operation, o, is any function on R to C.   **Definition**

Ordinarily, the domain set, R, is the universal relation. This definition connects two fundamental concepts, those of operation and relation. In Chapter 2, operations such as union and intersection were defined for sets. In the sense of this definition, they are seen to be functions. Thus, for example, a union is a function that maps two sets, A and B, into the new set, $A \cup B$. The reader should be convinced of the importance of this notion by observing that most arithmetic operations such as "+" and "−" are binary operations. This should make it clear that the sets A, B and C of 4.6.1 need by no means be distinct. Some of the most fruitful applications of binary operations are on sets of the form $A \times A$ to A.

In an earlier section, diagrams that represented relations were presented. A graphic representation of a binary operation requires three dimensions for complete clarity. One dimension would represent the elements in the set A; a second dimension would represent B; and the third dimension would represent the set C. Unfortunately, this is somewhat difficult to accomplish on a two-dimensional surface such as this page. A three-dimensional representation can be approximated, however, if the dots in our earlier diagrams are replaced with notations, as in the following representation of two binary operations on $A \times A$ to A where $A = \{a_1, a_2, a_3\}$.

Figure 4.2

$$
\mathbf{o}_1 = \begin{array}{c|ccc}
a_3 & a_3 & a_1 & a_2 \\
a_2 & a_2 & a_3 & a_1 \\
a_1 & a_1 & a_2 & a_3 \\
\hline
 & a_1 & a_2 & a_3
\end{array}
\qquad
\mathbf{o}_2 = \begin{array}{c|ccc}
a_3 & a_1 & a_2 & a_3 \\
a_2 & a_1 & a_2 & a_2 \\
a_1 & a_1 & a_1 & a_1 \\
\hline
 & a_1 & a_2 & a_3
\end{array}
$$

$$\text{a} \qquad\qquad\qquad\qquad \text{b}$$

Thus, the ordered pair $\langle\langle a_1, a_1\rangle, a_1\rangle$ is an element of the binary operation o_1 and $\langle\langle a_2, a_3\rangle, a_2\rangle$ is an element of o_2 in the operation of Figure 4.2. Notice that tables such as these provide the model for addition, multiplication, and similar tables, all of which represent listings of certain binary operations.

Exercises

4.27. Given a binary operation on $A \times A$ to $A = \{a, b, c\}$ defined by

$$
\mathbf{o} = \begin{array}{c|ccc}
 & c & a & b \\
c & c & a & b \\
b & b & c & a \\
a & a & b & c \\
\hline
 & a & b & c
\end{array}
$$

Find:

(a) $o(b, b)$.

(b) $o(c, a)$.

> Note that $o(c, c)$ may be—and conventionally is—written coc. (Relate this notation to the statement in the text that "$+$" and "$-$" are particular binary operations.)
> Find:

(c) aob.

(d) cob.

(e) $(aob)oc$.

(f) $co(coc)$.

4.28. In Exercise 4.27, is it true that, for each ordered triplet of letters, say $\langle x, y, z \rangle$ in $A \times A \times A$, $(xoy)oz = xo(yoz)$? For example, $(boc)oa = aoa = a$; $bo(coa) = boc = a$ so that, for this particular ordered triplet, $\langle b, c, a\rangle$, the identity is satisfied; but is this true for *all* triplets?

4.29. In Exercise 4.27, is it true that, for each x, y in A, there exists an element $z \in A$ such that $xoz = y$? For instance, let $x = a, y = b$. Then $z = b$ also, since $aob = b$.

4.30. In Exercise 4.27, is it true that, for each x, y in A, there exists an element $z \in A$ such that $zox = y$? (Compare the question carefully to that of 4.29.)

4.31. In set theory, a *group* is any binary operation, o, on $A \times A$ to A such that, for each x, y, z in A

    (1) $(xoy)oz = xo(yoz)$.

    (2) For each x, y in A there exists $z \in A$ such that $xoz = y$.

    (3) For each x, y in A there exists $z \in A$ such that $zox = y$.

(a) Is the binary operation of Exercise 4.27 a group?

(b) Construct a group on $A \times A$ to A if $A = \{1, 2, 3, 4\}$.

4.32.

(a) Is the arithmetic operation "$+$" a group?

(b) Is "$-$" a group?

(c) Is "$\div$" (division) a group?

Selected References

1. Allendoerfer, C. B., and Oakley, C. O. *Principles of Mathematics.* New York: McGraw-Hill Book Company, Inc., 1955. Chapter 6.

2. Kemeny, John G., Merkil, H., Snell, J. L., and Thompson, G. L. *Finite Mathematical Structures.* Englewood Cliffs, New Jersey: Prentice-Hall, Inc., 1959. Pages 70–79.

3. Kirshner, R. B., and Wilcox, L. R. *The Anatomy of Mathematics.* New York: The Ronald Press Company, 1950. Chapter 5.

4. Moore, John T. *Fundamental Principles of Mathematics.* New York: Rinehart and Co., Inc., 1960. Chapter 4.

5. Suppes, Patrick. *Axiomatic Set Theory.* Princeton, New Jersey: D. Van Nostrand Co., Inc., 1960. Chapter 3.

6. Suppes, Patrick. *Introduction to Logic.* Princeton, New Jersey: D. Van Nostrand Co., Inc., 1957. Chapter 11.

NUMBERS

II

Integers

This chapter and the next are concerned with the construction of numbers. In a sense this is a foolish business, because any educated person is familiar with numbers. Most people today can use addition and multiplication tables and can perform quite complicated operations with numbers. But all this represents familiarity with numbers as *tools*. The purpose of the next few chapters is to construct numbers as *abstract entities*.

This construction should be useful to the reader in at least two ways. First, it provides an opportunity for reviewing arithmetic operations, which so easily grow rusty in the mind through non-use. Second, and more important, it provides the first opportunity to make full and formal use of the axiomatic method. In this chapter the integers are constructed and investigated. In the next, integers are converted into rational and then into real numbers. In Chapter 7, some elementary operations are constructed on the set of real numbers.

What will and will not be accomplished in these chapters must be clear at the outset to the reader. In the first place, numbers are not defined here. Instead, they are *characterized* by axioms that dictate how they should behave. From these characterizing axioms, the familiar properties of numbers are derived, together with some that may be unfamiliar to many readers. Much of classical algebra will be treated abruptly or dismissed altogether. Our attention will be restricted to those aspects of numbers that are needed to construct the systems which make up the subject matter of this book.

5

5.1 The Set of Integers

Historically, the most primitive numbers are those with which we count. These are called *natural numbers* and are represented by the familiar symbols 1, 2, 3, $\cdots$. To get some idea of what entities these symbols represent, let us consider a class of sets. Each set in the class has a property usually called its *size* or *number*. It is possible to make certain statements about this property without in any way defining it. To do this, select a set arbitrarily and test it against every other set in the class to determine whether a one-to-one correspondence can be established. Suppose that a second set is found that can be placed in correspondence with the first. Then what can be said about the two sets? The reader who recalls that a correspondence is a function whose transpose also is a function should recognize that the two sets are equivalent in size. After all remaining sets have been tested in a similar manner, there exists a subclass of sets (called an *equivalence class*) such that each set in the subclass can be placed in one-to-one correspondence with every other set in the subclass but cannot be in such correspondence with any set that is not in it. Next, select a set from those that remain and use it to establish a second equivalence class. One may continue in this way until all sets in the original class have been allocated to a subclass. It should be clear that each set in the class must belong to one and only one such subclass. In this way we have *partitioned* the initial class of sets into subclasses that are mutually exclusive and exhaustive.

Each subclass of the partitioned class has a unique property. All its elements (sets) consist of elements that can be placed in a one-to-one correspondence with one another but not with any other subclass. It is this that we call the *number property* of a set. To many philosophers of mathematics, number is nothing more than a class of sets that can be placed in correspondence. Thus, by this view, the symbol 1, for example, represents the class of unit sets. It is not necessary for the reader to adopt or reject this position unless he feels that a definition of number is indispensable. It is important only that number be recognized as an abstract entity associated with a property of sets.

The number zero can be joined to the counting or natural numbers if it is considered as (or as the property of) the null set. What remains then, so far as integers are concerned, is to create the negative integers and to characterize the behavior of the set so constructed. To do this, we impose the familiar binary operations $+$ (addition) and $\cdot$ (multiplication) on the integers.

Just as numbers can be identified with properties of sets, operations on numbers, such as addition, can be identified with set operations. Addition, for example, can be identified with the operation of union of two disjoint sets. Thus, if a and b represent two numbers, then these can be said to be the size of two sets (or two classes of sets). The number $a + b$, which is called the sum of a and b, is said to be the size of the set obtained by taking the union of two disjoint sets with size a and b. In this sense, what would the operation of multiplication represent? (The answer is *not* the intersection of two sets.)

None of this constitutes a characterization of integers—far less a formal definition. In order to characterize the integers axiomatically, it is necessary first to construct a domain of definition. This is done by the following:

(5.1.1) Let $I = \{a, b, c, \cdots\}$ be any set for which two binary operations, $+$ (called addition) and $\cdot$ (called multiplication), are defined on $I \times I$. If I satisfies the axioms on addition (5.2.1), multiplication (5.3.1), and order (5.4.1), given below, then I is called an *integral set*.

Definition

Thus, any set that satisfies a particular list of axioms is an integral set. The integers, as we know them intuitively, will be seen to satisfy these axioms. Integers are not the only entities that satisfy the axioms, but this fact need not concern us for the present. In fact, an integral set hereafter will be identified with the set of integers.

Exercises

5.1.

(a) Before reading Section 5.2, list the properties that you think ought to be possessed by the binary operation of arithmetic, $+$.

(b) Which of these properties also is possessed by the binary operation $-$?

5.2. The numeric operation $+$ was identified with the set operation $\cup$. In a similar fashion, construct a set-theoretic analogue for each of the following:

(a) $-$

(b) $\cdot$

(c) $/$ (division)

5.2 The Binary Operation +

Let I represent any set of elements such that a binary operation, $+$, is defined on $I \times I$ to some set. If I is an integral set, it must satisfy the following axioms:

(5.2.1) Let I be a set of elements and $+$ a binary operation on $I \times I$. Let $=$ be a reflexive, symmetric, transitive relation on $I \times I$. If I is the set of integers, then

A1 (Closure) For all elements a, $b \in I$, the element $(a + b) \in I$.

A2 (Uniqueness) For every a, b, c, $d \in I$, if $a = c$ and $b = d$, then

$$(a + b) = (c + d).$$

A3 (Identity Element) There exists an element $0 \in I$ such that

$$a + 0 = a,$$

for every $a \in I$.

A4 (Commutativity) For every a, $b \in I$

$$(a + b) = (b + a).$$

A5 (Associativity) For every a, b, $c \in I$

$$(a + b) + c = a + (b + c) \; [= a + b + c].$$

A6 (Additive Inverse) For every $a \in I$, there exists an element $b \in I$ such that

$$(a + b) = 0.$$

The element b may be written $(-a)$ and the expression $a + (-b)$ may be written $a - b$.

These six axioms completely characterize the operation of addition (of *two* numbers) on the set of integers. Consider for a moment what the axioms say about numbers. They give principles that are familiar to nearly everyone. They tell us that the sum of two integers is an integer, that $+$ is an operation on $I \times I$ to I (A1); that the sum of any two numbers is a unique number (A2); that a number is un-

changed when 0 is added to it (A3); that the order of addition is unimportant (A4 and A5); that every integer, a, has
associated with it a second integer, called $-a$, such that
$a + (-a) = 0$ (A6).

Strictly speaking, these axioms characterize the operation
of addition only for *two* integers. However, they extend quite
directly to the operation of addition over *any* set of integers.
Since $+$ is a binary operation, the sum $(a + b)$ is just an
integer (by axioms A1 and A2) so that the sum $(a + b) + c$
is the sum of two integers, the result of a binary operation.
The sum $(a + b) + c$ is an integer, so we can write it
as $(a + b + c)$. Then the sum $(a + b + c) + d$ is also
the result of a binary operation on $I \times I$ to I. By this re-
cursive process, each of the six axioms applies over any
(finite) set of integers.

Some of the more immediate consequences of the rules
or axioms on addition follow. The reader would be wise to
read each part of the theorem carefully in an effort to grasp
precisely what it does and does not say. The first theorem,
for example, says that if a number a is added to a number b
and, separately, to a number c, and if the two sums are
equal, then the two numbers b and c are equal. On the other
hand, this does not tell us that, if $a + b = c + d$, then
$a = c$ and $b = d$ (which the reader should demonstrate to
be false by constructing a numerical counter-example using
an addition table).

ELEMENTARY
THEOREMS
ON
ADDITION

(5.2.2) If a, b, c, d, $\epsilon\ I$, then:

(1) $a + b = a + c \leftrightarrow b = c$.
(2) If $a + b = a$, all $a\ \epsilon\ A$ then $b = 0$.
(3) For each $a\ \epsilon\ I$ and $b\ \epsilon\ I$, there exists one and only one
    $c\ \epsilon\ I$ such that $a + c = b$.
(4) $a + c = b \leftrightarrow a = b - c$.
(5) $-(-a) = a$.
(6) $-(a + b) = -a - b$.
(7) $(a - b) - (c - d) = (a + d) - (b + c)$.
(8) $a - b = c - d \leftrightarrow a + d = b + c$.

Let $(a + b) = (a + c).$ *Proof (1)*

(1) There exists an element $x \in I$
such that $(a + x) = 0.$ (A6)

(2) $b = b + 0 = b + (x + a).$ (A3, A2 and Step 1)

(3) But (A4, A5, A2 and
$$b + (x + a) = (a + b) + x,$$ hypothesis,
$$= (a + c) + x.$$ $a + b = a + c$)

(4) $b = c + (a + x),$ (Steps 2, 3 and axioms A2, A4, A5)

(5) $= c + 0.$ (Step 1)

(6) $b = c.$ (Steps 4 and 5 and A3)

To prove the converse, let $b = c.$

(7) $a = a.$ ($=$ is reflexive)

(8) $a + b = a + c.$ (Hypothesis, Step 7 and A2)

Let $c = (b + (-a)).$ *Proof (3)*

(1) $a + c = a + (b + (-a)),$ (Hypothesis and (5.2.2.1))

(2) $= b + (a + (-a)),$ (A4, A5)

(3) $= b.$ (A6, A3, Steps 1 and 2)

Thus, a solution exists. To show that it is unique, let a second solution be $a + d = b$ (so that it becomes necessary to show that $c = d$).

(4) $a + c = b = a + d.$ (Hypothesis, Step 3, and transitivity of $=$)

(5) $c = d.$ (Step 4 and (5.2.2.1))

Proof (5)

(1) $a + (-a) = 0.$ (A6)

(2) $a = 0 - (-a).$ (Step 1 and (5.2.2.4), setting $c = -a$)

(3) $a = -(-a).$ (A3 and A4)

Proof (7)

(1) $-(c - d)$
$= -c - (-d),$ (A6 and 5.2.2.6)
(2) $= d - c.$ (A4 and 5.2.2.5)
(3) $(a - b) - (c - d)$ (Steps 1, 2 and
$= a - b + d - c,$ 5.2.2.1)
(4) $= (a + d) + (-b - c),$ (A4, A5)
(5) $= (a + d) - (b + c).$ (5.2.2.6 and Steps
3, 4)

The proof of the remaining parts of this theorem are left
as exercises, together with several other consequences of the
axioms on addition. The reader will be completely stumped
by these exercises unless he has followed carefully the development of the above proofs. It should be noted that the
transitivity property of equality is used so frequently that it
is noted only when the flow of reasoning does not make its
use apparent.

Exercises

5.3. Notice that the only segments of an addition table that can be reproduced from
the axioms on addition are those of the form $a + 0 = a$. You cannot prove, for
instance, that $1 + 1 = 2$. This identity is a matter of faith, or a convention adopted
when one accepts the "standard" addition table. On the other hand, prove, using
the axioms, that

(a) $(3 - 5) - (4 - 6) = (3 + 6) - (5 + 4).$
(b) $-(-4) = 4.$
(c) $12 - 8 = 5 - 1 \leftrightarrow 12 + 1 = 5 + 8.$

5.4. Prove that

(a) $a + (b + c) = (c + a) + b.$
(b) $a + (c - d) = -(d - a) + c.$
(c) $-(a - b) = b - a.$
(d) $a + [b + (d + c)] = a + b + c + d.$

5.5. Prove that

(a) $a + b = 0$ and $a + c = 0 \rightarrow b = c.$
(b) The converse, in general, is *not* true.

5.6. Suppose that, in place of A4: $(a + b) = (b + a)$, we substitute A'4: $(a + b) \neq$
$(b + a)$, all $a \in I, b \in I.$

(a) What parts of Theorem 5.2.2 would then be false?

(b) Use A'4 (keeping the other axioms as they are) to prove $a \neq a$.

5.7. Prove parts (2), (4), (6) and (8) of Theorem 5.2.2.

5.8. Two towns, say Oneville and Twoville, had identical populations at census period t. At the next census period, call it $t + 1$, their populations were unequal. Show that their respective populations could not have changed by the same number.

5.9. Interpret 5.2.2.5 in terms of a person erasing a debt of a dollar.

5.10. A region consists of two districts. District one loses a persons during a period of time and district two loses b persons. Interpret the loss to the *region* by means of 5.2.2.6.

5.11. In the same region as in Exercise 5.10 the number of voting-age males is a in district one, d in district two; the number of voting-age females is b in district one and c in district two. Interpret the sex disparity in persons of voting age within the *region*.

5.3 The Binary Operation ·

The operation of addition was seen to have a direct intuitive meaning in terms of the union of sets. The sum of two integers is just the "size" of the union of two (disjoint) sets if the size of each is given by one of the added numbers. What sort of parallel intuitive meaning can we pour into the operation of multiplication? Certainly, it does not correspond to taking intersections or complements. The only intuitive meaning given to this operation, the set operation to which it corresponds, is the following: If the sizes of two sets, A and B, are given by integers a and b respectively, then the size of the cartesian product, $A \times B$, is given by the product of the two integers, $a \cdot b$ (also written $a \times b$ or just ab). Or $a \cdot b$ may represent the union of a different disjoint sets, each of size b. The number $a \cdot b$ itself, then, is the sum of b taken a times.

Remember that this is only an informal attempt to convey the way in which the completely abstract notion of multiplication is used. Formally, multiplication will be defined no more directly than was addition. Multiplication is just a binary operation on $I \times I$ where I is a set of elements.

(5.3.1) Let I be a set of elements and $\cdot$ a binary operation on $I \times I$. If I is an integral set, then, in addition to the
axioms of 5.2.1, I satisfies the following:

M1   (Closure)   If a, $b \in I$, then the element $ab(= a \cdot b) \in I$.

M2   (Uniqueness)   For every a, b, c, $d \in I$, if $a = c$ and
$b = d$, then
$$ab = cd.$$

M3   (Identity Element)   There exists an element $1 \in I$
such that $1 \neq 0$ and such that, for all $a \in I$,
$$a1 = a.$$

M4   (Commutativity)   For every a, $b \in I$,
$$ab = ba.$$

M5   (Associativity)   For every a, b, $c \in I$,
$$a(bc) = (ab)c.$$

M6   (Distributivity)   For every a, b, $c \in I$,
$$a(b + c) = ab + ac.$$

M7   (Cancellation)   For every a, b, $c \in I$, if
$c \neq 0$, then $ca = cb \leftrightarrow a = b$.

These axioms complete all but one of the characterizing
properties of the integers. They are, in fact, the basic properties of *all* ordinary numbers. Notice that the first five axioms on multiplication parallel the first five on addition.
The so-called distributive axiom, M6, uses both the notions
of addition and multiplication. The cancellation axiom
parallels the first theorem on addition.

Consider again what these axioms assert. They tell us
that the product of two integers is a unique integer (M1
and M2); that a number is unchanged when multiplied by
one (M3); that the order of continued or *serial* multiplication is unimportant (M4 and M5); that multiplying an
integer by the sum of two integers is equivalent to multiplying each member of the sum separately by the first integer and adding the two products (M6); that identical
terms on both sides of an equality sign can be cancelled
(M7).

Again, most of these axioms square with an informal sense of the way in which integers ought to behave. Some, however, make little or no immediate intuitive sense. For example, the distributive axiom, M6, does not correspond to any *obvious* physical process; but this is not to say that such a correspondence does not exist. Remember that $a \cdot b$ is just the number a added to itself b times. Recall also that $(b + c)$ is a unique integer so that $a \cdot (b + c)$ is the result of adding a number, a, $(b + c)$ times. This in turn represents adding a b times and then adding to this the result of adding a c times, which is $ab + ac$. None of this, of course, is a *proof* of anything. It is no more than an intuitive justification for the inclusion of a particular axiom. Given these axioms, some basic theorems can be derived.

ELEMENTARY THEOREMS ON MULTIPLICATION

(5.3.2)

(1) $a \cdot 0 = 0$, all $a \epsilon I$.

(2) If there exists $b \epsilon I$ such that $ab = a$, all $a \epsilon I$, then $b = 1$.

(3) $(-a)(-b) = ab$.

(4) $(-a)(b) = (a)(-b)$ [to be written $-(ab)$].

(5) $-a = -1(a)$.

(6) $(a - b)c = ac - bc$.

(7) $(a + b)(c + d) = ac + ad + bc + bd$.

(8) $(a - b)(c - d) = ac + bd - (ad + bc)$.

(9) $(a + b)(c - d) = ac + bc - (ad + bd)$.

Proof (1)

(1) $a = a + 0$.	(A3)
(2) $aa = a(a + 0)$.	(Step 1 and M7)
(3) $aa = aa + a0$.	(Step 2 and M6)
(4) $a0 = 0$.	(Step 3, A3 which gives $aa = aa + 0$, and 5.2.2.1)

Proof (3)

(1) $a(-b) + (-a)(-b)$
   $= [a + (-a)](-b),$
   $= 0(-b) = 0.$ (M6, A6, A3 and
                                        5.3.2.1)

(2) $ab + [a(-b) + (-a)(-b)]$
   $= ab + 0 = ab.$ (Step 1, A3)

(3) $ab + (a)(-b)$ (M6, A6 and
   $= a[b + (-b)] = 0.$ 5.3.2.1)

(4) $[ab + a(-b)] + (-a)(-b)$
   $= 0 + (-a)(-b),$ (Step 3, A3)
   $= (-a)(-b).$

(5) $ab = (-a)(-b).$ (Steps 2, 4, A5, and
                                        transitivity of $=$)

(6) $(-a)(-b) = ab.$ (Symmetry of $=$)

Let $(a + b) = x.$ *Proof (7)*

(1) $x \epsilon I$ (A1)

(2) $(a + b)(c + d)$ (Hypothesis, M7,
   $= x(c + d),$ and Step 1)

(3) $= xc + xd,$ (M6)

(4) $= c(a + b) + d(a + b),$ (M4, A4, and
                                        hypothesis)

(5) $= ca + cb + da + db,$ (M6)

(6) $= ac + ad + bc + bd.$ (A4, M4)

Again, the remaining proofs are left as exercises. As with addition, these properties of multiplication extend directly from a binary operation on two integers to repeated or *serial* multiplication on any number of integers.

Exercises

5.12. Prove that:

(a) $-0 = 0.$
(b) $(ab)c = (cb)a.$
(c) $(a + b)c = ca + cb.$

5.13. Expand (that is, reduce to a simple sum of products as in 5.3.2.7)

(a) $(d + c)(b + a)$ and compare with 5.3.2.7.

(b) $(a + c)(b + d)$ and compare with 5.3.2.7.

5.14. Axiom M6 could be translated into "Multiplication distributes over addition." In this sense, is it true that addition distributes over multiplication? (HINT: Simply invert the operators $+$ and $\cdot$ in M6 and decide whether this violates any other axioms.)

5.15. Compare your conclusion in Exercise 5.14 with the two distributive laws of sets (Section 2.6).

5.16. Prove Theorem 5.3.2, Parts 2, 4, 5, 9.

5.17. In a region there are b thousands of residents. In this region there are a persons *per thousand* named Mary (suppose a and b to be integers). Interpret the integer $a \cdot b$.

5.18. Again, the region of Exercise 5.17 consists of two districts with b thousands of persons in district one and c thousands of persons in district two. Interpret M6 in terms of Exercise 5.17.

5.19. Suppose that in an interval of time, the population of district one increases from size a to size ca, that district two increases from size c to size bc, and that at the end of the period, the two populations are equal. What can you conclude from M7?

5.20. Interpret 5.3.2.6 in the following sense:

Of the purchasers in a given market in a given session, a number a per thousand purchase Abscondo Uranium stock and b per thousand purchase Gulp Oil stock. During this session there are c purchases of these stocks in the market.

5.21. In the manner of Exercises 5.17–5.20, interpret:

(a) M2

(b) M5

(c) 5.3.2.4

(d) 5.3.2.8

5.4 Ordered Sets

An especially important property of integers, not yet mentioned, is that of order. The notion of order is so basic to the number system that assertions such as "5 is less than 8" and "12 is greater than 0" are readily acceptable, even comprehensible, to most persons. But when it comes to explaining concisely what is meant by "more" or "less," matters are not so simple (before continuing, the reader might attempt to construct his own set of axioms on order). The following axioms invest the integers with all familiar order properties:

(5.4.1) A set of positive integers $I^+ \subset I$ is such that, for each $a \in I$

O1 just one of the following is true: $a \in I^+$, $-a \in I^+$, or $a = 0$.

O2 $a \in I^+$ and $b \in I^+ \leftrightarrow (a + b) \in I^+$ and $ab \in I^+$.

The first order axiom, sometimes called the *axiom of trichotomy*, says that a number is positive, or the negative of the number is positive, or it is the number zero (look again at Exercise 5.12.a to see why neither zero nor its negative is in I^+). Order axiom two requires that, if the sum *and* product of two numbers are in I^+, then the two numbers themselves must be positive. The reader should convince himself that neither of these two conditions alone would be sufficient to ensure that a and b are in I^+. Having constructed the positive integers, those that are not in I^+ and are not 0 deserve a name of their own.

(5.4.2) The set of integers, a, such that $-a \in I^+$, is called the set of *negative* integers, denoted I^-.   **Definition**

Notice that zero is no more a negative than it is a positive integer. Consider once again Theorem 5.3.2.3, which told us that $(-a)(-b) = ab$. This does not say that the product of two negative numbers is a positive number, for either a or b or both could be in I^-. Rather, the theorem says that the product of the negatives of *any* two numbers is identical to the product of the numbers.

To this point three sets—the negative integers, the positive integers, and zero—have been constructed. To extend the notion of order to any pair of integers, the following definition is needed:

(5.4.3) A relation called the *strict inequality*, denoted $<$ **Definition**
(read "is less than"), on $I \times I$ is such that, for any a, $b \in I$,

$a < b \leftrightarrow (b - a) \in I^+ (\leftrightarrow b > a$, read "$b$ is greater than a").

Notice first that, since $(b - a)$ is an integer (why?), the order axiom assures us that the relation $<$ is connected in

$I \times I$ (again, why?). This definition leads to the familiar notion of a negative number, which can now be stated as a theorem.

(5.4.4) Any integer a is a member of $I^- \leftrightarrow a < 0$. The proof of this theorem is left as an exercise.

In part because of the peculiar position of zero in the ordered integers, it will be convenient to use a so-called weak inequality at times in place of the strict inequality.

(5.4.5) A relation of weak inequality, noted $\leq$ (read "is less than or equal to") on $I \times I$ is such that, for each $a, b \in I$

$$a \leq b \leftrightarrow a < b \text{ or } a = b.$$

With this panoply of axioms and definitions, it is possible to deduce such consequences as that 1 is a positive number.

(5.4.6) (*Properties of Inequalities.*) For all $a, b, c, d \in I$

Addition

(1) $a < b \leftrightarrow a + c < b + c$, all $c \in I$.
(2) $a < b$ and $c < d \rightarrow a + c < b + d$.

Multiplication

(3) $a < b$ and $0 < c \rightarrow ac < bc$.
(4) $a < b$ and $c < 0 \rightarrow ac > bc$.
(5) $a^2 > 0$, where $a^2 = a \cdot a$, all $a \neq 0$ (read "a squared" or "a to the second power").

General

(6) $1 > 0$.
(7) The relation $<$ is (a) irreflexive, (b) assymetric, (c) transitive, and (d) connected in I.
(8) The relation $\leq$ is (a) reflexive, (b) antisymmetric, (c) transitive, and (d) strongly connected in I.

Let $a < b$ and $c < d$. Then

(1) $a + c < b + c$.   (5.4.6.1 and hypothesis)
(2) $b + c < b + d$.   (5.4.6.1 and hypothesis)
(3) $a + c < b + d$.   (Steps 1, 2 and 5.4.6.7.c)

Let $a < b$ and $c < 0$. Assume $bc - ac > 0$.   *Proof (4)*

(1) $c(b - a) > 0$.   (Hypothesis, 5.3.2.6, and M4)

(2) $b - a > 0$.   (Hypothesis and 5.4.3)

(3) $c > 0$ [contradiction].   (Steps 1 and 2 and O2 and 5.4.4)

These proofs should provide enough procedural hints to permit the reader to prove the remaining parts of the theorem for himself.

Several comments are in order at this point. First, 5.4.6 ignored the weak inequality relation for the most part. In parts 1–4, if weak inequalities are substituted consistently for the strict inequalities, the propositions would be equally true (of course, the reader should verify this for himself). In Part 5, if the restriction on the element a is dropped, a weak inequality could be substituted.

When one is confronted with inequalities, as certainly will be the case later in this book, it is convenient to remember that they are exactly like equalities insofar as all addition and multiplication of like-signed numbers are concerned. It is only when one must multiply (or divide) opposite-signed numbers that the inequality relation behaves in novel fashion. In this case, 5.4.6.4 says that the direction of the inequality must be reversed. For instance, $2 < 3$ and $-2 < 0$ so that $(-2)(2) > (-2)(3)$ which implies $-4 > -6$, which may be thought of intuitively as meaning that -6 is farther to the "left" of 0 on a scale of numbers (or has lower value) than -4.

Exercises

5.22. Prove parts (3) and (5) of 5.4.6.

5.23. Prove part (7) of 5.4.6.

5.24. Prove 5.4.6.6 by indirection. Note that M3 assures us that $1 \neq 0$, a fact that must be used in conjunction with the order axiom in this proof.

5.25. Prove part (8) of 5.4.6.

5.26. Suppose that the towns of Oneville and Twoville have populations P_1 and P_2, respectively. Suppose that at time t, $P_1 < P_2$.

(a) Suppose that at time $t + 1$, the two towns have increased by an identical number. What does 5.4.6.1 tell you?

(b) Suppose that the two towns have increased by a constant *rate* $k > 0$. What does 5.4.6.3 tell you about the relative increase?

(c) Suppose that $k < 0$. What does 5.4.6.4 tell you about the relative loss?

5.5 Well Ordering and Finite Induction

The notion of *well-ordered sets* is but a short step beyond the notion of ordered sets, but once we have it, we also have one of the most important principles in the entire realm of formal logic, the *principle of finite induction*.

(5.5.1) Any ordered set X is called *well ordered* if every non-empty subset, $Y \subset X$, contains an element x_0 such that $x_0 < x$, all $x \in Y$.   **Definition**

Consider, as an example, the ages of all university students recorded by rounding to the nearest year. Note carefully that this is not a set of people but, instead, a set of positive integers. Then, for any subset, say the set of (ages of) junior classmen, there is necessarily a youngest age. This may be the age of one, two, or hundreds of juniors, but the fact remains that there is a youngest age. In contrast, consider the set, X, of all possible test scores that report the number of correct responses as a proportion of the number of questions asked. Notice that the set includes scores on tests of all possible lengths in terms of number of questions asked. Let $Y \subset X$ be the set of all scores greater than zero. Can the reader convince himself that Y contains no least element?

It follows at once from 5.5.1 that *the set of integers is well ordered* because, for every pair of distinct integers, one is smaller than the other. The following theorem is based on this definition and, in turn, yields the logical principle of induction.

(5.5.2) Let X be any set of positive integers that contains 1 and that contains n whenever it contains $n - 1$. Then X is the set of all positive integers.   **THEOREM**

Let $X \subset I^+$ be such that $1 \, \epsilon \, X$ and $n \, \epsilon \, X$ whenever $(n - 1) \, \epsilon \, X$, n and $(n - 1)$ integers in I^+. Also let $c\{X\} = \{I^+ - X\}$.

Proof

(1) Suppose $c\{X\} \neq \phi$. ($\rightarrow$ there exists some positive integer, k, such that $k \, \not\epsilon \, X$.)

(2) Then there exists an integer, m, such that m is the least integer in $c\{X\}$. (Since the integers are well ordered.)

(3) $m \neq 1$.   (By hypothesis, since $1 \, \epsilon \, X$)

(4) $m - 1 > 0$.   (Since there exists no integer between 0 and 1. See 5.5.5 below.)

(5) But $m > m - 1$.   (5.4.3 and 5.4.6.6)

(6) $(m - 1) \, \epsilon \, X$.   (Since m is the least element in $c\{x\}$)

(7) $(m - 1) + 1 = m \, \epsilon \, X$
[contradiction].   (Hypothesis)

The real importance of this theorem is that it serves to justify the following:

(5.5.3) Let P_n be a proposition connected with n, a positive integer, that is either true or false for each n. Then,

(1) if P_1 is true, and
(2) if $P_{n-1} \rightarrow P_n$,

then P_n is true for all positive integers n.

Unless Theorem 5.5.2 is thoroughly understood, this principle may appear to be extremely arbitrary and unreliable. In light of the theorem and the fact that the integers are well-ordered, however, it makes perfectly good sense. The great worth of the principle is just this: Suppose it is felt that some proposition concerning the integers is true in general. Then, instead of taking on the overwhelming task of proving it separately for every different positive integer, it is necessary only to show two things in order to prove the proposition generally. These two necessary proofs consist of showing that the proposition is correct for the case $n = 1$ and that the hypothesis (which remains only an assumption) that the proposition is valid for the number $n - 1$ implies that it must be correct also for n.

To exemplify the uses of the finite induction principle, a proposition will be proved that may not be obvious to the reader. The proposition asserts that the sum of a finite sequence of numbers $(1 + 2 + 3 + \cdots + n)$ always equals $\dfrac{n(n + 1)}{2}$.

(5.5.4) $(1 + 2 + \cdots + n) = \dfrac{n(n + 1)}{2}.$　　　　**THEOREM**

Proof
(By induction)

(1) $1 = \dfrac{1(2)}{2} = 1$ (so that P_1 is true).

(2) Assume $(1 + 2 + \cdots + (n - 1)) =$

$$\dfrac{(n - 1)(n)}{2}. \quad \text{(Inductive assumption)}$$

(3) $(1 + 2 + \cdots + n)$
$$= (1 + 2 + \cdots + n - 1) + n, \quad \text{(A5)}$$

(4) $\quad = \dfrac{(n - 1)(n)}{2} + n, \quad\quad\quad \text{(By 2 and 3)}$

(5) $\quad = \dfrac{n(n + 1)}{2}.$

Step (1) of this proof establishes the truth of P_1, that the "sum" of the first positive integer, the number 1, equals $(1)(1 + 1)/2$. Step (2) contains the inductive assumption about $P_{(n-1)}$. Notice carefully that this is only an assumption, that it is *not* proven. The crucial portion of the proof consists of demonstrating that this assumption necessarily implies P_n. Step (3) makes the connection between $P_{(n-1)}$ and P_n by expressing the sum of the first n integers as the sum of the first $(n - 1)$ integers plus n. In Step (4) the assumed identity is substituted for the first $(n - 1)$ integers in Step (3). Finally, Step (5) completes the proof by establishing a common denominator and cancelling (this assumes familiarity with division, which is introduced in the next chapter).

In order to see more clearly the conclusive nature of this kind of proof, let us consider a particular case of Proposition 5.5.4, say, $P_{10}: 1 + 2 + \cdots + 10 = \dfrac{10(11)}{2}$. We have established that $P_{(n-1)}$ implies P_n and that P_1 is true. Thus, it follows immediately that P_2 is true because P_1 implies P_2. The truth of P_2 implies P_3 in the same way. Once again, since P_3 is true and since $P_{(n-1)}$ implies P_n, it follows that P_4 is true. We can continue in this way until the truth of P_9 is established. But if P_9 is true and $P_{(n-1)}$ implies P_n, then P_{10} is true. This iterative procedure could be used just as readily to establish any special case of Theorem 5.5.4. But, of course, none of this is necessary because the proposition, in its generality applies immediately to propositions about *every* positive integer, n. In five relatively simple steps, an infinitely large set of propositions has been proven.

As a second illustration of finite induction, we have the following theorem (which was necessary to the proof of 5.5.2), which says that there is no integer between zero and one. Theorem 5.5.5 can be proven without induction if the well-ordering principle is appealed to (see Exercise 5.29), so our reasoning is not circular.

(5.5.5) $n \geq 1$, all $n \in I^+$ **THEOREM**

Proof

(1) $1 \geq 1$.	(5.4.6.8.a)
(2) Assume $(n - 1) \geq 1$.	
(3) $n - (n - 1) = 1 > 0$.	(Exercise 4.c and 5.4.6.6)
(4) $n \geq (n - 1)$.	(Step 3 and 5.4.3)
(5) $n \geq 1$.	(Steps 2, 4 and 5.4.6.8.c)

Notice that this proof uses induction but that it does not make direct use of the well-ordering principle.

Exercises

5.27. Using mathematical induction, prove:

$$1^2 + 2^2 + \cdots + n^2 = \frac{n(n + 1)(2n + 1)}{6}.$$

5.28. Is either of the following two expressions correct?

(a) $1^3 + 2^3 + \cdots + n^3 = \dfrac{n^3(n+1)}{2}$.

(b) $1^3 + 2^3 + \cdots + n^3 = \dfrac{n^2(n+1)^2}{4}$.

5.29. Prove 5.5.5 without using induction. (HINT: Assume that $K \neq \phi$, where $K = \{k : k \in I^+ \text{ and } 0 < k < 1\}$ and locate a contradiction of the well-ordering principle.)

5.30. Prove 2.6.8, the second law of dualization:

$$c \left(\bigcap_{i=1}^{n} (A_i) \right) = \bigcup_{i=1}^{n} (c(A_i)).$$

5.31. Prove Theorem 2.6.6 by induction. Theorem 2.6.6, the first law of dualization, states that

$$c \left(\bigcup_{i=1}^{n} (A_i) \right) = \bigcap_{i=1}^{n} (c(A_i)).$$

Selected References

1. Allendoerfer, C. B., and Oakley, C. O. *Principles of Mathematics.* New York: McGraw-Hill Book Company, Inc., 1955. Pages 47–51.
2. Birkhoff, Garrett, and Mac Lane, Saunders. *A Survey of Modern Algebra* (Revised Edition). New York: The Macmillan Company, 1953. Chapter 1 and pages 51–57.
3. Dantzig, Tobias. *Number, The Language of Science* (Fourth Edition, Revised and Augmented). New York: Doubleday Anchor Books, 1954. Chapters 1–4.
4. Hardy, G. H., and Wright, E. M. *An Introduction to the Theory of Numbers* (Second Edition). Oxford: The Clarendon Press, 1945. Chapter 1.
5. Suppes, Patrick. *Axiomatic Set Theory.* Princeton, New Jersey: D. Van Nostrand Co., Inc., 1960. Chapter 4.
6. Van DerWaerden, B. L. *Modern Algebra*, Volume I. New York: Frederick Ungar Co., 1949. Chapter 1.

Real Numbers

The integers comprise a large set indeed, running on in both directions forever as they do. It is, nonetheless, far too small a set to serve man's intellectual needs adequately. The integers were constructed to represent physical operations on sets. Some conceptual operations, however, cannot be represented by the integers, at least not as they have been used to this point.

To clarify this, consider the following situation. Suppose that two men are candidates for mayor in two different cities. Now, if the first candidate received 4,000 of his city's votes and the second candidate received 6,000 of his city's votes, then our entire knowledge about the integers tells us just one thing: that the first candidate received fewer votes than did the second. Intuitively, it ought to be clear that this information is virtually meaningless. It fails to convey which of the two was more popular and which, if either, won his race for office. What is needed is a second set of "benchmark" integers, against which the vote figures can be compared. These, of course, would be the number of votes cast in the two cities. If 6,000 votes were cast in the first city and 20,000 were cast in the second, the story would be quite different from that in which each town had 10,000 votes. In this sense, the integers do not serve us well. Rather than discarding them for something altogether new, however, we shall see that they can be built up into a set of numbers that are better suited to the expression of certain ideas, such as that of relative popularity.

6

6.1 Fields and Division

The point of the preceding illustration is that integers can be made to represent quite different things when considered with regard to different base numbers. In the illustration, the base number would be the total number of votes cast. Unfortunately, we are not equipped thus far even to discuss numbers relative to different bases. Besides the now familiar properties of an integral set, we need something called the *multiplicative inverse* of each element.

(6.1.1) If F is an integral set, then F is called a field if for each $x \in F$, $x \neq 0$, there exists an element, $x^{-1} \in F$ (called "x inverse") such that **Definition**

$$(x)(x^{-1}) = 1.$$

Thus, the inverse of a (nonzero) number is simply a second number that, when multiplied by the first, gives the product of one.

The multiplicative inverse has some useful properties that are summarized by:

(6.1.2) If F is a field and a, $b \in F$ are such that $a \neq 0$ and $b \neq 0$ (so that a^{-1}, $b^{-1} \in F$), then: **THEOREM**
(1) $a^{-1} = b^{-1} \leftrightarrow a = b$.   (4) $a^{-1} \neq 0$ all $a \in F$.
(2) $(ab)^{-1} = a^{-1}b^{-1}$.   (5) $a^{-1} > 0 \leftrightarrow a > 0$.
(3) $(a^{-1})^{-1} = a$.   (6) $a^{-1} < 0 \leftrightarrow a < 0$.

All proofs are left as exercises.

This theorem states that the inverse of a number is a unique number; that the inverse of a product of two numbers is the product of their inverses; and that the inverse of the inverse of a number is just that number. Note carefully that the inverse of the sum of two numbers is not necessarily the sum of their inverses. (When would this be the case?)

Thus far, the integers have been characterized as a well-ordered integral set. Definition 6.1.1 creates a question as to whether this set also is a field. That it is not should be immediately obvious; almost no integers have inverse elements that also are integers. (Can the reader think of an exception?) To prove that the integers do not constitute a field, we need find only a single counterexample, for which the number 2 works well.

(6.1.3) The inverse of 2 is not an integer. **THEOREM**

Suppose there exists an integer, x, such that $2x = 1$ (so that $x = 2^{-1}$). But we know that $x > 0$ by O2 and 5.4.6.6. Moreover, $x < 1$ since $2x = 1 \rightarrow x = 1 - x$. Thus, x is an integer between 0 and 1; but no such integer exists, according to 5.5.5. *Proof*

As the reader should have suspected by now, fields of elements are introduced in order to provide a basis for constructing the operation of division. Intuitively, one recognizes that the sentence "divide a by b" means "locate an element, x, such that $bx = a$." With the notion of a multiplicative inverse, this intuitive correspondence can be formalized as follows:

(6.1.4) If I is any integral set, then $/$ (called division) is a mapping of $I \times (I - 0)$ into a set X subject to

$$a/b = x \leftrightarrow (a)(b^{-1}) = x, \langle a, b \rangle \, \epsilon \, I \times (I - 0), x \, \epsilon \, X,$$

and x is called the quotient of the ordered pair, $\langle a, b \rangle$.

Definition

This is equivalent to saying that division locates a solution for x of the equation $bx = a$ for each $\langle a, b \rangle$ in which $b \neq 0$. That is,

(6.1.5) $(a)(b^{-1}) = x \leftrightarrow bx = a$.

PROPOSITION

Let $(a)(b^{-1}) = x$. Then:

Proof

(1) $(a)(b^{-1})b = xb$. (M7)
(2) $(a)(1) = xb$. (6.1.1 and M5)
(3) $a = bx$. (M3 and M4)

Proof of the converse is left as an exercise.

The notions of field and division are brought together by the following:

(6.1.6) If F is a field, then F is closed under division (except for division by zero).

THEOREM

Since F is a field, $b^{-1} \epsilon F$ for each $b \epsilon F$, $b \neq 0$. Since a field is an integral set, $(ab) \epsilon F$ for each $a \epsilon F$ and $b \epsilon F$. Hence, in particular, $(a)(b^{-1}) \epsilon F$.

Proof

The next major task will be to reconstruct the integers as a field so that this new operation, division, can be used. A preliminary examination of the behavior of division will help in this investigation. The reader might attempt to anticipate the characteristics of division before he proceeds. For example, if $a/b = x$, is x unique? is division associative? What must be true of elements a and b in order for x to be positive? Several questions such as these are answered by the following:

(6.1.7) If F is a field and a, b, c, d, $x \in F$, with $b \neq 0$ and $d \neq 0$, then: **THEOREM**
(1) $a/b = c/d \leftrightarrow ad = bc$.
(2) $a/b \pm c/d = (ad \pm bc)/bd$.
(3) $(a/b)(c/d) = ac/bd$.
(4) $a/b = x$ and $a/b = y \to x = y$.
(5) $(a/b)(d/d) = a/b$.
(6) If $a/b = x$ then:

    (a) $x > 0 \leftrightarrow ab > 0$.
    (b) $x = 0 \leftrightarrow a = 0$.
    (c) $x < 0 \leftrightarrow ab < 0$.

(7) If inequalities are substituted for equalities in (1), the statement remains true.

Let $a/b = c/d$.		*Proof (1,*
(1) $ab^{-1} = cd^{-1}$.	(Hypothesis and 6.1.4)	*implication.)*
(2) $ab^{-1}(bd) = cd^{-1}(bd)$.	(M7)	
(3) $a(b^{-1}b)d = b(d^{-1}d)c$.	(M4 and M5)	
(4) $a(1)d = b(1)c$.	(6.1.1)	
(5) $ad = bc$.	(M3)	

Proof (2)

(1) $a/b \pm c/d$		
$= ab^{-1} \pm cd^{-1}$,	(6.1.4 and A2)	
(2) $= (bd)(bd)^{-1}(ab^{-1} \pm cd^{-1})$,	(6.1.1 and M3 since $(bd)(bd)^{-1} = 1$)	
(3) $= [a(bb^{-1})d \pm bc(dd^{-1})](bd)^{-1}$,	(Steps 1, 2, M4, M5, M6)	
(4) $= (ad \pm bc)(bd)^{-1}$,	(6.1.1 and M3)	
(5) $= (ad \pm bc)/bd$.	(6.1.4)	

The remaining proofs are left as exercises. Parts (1)–(3) of the theorem stipulate the conditions of equality, addition, and multiplication respectively (we know, of course, that sums and products are in F because F is an integral set). Part (4) gives the uniqueness property of the number b^{-1}, similar to Axiom (2) on addition and multiplication of integers. Part (5) gives an identity element for division, namely (d/d) for any element $d \neq 0$. This could be rewritten as $da/db = a/b$, which resembles the cancellation axiom of multiplication, M7. Note that there are no parallels in this theorem to the commutative, associative, and distributive axioms on multiplication. (Why?)

Exercises

6.1. Prove 6.1.2.1. (HINT: Investigate $(ab)b^{-1}$ and $(ab)a^{-1}$.)

6.2. Prove 6.1.2.2. (HINT: $(ab)(ab)^{-1} = 1$. Multiply both sides by a^{-1} and proceed from there.)

6.3. Prove 6.1.2.3. (HINT: Note that $a^{-1}(a^{-1})^{-1} = 1$. Why?)

6.4. Prove 6.1.2, parts (4)–(6).

6.5. Suppose that the restriction $x \neq 0$ were removed from 6.1.1. What sort of contradictions would result?

6.6. Carefully explain how 6.1.4 expresses division as a special case of multiplication.

6.7. Proposition 6.1.5 expresses division as the solution of an equation, $bx = a$. Restate this proposition in English and compare the result with that of Exercise 6.6.

6.8. When is an integral set a field? a field an integral set?

6.9. Prove the converse of 6.1.7.1.

6.10. Prove 6.1.7.4.

6.11. Prove 6.1.7.6. (HINT: There are six parts to the exercise.)

6.12. Prove that $a/b < c/d \leftrightarrow ad < bc$.

6.13. Assume that $/$ is commutative. What contradictions result?

6.14. Assume that $/$ is associative. What contradictions result? (HINT: Investigate $(a/b)/c$ and $a/(b/c)$.)

6.2 Rational Numbers

At this point we are in a rather odd situation. The operation of division was seen to be a useful, even necessary tool for numerical analysis. In order to get at this operation, a set called a *field* was constructed and investigated. This yielded division, which in turn was explored in some detail. Despite this effort, we have no set of numbers that comprise a field. Theorem 6.1.3 showed that the set of integers does not contain all the multiplicative inverses of the integers and, hence, is not closed under division as a field is.

In order to set matters straight and to uncover a set on which we can impose division, a new construction is needed. The strategy here is to build up from the integers a set that preserves all properties of the integers and, besides, contains all its inverses. This set is, of course, the rational numbers. The blueprint for this construction is provided by the results of the preceding section, especially Theorem 6.1.7. The first three parts of that theorem suggest that our new set must consist of *ordered pairs* of integers and must tell us how to define equality, addition, and multiplication. The reader should review these parts of Theorem 6.1.7 carefully in order to see how they motivate the following:

(6.2.1) If I is the set of integers, then $R' = \{\langle a, b \rangle : a, b \, \epsilon \, I$ and $b \neq 0\}$ is called the set of *rational numbers*, and R' is governed by: **Definition**

$$R' = \{\cdots\}.$$

(1) $\langle a, b \rangle \cong \langle c, d \rangle \leftrightarrow ad = bc$ (where $\cong$ is called *congruence*).
(2) $\langle a, b \rangle \pm \langle c, d \rangle = \langle (ad \pm bc), bd \rangle$.
(3) $\langle a, b \rangle \cdot \langle c, d \rangle = \langle (ac), (bd) \rangle$.
(4) $\langle a, b \rangle > 0 \leftrightarrow (ab) > 0$.

An element $\langle a, b \rangle \, \epsilon \, R'$ may be written a/b or $\frac{a}{b}$, in which a is called the numerator and b, the denominator of the ordered pair.

Several remarks are in order about this definition. First, notice that $R' = I \times (I - 0)$ in which $(I - 0)$ is the set of integers excluding zero. This is equivalent to saying that numbers of the form $\frac{a}{0}$ are not contained in R' or that division by zero is inadmissible. Recall from exercise 6.5 that such a number would create contradictions.

Part 1 of definition 6.2.1 introduces a new relation, that of congruence, which is similar but not identical to the relation of equality. Recall that $\langle a, b \rangle = \langle c, d \rangle$ if and only if $a = c$ and $b = d$. But Part 1 of Theorem 6.1.7 suggests that two ordered pairs of a field may be the same number even though their domain and range members are not identical. In this sense, the ordered pairs $\langle 2, 4 \rangle$ and $\langle 4, 8 \rangle$ are the same number even though they are not equal in the set-theoretic sense. The number $2/4$ is said to be congruent to the number $4/8$, according to 6.2.1.1, because $(2)(8) = (4)(4)$. Although this is a necessary refinement because equality must mean one thing only, it is unimportant in the sense that congruence *behaves* exactly as does equality. In 3.7 we saw that the relation of equality was reflexive, symmetric, and transitive.

(6.2.2) The congruence relation, $\cong$, is   **THEOREM**
(1) reflexive,
(2) symmetric,
(3) transitive.

Let $\langle a, b \rangle \cong \langle c, d \rangle$ and $\langle c, d \rangle \cong \langle e, f \rangle$. Then, we must show   *Proof (3)* that $\langle a, b \rangle \cong \langle e, f \rangle$ so that, by 6.2.1.1, $af = be$.

(1) $ad = bc$ and $cf = de$.	(Hypothesis and 6.2.1.1)
(2) $ade = bce$ and $acf = ade$.	(Step 1 and M7)
(3) $acf = bce$.	(Step 2 and, transitively, of $=$)
(4) $af = be$.	(Step 3 and M7)
(5) $\langle a, b \rangle \cong \langle e, f \rangle$.	(Step 4 and 6.2.1.1)

Proofs of parts 1 and 2 are immediately obvious.

Equality and congruence are two examples of what is called an *equivalence relation*. An equivalence relation is any relation that is reflexive, symmetric, and transitive. Such a relation generates disjoint and exhaustive sets of elements that are called *equivalence classes*. In Chapter 5, we partitioned any given class of sets into equivalence classes by establishing one-to-one correspondences on their elements. The definition of congruence of ordered pairs permits a similar partition of the set of rational numbers. Thus, some typical equivalence classes in this partition would be $\{\langle 1, 2 \rangle, \langle 2, 4 \rangle, \langle 4, 8 \rangle, \cdots\}$, $\{\langle 1, 3 \rangle, \langle 2, 6 \rangle, \langle 3, 9 \rangle, \cdots\}$, $\{\langle 3, 5 \rangle, \langle 6, 10 \rangle, \langle 12, 20 \rangle, \cdots\}$. In this view, R', the set of rational numbers, is just a set of equivalence classes of ordered pairs of integers, $\langle a, b \rangle$, $b \neq 0$.

Parts 2 and 3 of 6.2.1 define addition and multiplication of the rationals. These particular definitions were chosen, of course, so as to be consistent with Theorem 6.1.7, parts 2 and 3, the strategy being to construct the rationals so that they are closed under division. Notice that equality rather than congruence is used in these two parts of the definition. (Why?) The definition of addition, $\langle a, b \rangle \pm \langle c, d \rangle = \langle (ad \pm bc), bd \rangle$ makes good sense intuitively in light of 6.1.7.5, which said that $(a/b)(d/d) = a/b$. The elements $\langle a, b \rangle$ and $\langle c, d \rangle$ can be thought of as integers a and c expressed relative to different bases, b and d respectively. To be added, these numbers must be made comparable, that is, expressed relative to a common base. The strategic choice of base clearly is bd, since $\langle a, b \rangle \cong \langle ad, bd \rangle$ and $\langle c, d \rangle \cong \langle bc, bd \rangle$. Thus, $\langle a, b \rangle \pm \langle c, d \rangle \cong \langle ad, bd \rangle \pm \langle bc, bd \rangle$, in which the integers now have the common base bd and the sum is just $\langle ad + bc, bd \rangle$. The reader should make a similar intuitive justification of the definition of multiplication, 6.2.1.3.

Part 4 of 6.2.1, which says that $\langle a, b \rangle > 0 \leftrightarrow ab > 0$, gives a definition of order in terms of the order property of integers. Thus, whatever else it may or may not be, R' is an ordered set. Of course, this does not mean that it is well-ordered. The reader should review 5.5.1, the definition of a well-ordered set, and decide whether or not R' has this property.

Three questions remain unanswered at this point. These are whether R' is an integral set, whether it is a field, and whether it is well-ordered. Of course, we would hope that R' is both an integral set and a field because we need the properties of the former as well as division, which can occur in a field. If R' is well-ordered, then it is subject to proofs by finite induction; if not, matters become more complicated.

To answer the first of these three questions, it must be decided whether or not R' has all properties invested in I by the axioms of Chapter 5. We should have to show, for example, that R' is commutative under both addition and multiplication so as to satisfy A4 and M4. The question is answered by the following:

(6.2.3) R' is an integral set.   **THEOREM**

The proof of this theorem can be displayed as a series of proofs about propositions, one concerning each axiom on the integers. For example, M6, the distributive axiom, says that $a(b + c) = ab + ac$, where a, b, and c are integers. This leads to the following:

(6.2.4) If $\langle a, b \rangle, \langle c, d \rangle, \langle e, f \rangle \in R'$, then $\langle a, b \rangle(\langle c, d \rangle \pm \langle e, f \rangle)$ **PROPOSITION**
$\cong \langle a, b \rangle \langle c, d \rangle \pm \langle a, b \rangle \langle e, f \rangle$.

Let $\langle a, b \rangle, \langle c, d \rangle, \langle e, f \rangle \in R'$.   *Proof*

(1) $\langle c, d \rangle \pm \langle e, f \rangle = \langle (cf \pm de), df \rangle$.   (6.2.1.2)
(2) $\langle a, b \rangle(\langle c, d \rangle \pm \langle e, f \rangle)$
$\qquad\qquad = \langle a, b \rangle \langle (cf \pm de), df \rangle$,   (Step 1)
(3) $\qquad\quad = \langle a(cf \pm de), bdf \rangle$,   (6.2.1.3)
(4) $\qquad\quad = \langle (acf \pm ade), bdf \rangle$,   (M6)
(5) $\qquad\quad \cong \langle b, b \rangle \langle (acf \pm ade), bdf \rangle$,   (6.2.1.1)
(6) $\qquad\quad = \langle (abcf \pm abde), bbdf \rangle$,   (as in steps 1–4)
(7) $\qquad\quad \cong \langle ac, bd \rangle \pm \langle ae, bf \rangle$,   (6.2.1.2)
(8) $\qquad\quad \cong \langle a, b \rangle \langle c, d \rangle \pm \langle a, b \rangle \langle e, f \rangle$.   (6.2.1.3)

The only trick to this proof consists of multiplying in the identity element, $\langle b, b \rangle$, in step 5. Proofs of the remaining parts of 6.2.3 are left as exercises.

As matters now stand, we have two sets, I and R', both of which are integral sets and, thus, are indistinguishable. However, we know from 6.1.3 that I is not a field. If it could be shown that the inverse of each nonzero element $x \in R'$ (where x is an ordered pair) also is in R', then we would have a first distinguishing property between I and R'.

Before it is possible to discover whether R' is a field, it is necessary to decide what the symbols 0 and 1 in 6.1.1, the definition of a field, represent so far as elements in R' are concerned. That is, a connection between integers and rational numbers must be provided. An integer cannot be called a rational number because an integer is not the same thing as an ordered pair of integers. However, the intuitively satisfactory connection also works well formally. That is, if we think of an integer, a, as a rational number to the base 1, $\langle a, 1 \rangle$, then this number behaves exactly like an integer under addition and multiplication. That is,

PROPOSITION

(6.2.5) Let a and b be integers; then:
(1) $\langle a, 1 \rangle \cong \langle b, 1 \rangle \leftrightarrow a = b$.
(2) $\langle a, 1 \rangle \pm \langle b, 1 \rangle = \langle (a \pm b), 1 \rangle$.
(3) $\langle a, 1 \rangle \cdot \langle b, 1 \rangle = \langle (ab), 1 \rangle$.
(4) $\langle a, 1 \rangle < \langle b, 1 \rangle \leftrightarrow a < b$.
(5) $\langle a, 1 \rangle > 0 \leftrightarrow a > 0$.

The proof follows immediately from 6.2.1. Thus, the zero of R' is just the equivalence class $\langle 0, b \rangle$, and the unit is $\langle b, b \rangle$. Hereafter, the integer a and the ordered pair $\langle a, 1 \rangle$ will be treated as though they were the same thing.

With this, it is possible to show that R', unlike I, is a field.

THEOREM

(6.2.6) If $x = \langle a, b \rangle \, \epsilon \, R'$, such that $a \neq 0$, then $x^{-1} \, \epsilon \, R'$.

Proof

Let $\langle a, b \rangle \, \epsilon \, R'$ and $a \neq 0$. Then, $\langle b, a \rangle \, \epsilon \, R'$.
(1) $\langle a, b \rangle \langle b, a \rangle = \langle ab, ba \rangle$,   (6.2.1.3)
(2) $= \langle ab, ab \rangle$,   (M4)
(3) $\cong \langle 1, 1 \rangle$,   (6.2.1.1)
(4) $x^{-1} = \langle b, a \rangle$.   (6.1.1 and step 3)

Thus, the inverse of any nonzero element, $\langle a, b \rangle \, \epsilon \, R'$, is the element $\langle b, a \rangle$, which also is in R', since $a \neq 0$. Both I and R' are integral sets and, hence, are closed under addition and multiplication. But only R' is a field and, hence, by 6.1.6, is closed under division as well. Informally, I has been imbedded in R' by the correspondence $a \leftrightarrow \langle a, 1 \rangle$, where a is an integer.

One other property serves to separate I and R'. That is

the well-ordering property. Recall from 5.4.1 that an integral set is ordered if it contains a positive subset. Thus, both I and R' (by virtue of 6.2.1.4) are ordered. To be well-ordered, each subset of an ordered positive set must contain a least element. We know that the positive integers are well-ordered, but it happens that the rational numbers are not. The proof of this fact, moreover, provides an apparent, although somewhat misleading, insight into the size of R'. The proof requires the following:

PROPOSITION

(6.2.7) If a and c are any rational numbers such that $a < c$, then there exists a rational number b such that $a < b < c$.

Proof

Let $a, c \in R'$ and $a < c$. Then let $b = \langle (a + c), 2 \rangle$, that is $\dfrac{a + c}{2}$, so that $b \in R'$.

Assume that $b < a$.

(1) $\dfrac{a + c}{2} < a$.   (Hypothesis about b and assumptions)

(2) $a + c < 2a$.   (M7 and 6.26)
(3) $c < a$.   (5.4.6.1)

But (3) contradicts the hypothesis, $a < c$, so it must be that $a < b$. It remains to be shown that $b < c$. Assume $c < b$.

(4) $c < \dfrac{a + c}{2}$.   (Hypothesis about b and assumptions)

(5) $2c < a + c$.   (M7)
(6) $c < a$.   (5.4.6.1)

This contradicts the hypothesis, so $a < b < c$. Notice that there are no restrictions on the rational numbers a and c. They can be squeezed together as tightly as one pleases, and still there is another rational number between them. Since we identify the integers 0 and 1 with rational numbers, there are, in particular, rational numbers between 0 and 1. Obviously, then, R' is indeed a crowded set. Since I does not have this property (how do we know?), it would appear that R' is much larger than I. That this is not at all the case will be made clear later in this chapter. From all of this, it follows that:

(6.2.8) The positive rational numbers are not well-ordered.

Consider $X = \{\langle a, b \rangle : 0 < \langle a, b \rangle < 1\}$. Thus $X \subset R'$. If R' is well-ordered, X contains a least element, x_0. Assume that $x_0 = \langle a_0, b_0 \rangle$ is the least element of X.

(1) $\langle 1, 2 \rangle \langle a_0, b_0 \rangle = \langle a_0, 2b_0 \rangle$.   (6.2.1.3 and M3)
(2) $\langle a_0, 2b_0 \rangle < \langle a_0, b_0 \rangle$.   (6.1.7.7 and $a_0 b_0 < 2a_0 b_0$)
(3) $2a_0 b_0 > 0$.   (Since $a_0 b_0 > 0$ by hypothesis
                                    and 5.4.6.3)
(4) $0 < \langle a_0, 2b_0 \rangle < \langle a_0, b_0 \rangle$.   (Steps 2 and 3)
(5) $\langle a_0, b_0 \rangle$ is not the least element of X (since $\langle a_0, 2b_0 \rangle \in X$
    and is less than $\langle a_0, b_0 \rangle$ by step 4).

Thus, the integers comprise a well-ordered set that is not a field, while the rational numbers comprise both an integral set and a field but are not well-ordered. Despite these differences, we see that the integers can be imbedded in the rationals, that is, $I \subset R'$.

Exercises

6.15. Construct an equivalence relation on the set $A = \{a, b, c, d\}$.

6.16. Substitute $\langle a, d \rangle \pm \langle b, c \rangle = \langle (ab \pm cd), cd \rangle$ (in 6.2.1.2) and show that the resultant set is not an integral set.

6.17. If $\langle a, b \rangle > 0$, then we write $-\langle a, b \rangle < 0$, and $-\langle a, b \rangle$ can be written $\frac{-a}{b}$. Show

that $\frac{-a}{b} = \frac{a}{-b}$.

6.18. Since R' is an ordered integral set, it should satisfy all properties of inequalities of Section 5.4. Use definition 5.4.3 to prove that the rationals satisfy 5.4.6, parts 1, 4, and 5.

6.19. Prove 6.2.2.2.

6.20. Which of the following are positive?

(a) $-2/-4$
(b) $2/-4$
(c) $-1(-2/4)$
(d) $(-2/-4)/-8$
(e) $(-2/-4)/0$
(f) $(-2/-4)/(0/-4)$

6.21. Prove that R' satisfies the following integral axioms on addition:

(a) A2
(b) A3
(c) A5
(d) A6

6.22. Prove that R' satisfies the following axioms on multiplication:

(a) M2
(b) M5
(c) M7

6.23. Prove 6.2.5.

6.24. Locate the inverse of each of the following and verify it by the property $(x)(x^{-1}) = 1$:

(a) $\langle 3, 2 \rangle$
(b) $\langle \langle 3, 2 \rangle, 2 \rangle$
(c) $\langle 4, \langle 4, 4 \rangle \rangle$
(d) $\langle \langle a, b \rangle, \langle c, d \rangle \rangle$
(e) $\langle \langle \langle a, b \rangle, \langle c, d \rangle \rangle, \langle e, f \rangle \rangle$ (HINT: Write this as $[(a/b)/(c/d)]/(e/f)]$.)

6.25. Explain why statements that are axioms on integers are theorems on rationals.

6.26. Simplify the following, justifying each step by an appropriate axiom or theorem:

(a) $\frac{1}{2} + \frac{2}{5} - \frac{1}{10}$
(b) $\frac{1}{3}(\frac{2}{5} + \frac{3}{5})$
(c) $(\frac{1}{3})(\frac{1}{4})(\frac{1}{5})$
(d) $(\frac{1}{3})(\frac{2}{5}) + (\frac{3}{5})(\frac{1}{3}) + (\frac{2}{5})(\frac{8}{10})$
(e) $(\frac{1}{3})(\frac{1}{4}) + (\frac{2}{3})(\frac{6}{8}) + (1)(\frac{3}{2})$
(f) $2(\frac{1}{2}) + 3(\frac{3}{9}) + 4(\frac{4}{16})$

6.27. Simplify:

(a) $\dfrac{ax}{c} \Big/ \dfrac{a}{bc}$

(b) $\left\{ \left[\left(\dfrac{3}{5}\right) + \left(\dfrac{5}{7}\right) \right] \left[\dfrac{1}{2}\right] - \dfrac{\left(\dfrac{4}{4-1}\right)}{(2/-3)} \right\} \dfrac{7}{20}$

(c) $4\left(\dfrac{3x + 4}{15 - 3}\right) + \dfrac{\frac{11}{9} + \frac{3}{27}}{-3}$

6.28. Each of the following illustrates a common error of algebra. State the axiom or theorem that was violated and point out the reasoning that led to the false conclusions in each:

(a) $a\left(\dfrac{b}{c} + \dfrac{d}{e}\right) = \dfrac{ab}{c} + \dfrac{d}{e}.$

(b) $\dfrac{a + b}{c} = \dfrac{a}{c} + b.$

(c) $\left(\dfrac{a}{c}\right)\left(\dfrac{b}{c}\right) = \dfrac{ab}{c}.$

(d) $\dfrac{a}{b}\bigg/\dfrac{c}{d} = \dfrac{ac}{bd}.$

(e) $\dfrac{ab}{c} + \dfrac{ad}{e} = \dfrac{a}{ce}(b + d).$

6.29. Find each of the following:

(a) $((a/b)^{-1})^{-1}$

(b) $(a/b)^{-1}(c/d)$

(c) $(a/b)^{-1}(c/d)^{-1}$

(d) $[(a/b)(c/d)]^{-1}$

6.30. Find the value of x, justifying each step:

(a) $2x - 1 = 0.$

(b) $3x - \left(\dfrac{2 - x}{5}\right)\left[\dfrac{2}{3} + \dfrac{1}{-6}\right] = 6.$

(c) $x - 3 = \dfrac{3}{2}\left(\dfrac{1 + 3}{3 - 1}\right).$

(d) $3(1 - x) = 3.$

6.31. For what values of x are the inequalities satisfied?

(a) $3x - 15 < 0.$

(b) $\dfrac{1}{x} < \dfrac{1}{5}$ if $x > 0$; if $x < 0.$

(c) $2x + 5 > 4x - 9.$

(d) $3 < \dfrac{x + 2}{5} < 6.$

(e) $-2 < \dfrac{20 - x}{5} < 2.$

6.32. The sum of a number and its inverse is 2. Find the number.

6.3 Decimals

A rational number is neither more nor less reasonable than is any other number. It is, instead, a ratio-nal number, that is, the *ratio* of two integers. There is nothing inherently frightening about such numbers, but it is certainly true that they are often awkward, inconvenient things with which to work. For purposes of computation, it is frequently much more convenient to work with numbers in decimal form.

The decimal form of a rational number, a/b, is usually found by dividing the value assigned to b into that assigned to a according to the rules familiar from elementary arithmetic. It will be worthwhile to formalize this idea somewhat and to investigate the set of decimal numbers. To do this, it is necessary to anticipate some of the work of the next chapter.

(6.3.1) If a is any number and n is a positive integer, then a^n is the number obtained by serially multiplying a n times. The number $a^{-n} = \dfrac{1}{a^n}$ and $a^0 = 1$. The number 0^0 is undefined.

Definition

In this definition n is called an integral exponent of the base number a. Thus $10^0 = 1, 10^1 = 10, 10^2 = 100, 10^3 = 1,000$. For the present, we shall consider only the base number 10.

A number, in this context, is just an ordered $n$tuple of *digits*, which are the numbers from 0 to 9. Thus, the number 2,161 is just the ordered quadruple of digits $\langle 2, 1, 6, 1 \rangle$. Moreover, this can be represented as a sum of numbers as follows:

(6.3.2)

PROPOSITION

$$2{,}161 = 2(10^3) + 1(10^2) + 6(10^1) + 1(10^0),$$

a fact that the reader should verify. The position of a digit in the $n$tuple indicates the power of 10 by which it is multiplied. In order to establish a clear starting place, the decimal point has been introduced. This little dot is used to indicate that the digit to its left is multiplied by 10^0, that the digit next to the left is multiplied by 10^1, and so on. In 6.3.2, the integer thus could be written $(2{,}161.)$. The first number to the right of the point is taken as a multiple of 10^{-1}, the next, as a multiple of 10^{-2}, and so on. Thus, the number 3,624.36 is

(6.3.3)

PROPOSITION

$$3{,}624.36 = 3(10^3) + 6(10^2) + 2(10^1) + 4(10^0)$$
$$+ 3(10^{-1}) + 6(10^{-2}).$$

Now, this clearly is a rational number, since R' is closed under addition and since $k(10^n)$ is a rational number for any integers k and n. Division in the common form is just a way of finding the correct k and n so that $k(10^n) = \dfrac{a}{b}$.

The reader certainly is familiar with the class of decimal numbers called *terminating*. A decimal number is called terminating if there exists a point beyond which only the digit zero occurs. For example, the number $\frac{1}{2} = 0.5000 \cdots$. A second class of decimals is nonterminating but behaves in an orderly fashion. This is called the class of *periodic* or *repeating* decimals. A periodic decimal is an *n*tuple that is endless but repeats a particular pattern "in blocks" beyond some point. For instance, the rational number $\frac{5}{7}$ is equal to $0.857142\ 857142\ 857142 \cdots$, the digits of which can be partitioned into the repeating sextuple $\langle 8, 5, 7, 1, 4, 2 \rangle$. With these two classes of decimals, we have the following:

(6.3.4) A number is a rational number if and only if its decimal expansion is terminating or repeating.   **THEOREM**

This theorem, which is not proven here (see Moore, *Fundamental Principles* [6], pp. 37–41), does two things. First, it assures us that a rational number takes on a specific decimal form. Second, and much more interesting, it opens the door to an important question: Are all decimal numbers either repeating or terminating? If the answer is no, as the reader ought to suspect is the case, then what would the remaining decimal numbers—call them *nonperiodic*—represent? In the event that there are nonperiodic decimals, then there must be numbers that are not rational. This is precisely the case. Such numbers are considered in the following section.

Exercises

6.33. Determine whether each of the following is terminating or periodic in its decimal expansion:

(a) $\frac{1}{8}$
(b) $\frac{2}{8}$
(c) $\frac{3}{8}$
(d) $\frac{1}{7}$
(e) $\frac{4}{7}$
(f) $\frac{1}{8}$

6.34. Consider carefully the process of decimally expanding the numbers $\frac{1}{7}$ and $\frac{1}{8}$. Explain why the periodic blocks cannot be any longer than they are.

6.35. Let n be any positive integer. If the decimal expansion of $1/n$ is periodic, the size of the periodic blocks can be no longer than a certain number. What is that number? Why?

6.4 Irrational Numbers

It is not difficult to show that there are numbers whose decimal expansions are neither terminating nor periodic. Such numbers are called *irrationals*, that is, numbers that cannot be expressed as a ratio of integers. To demonstrate this fact we shall need the additional equipment provided by the following definition and lemmas (auxiliary theorems used primarily to prove other theorems).

(6.4.1) An integer, n, is said to be *even* if there exists an integer k such that $n = 2k$. Otherwise, it is said to be *odd*.

Definition

Thus, the sequence of integers 2, 4, 6, 8, $\cdots$, is the even set, while 1, 3, 5, 7, $\cdots$ is the odd set. It should be clear that, if n is odd, $n + 1$ is even, and if n is even, $n + 1$ is odd. Moreover, if n is odd, there exists an integer k such that $n = 2k + 1$.

(6.4.2) For any integer, n,

LEMMA

(1) n is even $\leftrightarrow n^2$ is even.
(2) n is odd $\leftrightarrow n^2$ is odd.

Let n be even so that $n = 2k$, k being an integer. Then $n^2 = (2k)(2k) = 2(2k^2)$. But $2k^2$ is an integer, so that n is even by 6.4.1. To prove the converse, let n^2 be even. Then, if n were odd, this fact would contradict the implication of 6.4.2.2.

Proof (1)

Let n be odd, so that $n = 2k + 1$, k being an integer, and *Proof (2)*
$n^2 = (2k + 1)(2k + 1) = (4k^2 + 4k) + 1$. But $4k^2 + 4k = 2(2k^2 + 2k)$, an even integer, so that n^2 is odd. The converse
follows from the implication of 6.4.2.1.

Notice that the proof of the two converses depends on the
truth of the implications. This is quite proper, because the
proof of the implications does *not* depend on the truth of the
converses.

(6.4.3) Every rational number is congruent to a rational **LEMMA**
number at least one of whose members is odd.

Let $x = a/b$ be a rational number such that both a and b *Proof*
are even. Then $x = 2k_a/2k_b \cong k_a/k_b$. If k_a and k_b are even,
then $x \cong 2k_a'/2k_b' \cong k_a'/k_b'$. If both k_a' and k_b' are even, this
process is repeated. If the process can be repeated until
k_a or k_b equals 2 and the other member is even, then one
final iteration necessarily produces the integer 1, an odd
number.

With this it can be shown that there are irrational numbers. As a case in point, consider the number, x, such that
$x^2 = 2$. The number x, of course, is usually written $\sqrt{2}$.
This is certainly an entity that ought to be in our set of numbers. Geometers, who make numbers correspond to lengths,
recognize this as the length of a diagonal line drawn through
a square with unit length (that is, as the hypotenuse of a
right triangle with unit base and altitude). The question
then is whether the number x such that $x^2 = 2$ is actually a
rational number. The following shows by contradiction that
it is not.

(6.4.4) Let x be a number such that $x^2 = 2$. Then x is **THEOREM**
not a rational number.

Let $x^2 = 2$ and assume x to be rational, so that $x \cong a/b$, *Proof*
a and b being integers in which a or b can be chosen odd by
6.4.3. Let a or b be odd.

(1) $x^2 = a^2/b^2 = 2$.   (Hypothesis and 6.2.1.3)

(2) $a^2 = 2b^2$.   (Step 1 and 6.1.5)

(3) a is even.   (Since a^2 is even by step 2, 6.4.1, and 6.4.2.1)

(4) $a^2 = 4k^2$.   (By Step 3 and 6.4.1)

(5) $2b^2 = 4k^2 \rightarrow b^2 = 2k^2$.   (Steps 2, 4, and M7)

(6) b^2 also is even so that b is even, which with Step 3 contradicts the hypothesis.

Thus, there exists at least one irrational number. This exercise could be repeated substituting for x numbers such as $\sqrt{3}$ or $\sqrt{5}$ and lemmas about multiples of 3 and 5 for those about odd and even numbers. We could show that there are several irrational numbers. It turns out, as we shall see later, that actually there are far more irrational than rational numbers.

Exercises

6.36. Prove that n is odd $\rightarrow n^3$ is odd.

6.37. Prove that n^3 is even $\rightarrow n$ is even.

6.38. Prove that $n/3 \notin I \rightarrow n^2/3 \notin I$.

6.39. Let n be even.

(a) Prove that m even $\rightarrow (m + n)$ even.

(b) Prove that (mn) is even, m being any integer.

6.40. Let x be such that $x^4 = 2$, that is $x \cdot x \cdot x \cdot x = 2$. (By convention $x = \sqrt[4]{2}$.) Show that x is irrational.

6.41. Let x be such that $x^2 = 5$. Show that x is irrational.

6.42. Prove that n odd $\rightarrow n = 2k + 1$, k an integer.

6.5 Real Numbers

We are now in a dilemma. We have put a great deal of effort into the construction of rational numbers, only to discover that they are not complete in the sense that they do not contain numbers such as $\sqrt{2}$ and $\sqrt{5}$. Although this dilemma was known to the ancients (the irrationality of $\sqrt{2}$ is sometimes called the *Pythagorean dilemma*), a reasonably satisfactory resolution within arithmetic was not offered prior to the final years of the past century. This resolution consists in building up the real numbers from a rational field.

A construction of the real numbers will be sketched in the briefest detail here. More thorough treatments can be found in the list of suggested readings at the chapter's end. An entirely new notion is required at this point.

(6.5.1) Let F be an ordered field and let $X \subset F$. Then   **Definition**
an element a is an *upper bounds* of $x \leftrightarrow x \leq a$, all $x \in X$. Let
$B = \{b: b$ is an upper bound of $X\}$. Then a is a *least upper
bounds* of X (denoted lub of X) $\leftrightarrow a \in B$ and $a \leq b$, all $b \in B$.
Lower bound and *greatest lower bound* (denoted "glb") are defined by reversing all inequalities in the above.

Consider the set of numbers n^{-1}, $n \in I^+$. This forms a set of numbers $X = \{1/1, 1/2, 1/3, \cdots\}$. This is clearly a subset of F. Its set of upper bounds is $B = \{b: b \geq 1\}$. Since $b = 1$ is the least element of this set, the lub of X is the number 1. Since $1/n > 0$, all $n > 0$, the set of lower bounds X is $C = \{c: c \leq 0\}$ and the *glb* of X is the number 0. Since $1 \in X$ and $0 \notin X$ we see that a lub or glb need not be in the domain set. Now let $Y = \{y: y \in R'$ and $y > 0\}$. Then Y has a set of lower bounds, a glb $= 0$, but it is not bounded above. Thus, not every set has upper or lower bounds.

Let us return to the irrational number x, which satisfies $x^2 = 2$. This number can be trapped in an ever narrower cage by the following device:

(6.5.2)
$$(1.4)^2 = 1.96 < 2 < (1.5)^2 = 2.25.$$
$$(1.41)^2 = 1.9881 < 2 < (1.42)^2 = 2.0164.$$
$$(1.414)^2 = 1.999396 < 2 < (1.415)^2 = 2.002225.$$
$$(1.4142)^2 = 1.99996164 < 2 < (1.4143)^2 = 2.00024449.$$

The set of numbers can be expanded endlessly because $\sqrt{2}$ is an irrational number. The number 1.4143 is less than .0001 in error as an approximation of $\sqrt{2}$ (why?) and this provides a good working estimate. The important point, however, is that this endless set of decimal numbers has a set of lower bounds, $X = \{x: x \leq \sqrt{2}\}$ and, vastly more important, it has a glb, which is just the number $\sqrt{2}$. This is precisely the way in which real but irrational numbers are characterized: as greatest lower bounds of subsets of rational numbers.

To formalize this, a new structure once again can be erected on a familiar foundation, in this case a field:

(6.5.3) If F is an ordered field (thus containing a positive subset, F^+) then F is said to be *complete* if and only if each nonempty subset $X \subseteq F^+$ has a glb, x, such that $x \in F$.

Definition

This definition hinges on the positive subset of F. It could just as readily have been constructed on the negative set by substituting lub's for glb's. In the sense of 6.5.3, although R' is an ordered field, it is not complete because some glb's of subsets are missing. For example, $\sqrt{2}$ is the glb of a rational subset, but is not itself in R'. A complete ordered field, since it is a field, would contain the rational numbers and the integers. In addition, it contains all irrational numbers such as $\sqrt{2}$ and $\sqrt{5}$. This new set is called the set of *real numbers*.

(6.5.4) If R is the set of real numbers, then R is a complete ordered field. Since the set of real numbers, R, is a field, it has the general characteristics of the rational numbers and the integers. The integers were identified as a subset of the rationals, and the rationals now are identified as a subset of the reals, that is, $I \subset R' \subset R$.

AXIOM (ON REAL NUMBERS)

The number system is now complete in that it contains all sums, products, and quotients (except for division by zero), and roots of *positive* numbers. In one sense, however, it remains incomplete. We know from 5.4.6.5 that $a^2 > 0$, all $a \in R$. Thus, there is no real-number solution of an equation of the form $a^2 = -1$. This fact gives rise to a system called the set of *complex numbers*, which will not be explored here. All the mathematical constructions to be considered in this book are based on the real-number system.

Exercises

6.43. Let $S = \{a + b\sqrt{2}: a, b \in R' \text{ and } b \notin 0\}$. Show that all $x \in S$ are irrational numbers.

6.44. Show that S, of Exercise 6.43, is closed under

(a) addition. (HINT: Investigate $(a + b\sqrt{2}) + (c + d\sqrt{2})$.)
(b) multiplication.
(c) division.

6.45. Show that the set S of Exercise 6.43 is

(a) commutative and associative under addition and multiplication.
(b) distributive.

6.46. Determine the glb and lub of each of the following sets and state whether or not these numbers are members of their sets. Also state what kind of number (integer, rational, etc.) each bound is.

(a) $S = \{x: 0 < x^2 < 5\}$.
(b) $T = \{x: x^3 \leq 5\}$.
(c) $U = \{x: x = 1\}$.
(d) $V = \{x: x \in I\}$.
(e) $W = \{x: x \in I \text{ and } 0 < x < 1\}$.

6.6 Cardinality

To ask "How large is a set?" may appear ludicrous. A set of 10 elements is larger than a set of 5 and, so long as order axioms and the arithmetic table of addition remain, no one can dispute such an assertion. Still, the question is important and raises some magnificently paradoxical problems. Once it is addressed seriously, for instance, such weird consequences spring up as the fact that two sets, one of which appears to contain far more elements than the other, may have exactly the same number of elements. The world of the infinite (or transfinite, as it is often called) awaits the reader.

A set of 5 or 20 or 10,000,000 is easily understood. Order

can be established among such sets and all, apparently, is reasonable. But what about the set of all integers as compared, say, to the set of all positive integers? Surely one is much larger than the other. However, the integers never "stop" and neither do the positive integers. Is one, then, really larger than the other? Add to this the question, "How large is R'?", the set of rational numbers and the very notion of size becomes muddy. Only in the most recent years of mathematical construction have these problems been attacked with some semblance of system.

To establish adequate pigeonholes, some definitions are needed. A first step consists of lumping together all sets that can be counted without exhausting the counting numbers.

(6.6.1) Any set is called *finite* (or is said to have *finite cardinality*) if its elements can be placed in 1-1 correspondence with the first n positive integers for some positive integer, n.

Definition

Suppose that a set consists of all persons living on earth at a given instant in time. This teeming set of mortals could, ideally at least, be lined up by alphabetical order within each living area and then ordered by living area. They could be counted off, and sooner or later they would all be counted. The last number would be rather large (2,910,000,000 is a reasonable guess*) but still there is a *larger* integer (such as 3,000,000,000). In this respect, the number of all persons is no different from the number of all sociologists who are also professional drummers. As radically different as the size of such sets may seem, they are lumped together in a class, the class of all finite sets. A grouping such as this may appear to be altogether useless because it evidently fails to differentiate among any sets. To show that this is an incorrect idea, it is necessary only to show that at least one important set exists that is not finite. The shrewd reader will have guessed already that such a set must consist not of physical objects but of conceptual elements,

* Supplied by Professor Leo A. Schnore some years ago.

which when assembled together in a set are useful as theoretical models. The positive integers (who could deny the utility of this set?) provide an example.

(6.6.2) The positive integers are not finite.

By the closure axiom on addition of the integers (A1),
$n + 1$ is an integer if n is an integer. Thus, no integer, n, can be found such that the positive integers can be placed in 1–1 correspondence with the first n positive integers.

In other words, the counting numbers reach no end. In this light the set of all living persons is indeed similar to much smaller sets in that they are smaller than the positive integers. So far as nonfinite sets are concerned:

(6.6.3) Any set that can be placed in one-to-one correspondence with the positive integers is called *countable* (or *countably infinite*).

Thus, the positive integers are themselves countably infinite. Can the same be said for any other familiar set? The answer to this question, at first blush, seems more enigmatic than any conclusion encountered to this point. Consider the set of *all* integers, I. Certainly, this seems to be a larger set than is that of the positive integers, I^+, since for every integer, such as 20, which is in I^+, its negative, such as -20, is in I. Nevertheless, the conclusion is inescapable that the two sets, I and I^+, contain the same number of elements:

(6.6.4) The set of all integers, I, is countable.

By 6.6.3, it is required only that a one-to-one correspondence between I and I^+ be established. This is done by the following function, whose domain consists of all integers:

$$f(x) = \begin{cases} -2x + 1 & \text{if } x \leq 0 \\ 2x & \text{otherwise} \end{cases} \quad \text{all } x \in I.$$

The range of f is clearly in I^+. To show that it is a one-to-one correspondence, suppose that there exist different integers x and y such that $f(x) = f(y)$. This could occur only if one were less than zero and the other larger. Let $x \leq 0 < y$:

(1) $-2x + 1 = 2y$.   (by hypothesis)
(2) $y = -x + \frac{1}{2}$.   (which is impossible because x and y are integers)

This odd result shows that some infinite sets can be placed in correspondence with what appear to be much smaller sets. It should be clear intuitively that such a situation can arise only among sets that are at least countably infinite.

One might well ask at this point how much farther the preceding result can be pushed. Can the yet larger set of all rational numbers be placed in correspondence with the positive integers? If so, what about the set of all real numbers? Consider first the rationals, which obviously are vastly "larger" than the positive integers. Thanks primarily to the investigations of Georg Cantor, a German mathematician, it is now clear that the rational numbers have the same cardinality as the set of positive integers.

To prove that the positive rational numbers are countable, we must locate a binary operation, **O**, that assigns to each ordered pair of positive integers, $\langle m, n \rangle$ a unique integer, k. Further, it must be shown that if $\mathbf{O}\langle m, n \rangle = k$ and if $\mathbf{O}\langle p, q \rangle = k$, then $m = p$ and $n = q$. (Why?) Cantor suggested that the trick was to array the rational numbers in such a way that one could begin counting them without ever losing his place. His suggestion as to the appropriate arrangement consisted of constructing an array of rows and columns by assigning to each row the set of rationals with a particular denominator and to each column the set with a given numerator. The result looks like this:

$$
\begin{array}{cccccccc}
\dfrac{1}{1} & \dfrac{2}{1} & \dfrac{3}{1} & \dfrac{4}{1} & . & . & . \\[2ex]
\dfrac{1}{2} & \dfrac{2}{2} & \dfrac{3}{2} & \dfrac{4}{2} & . & . & . \\[2ex]
\dfrac{1}{3} & \dfrac{2}{3} & \dfrac{3}{3} & \dfrac{4}{3} & . & . & . \\[2ex]
. & . & . \\
\end{array}
$$

Notice that this is an inefficient procedure because, for each ordered pair of positive integers, the array contains the entire set of ordered pairs that are congruent to it. We can afford this enormous redundancy because, even with it, the elements of the array are countable.

The sticky problem in this is to decide *how* to go about the counting process, which is equivalent to assigning a unique positive integer to each element in the array. If one begins in the usual manner of the Western world, starting in the first row and proceeding from left to right, he must lose the game, for he will never finish counting the countably infinite elements of that row. Clearly, the result would be similarly unhappy if one chose instead to begin counting down a column. Cantor's amazing trick for overcoming this problem consisted of counting *diagonally*, with a resulting assignment of integers to the elements of the array as follows:

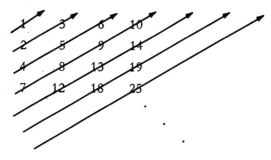

An explicit binary operation on the product set of positive integers may give the Cantor proof a more convincing appearance. That is, if we can construct a binary operation on ordered pairs of positive integers to positive integers that reproduces the above array, then we would have an algebraic expression for Cantor's proof of the assertion that positive rational numbers are countable. First, consider the general characteristics of such an operation and whether they are encapsulated in the following:

(6.6.5) A binary operation, **O**, on $I^+ \times I^+$ is a Cantor diagonal operation $\leftrightarrow$ for each $m, n \in I^+$

Definition

$$\mathbf{O}\langle m, n \rangle = \begin{cases} 1 \text{ if } m = n = 1, \\ 0(n - 1, 1) + 1 \text{ if } m = 1, n > 1, \\ 0(m - 1, n + 1) + 1 \text{ if } m > 1, \end{cases}$$

subject to $0\langle m, n \rangle = 0\langle p, q \rangle \leftrightarrow m = p$ and $n = q$.

Careful consideration should convince one that an operation satisfying these conditions must indeed reproduce Cantor's counting process. It remains only to specify an algebraic form for $\mathbf{O}$. This is given by:

(6.6.6) If a binary operation, $\mathbf{O}$, on $I^+ \times I^+$ is given by $\mathbf{O}\langle m, n \rangle = \frac{1}{2}[(m + n)(m + n - 1) - 2(n - 1)]$, then $\mathbf{O}$ is a Cantor diagonal operation. **THEOREM**

Let $\mathbf{O}\langle m, n \rangle$ be as above, each $m, n \in I^+$. *Proof*

(1) $\mathbf{O}\langle 1, 1 \rangle = \frac{1}{2}(2 \cdot 1 - 2(1 - 1)) = 1$, thus satisfying the case $m = n = 1$.

(2) $\mathbf{O}\langle 1, n \rangle = \frac{1}{2}[(1 + n)n - 2(n - 1)]$
$= \frac{1}{2}n(n - 1) + 1$. (clearing terms in Step 2)

(3) $\mathbf{O}\langle n - 1, 1 \rangle$
$= \frac{1}{2}[n(n - 1) - 2(1 - 1)]$, (since $n - 1 + 1 = n$)

(4) $= \frac{1}{2}n(n - 1)$. (clearing terms in Step 3)

(5) $\mathbf{O}\langle 1, n \rangle = \mathbf{O}\langle n - 1, 1 \rangle + 1$. (Steps 2–4)

The proof that $\mathbf{O}\langle m, n \rangle = \mathbf{O}\langle m - 1, n + 1 \rangle + 1$ is left as an exercise. The fact that $\mathbf{O}$ is a one-to-one correspondence will not be proven here, although it should be intuitively clear that this is the case.

All this amounts to saying that the rational numbers formed from pairs of positive integers have the cardinality of the positive integers. That is, the positive rational numbers, and, hence, the set of all rational numbers, are countable. Actually, the theorem is yet more general than this. Suppose that A is a countably infinite class, each of whose elements is a countably infinite set. Then A may be called a *countable union of countable sets*, and the theorem tells us that A itself is countable.

The real numbers consist of the union of the rationals (now seen to be countable) and the irrationals. Are the real numbers much more numerous than the rationals? If R turns out to be countable, then of course the irrationals have added little in size. As it turns out, however, the irrationals are so numerous that when they are added to the rationals the resultant set of real numbers cannot be counted.

(6.6.7) The set R of real numbers is uncountable.   **THEOREM**

It is sufficient to show that a subset of the real numbers   *Proof*
is uncountable. Consider all real numbers r such that $0 < r < 1$. Any such number can be expressed in decimal form, as $0.d_1d_2d_3 \cdots$ where $d_n (n = 1, 2, 3, \cdots)$ is a digit between 0 and 9 which is located in the nth position of the decimal expansion. Suppose that the real numbers between 0 and 1 are countable. Then they can be arrayed as in 6.6.5.

$$0.d_{11}d_{12}d_{13} \cdots$$
$$0.d_{21}d_{22}d_{23} \cdots \qquad (m, n = 1, 2, 3, \cdots)$$
$$0.d_{31}d_{32}d_{33} \cdots$$
$$\begin{matrix} \cdot & \cdot & \cdot \\ \cdot & \cdot & \cdot & d_{m,\,n} \cdots \\ \cdot & \cdot & \cdot \end{matrix}$$

And this set should contain all real numbers between 0 and 1. But no matter how they are ordered, a real number can be found that is not in the set. Construct this number, $0.d_1d_2 \cdots d_k \cdots$, $(k = 1, 2, 3, \cdots)$ by choosing $d_1 \neq d_{11}$, $d_2 \neq d_{22}$, and in general $d_k \neq d_{mm}$ wherever $k = m$. In this way, the newly constructed real number differs from every other real number in *at least* one place. Thus, no matter what ordering scheme is used, the real numbers are uncountable.

This demonstrates that the real numbers are much more numerous than are the rationals, which suggests that the irrationals comprise what is indeed a large set. To distinguish sets that are as large as that of the real numbers, a new phrase is needed:

(6.6.8) Any set that is neither finite nor countable is said to be *uncountable*, or *nondenumerably infinite*.   **Definition**

Exercises

6.47. Prove that the set of even integers is countable. That is, construct a one-to-one correspondence such as that of 6.6.4 on $2I \times I^+$.

6.48. Carefully describe and contrast the proofs of 6.6.5 and 6.6.6.

Selected References

1. Allendoerfer, C. B., and Oakley, C. O. *Principles of Mathematics*. New York: McGraw-Hill Book Company, Inc., 1955. Chapter 2.
2. Birkhoff, Garrett, and Mac Lane, Saunders. *A Survey of Modern Algebra* (Revised Edition). New York: The Macmillan Company, 1953. Chapters 2 and 4.
3. Dantzig, Tobias. *Number, The Language of Science* (Fourth Edition, Revised and Augmented). New York: Doubleday Anchor Books, 1954. Chapters 6–12.
4. Hardy, G. H., and Wright, E. M. *An Introduction to the Theory of Numbers* (Second Edition). Oxford: The Clarendon Press, 1945. Chapters 4, 9, 11.
5. Kelley, John L. *Introduction to Modern Algebra*. Princeton, New Jersey: D. Van Nostrand Co., Inc., 1960. Chapters 1–2.
6. Moore, John T. *Fundamental Principles of Mathematics*. New York: Rinehart and Co., Inc., 1960. Chapter 2.
7. Rudin, Walter. *Principles of Mathematical Analysis* (Revised Edition). New York: McGraw-Hill Book Company, Inc., 1964. Chapters 3–4.
8. Suppes, Patrick. *Introduction to Logic*. Princeton, New Jersey: D. Van Nostrand Co., Inc., 1957. Chapter 6.

Operations on Real Numbers

From this point on, the basic working tool of this book will consist of R, the set of real numbers. In this chapter some details are added to the characteristics of R. The remaining chapters are given over to the construction of functions on subsets of R.

7.1 Summation

Thus far, addition and multiplication have been considered primarily for pairs of numbers. In many situations, especially in statistical work, it is necessary to add or multiply not just two but great strings of numbers. Because writing out these operations becomes quite tedious, convenient notation has been developed. To understand the notation of the following definition, the reader must recall that x_i represents the ith member of an arbitrarily ordered set of numbers. Notation for repeated addition then is given by the following, in which $\sum$, the Greek upper-case letter sigma, stands for "sum of."

(7.1.1) If $x_i(i = 1, 2, \cdots, n)$ are n real numbers, then

$$\sum_{i=1}^{n} x_i = \begin{cases} x_1 \text{ if } n = 1 \\ \sum_{i=1}^{n-1} x_i + x_n \text{ if } n > 1, n \in I^+ \end{cases}$$

Definition

7

$\sum_{i=1}^{n} x_i$ is read "the sum of x_i over the range of i from x_1 through x_n." When there is no danger of confusion, this will be written $\sum_{i} x_i$ (read "the sum of x_i over the range of i"), or simply $\sum x_i$. If $x_i = k$, for any real number k and for each i, then, we write $\sum_{i=1}^{n} x_i = \sum_{i=1}^{n} k$.

A common first reaction to such a definition is that it violates all rules of definitional logic in that the thing to be defined (the operator $\sum$ in this case) is contained in the definition. Before proceeding, the reader must convince himself that 7.1.1, which is an example of an *inductive* definition, is perfectly proper.

Consider, for example, a set of four numbers that are arbitrarily ordered by attaching index numbers, $i = 1, 2, 3, 4$, so that the numbers are the ordered quadruple, $\langle x_1, x_2, x_3, x_4 \rangle$. Does 7.1.1 actually tell us what to do, even though the thing defined, Σ, is contained in the definition? Since $n = 4$, which is greater than 1, the definition says that

$$\sum_{i=1}^{4} x_i = \sum_{i=1}^{3} x_i + x_4.$$

But the definition also tells us exactly what $\sum_{i=1}^{3} x_i$ is. That is,

$$\sum_{i=1}^{3} x_i = \sum_{i=1}^{2} x_i + x_3.$$

In turn, 7.1.1 says that

$$\sum_{i=1}^{2} x_i = \sum_{i=1}^{1} x_i + x_2.$$

Finally, according to 7.1.1, in the case $n = 1$,

$$\sum_{i=1}^{1} x_i = x_1.$$

When the various parts are assembled, the result looks like this:

$$\sum_{i=1}^{4} x_i = \sum_{i=1}^{3} x_i + x_4 = \left(\sum_{i=1}^{2} x_i + x_3 \right) + x_4,$$

$$= \left(\left[\sum_{i=1}^{1} x_i + x_2 \right] + x_3 \right) + x_4 = x_1 + x_2 + x_3 + x_4.$$

Thus, the initial appearance of the definition is deceiving; 7.1.1 is entirely proper. Nonetheless, it is cumbersome. In many elementary books, 7.1.1 is replaced by a neater looking definition that usually says something to the effect that $\Sigma x_i = x_1 + x_2 + \cdots + x_n$. There are two reasons for dissatisfaction with such a definition. First, and less important, is the fact that the three little dots it contains may easily be confusing. When a definition is being used in a proof, this may contribute to false results. Second, as the term *inductive definition* suggests, a definition of the form of 7.1.1 is constructed with the idea of using it in proofs by induction (see Section 5.5), as will be seen in the next theorem. Definitions of this sort will be employed only when the subject comprises a well-ordered integral set, so that the principle of induction can be employed.

The Σ notation will be used throughout this book because summation is an operation indispensible to mathematics. Thus, the reader should pay especially close attention to the following:

(7.1.2) For any n numbers, n a positive integer, x_i, and any second set of n numbers, y_i,

THEOREM

(1) $\sum\limits_{i=1}^{n} (x_i \pm y_i) = \sum\limits_{i=1}^{n} x_i \pm \sum\limits_{i=1}^{n} y_i$.

(2) $\sum\limits_{i=1}^{n} k = nk$, k any real number.

(3) $\sum\limits_{i=1}^{n} kx_i = k \sum\limits_{i=1}^{n} x_i$.

Proof (1)
(By induction)

(1) $\sum\limits_{i=1}^{1} (x_i \pm y_i) = (x_1 \pm y_1)$.   (7.1.1)

(2) Assume $\sum\limits_{i=1}^{n-1} (x_i \pm y_i) = \sum\limits_{i=1}^{n-1} x_i \pm \sum\limits_{i=1}^{n-1} y_i$.   (Inductive assumption)

(3) $\sum\limits_{i=1}^{n} (x_i \pm y_i)$

    $= \sum\limits_{i=1}^{n-1} (x_i \pm y_i) + (x_n \pm y_n)$,   (7.1.1)

(4) $= \sum\limits_{i=1}^{n-1} x_i \pm \sum\limits_{i=1}^{n-1} y_i + (x_n \pm y_n)$,   (Step 2)

(5) $= \left(\sum\limits_{i=1}^{n-1} x_i + x_n \right) \pm \left(\sum\limits_{i=1}^{n-1} y_i + y_n \right)$, (A3, A4)

(6) $= \sum\limits_{i=1}^{n} x_i \pm \sum\limits_{i=1}^{n} y_i$.   (Step 5 and 7.1.1)

Proofs of parts 2 and 3 are left as exercises.

Thus, the sum of a series of pairs $(x_i \pm y_i)$ is the sum of the first series plus or minus the sum of the second, according to Part 1 of the theorem. When a number, k, is added to itself n times, the result is nk, by Part 2. Part 3 says that the sum of a series of numbers, each multiplied by the same number, k, is k times the sum of the original series.

Analysis involving two or more variables together is at the very heart of scientific research. Since summation operations are so vital to this kind of analysis, a mathematical system for summation over two or more variables is necessary.

(7.1.3) Let A and B be two partitions of a set such that   **Notation**
$A = \{A_i: i = 1, 2, \cdots, r\}$ and $B = \{B_j: j = 1, 2, \cdots, c\}$, and let x_{ij} be a number associated with the ordered pair of classes $\langle A_i, B_j \rangle \in A \times B$.

This notation provides the basis for the construction of *joint* distribution tables or matrices, which will be more thoroughly explored in later parts of this book. The reader should think through this notation carefully in order to see that it generates a binary operation on $A \times B$ to the set of numbers. Such an operation can be represented conveniently in tabular form. As an example, let A be a set of college students partitioned into the four subsets freshman, sophomore, junior, senior. Let these subsets be represented by the symbols A_1, A_2, A_3, and A_4, respectively. Let B be a second partition on this set, say the variable of academic major. Suppose that these subsets can be represented by B_1 = social science, B_2 = physical science, B_3 = humanities, B_4 = journalism, B_5 = basket-weaving. Let x_{ij} (which could be any number associated with $\langle A_i, B_j \rangle$) be the *frequency* of students who are both A_i and B_j. Thus, in this illustration, $x_{45} = 10$, is the number of those who are both seniors and basket-weaving majors. (In particular, x_{45} is not "x forty-five," but is "x-row 4-column 5.") Suppose that a particular set of students generates the distribution of Table 7.1. If the reader has followed this discussion, he should recognize, among other facts, that Table 7.1 represents a total of 790 students, that there are 195 sophomores, and that there are 5 freshman journalism majors (but no senior journalism majors).

Table 7.1

	B_1 (Social Science)	B_2 (Physical Science)	B_3 (Human- ities)	B_4 (Jour- nalism)	B_5 (Basket- weaving)	
A_1 (Freshman)	25	10	50	5	200	290
A_2 (Sophomore)	25	15	50	5	100	195
A_3 (Junior)	55	15	40	5	50	165
A_4 (Senior)	75	25	30	0	10	140
	180	65	170	15	360	790

In order to discuss the operation of addition with two variables, somewhat more complicated equipment is needed.

Definition

(7.1.4) Let x_{ij} be as in 7.1.3, and let $x._j = \sum\limits_{i=1}^{r} x_{ij}$ and $x_{i.} = \sum\limits_{j=1}^{c} x_{ij}$. Then:

$$\sum_{i=1}^{r} \sum_{j=1}^{c} x_{ij} = \sum_{i} x_{i.},$$

and

$$\sum_{j=1}^{c} \sum_{i=1}^{r} x_{ij} = \sum_{j} x._j,$$

in which $\sum\limits_{i=1}^{r} \sum\limits_{j=1}^{c} x_{ij}$ may be written $\sum\limits_{i,j} x_{ij}$ when the indices of summation, i and j, are made clear elsewhere. Similarly, $\sum\limits_{j=1}^{c} \sum\limits_{i=1}^{r} x_{ij}$ may be written $\sum\limits_{j,i} x_{ij}$.

Note carefully that $x_{i.}$ is the sum of the frequencies in the ith row and that $x._j$ is the sum of the frequencies in the jth column. These numbers are often called *marginal values* (or *marginal frequencies* if the numbers x_{ij} are simple frequencies, as in Table 7.1) because they appear conventionally along the lower and right-hand margins of a joint distribution matrix. Thus, in Table 7.1,

$x_{3.} = \sum\limits_{j=1}^{5} x_{3j} = 55 + 15 + 40 + 5 + 50 = 165.$ Similarly,

$x_{.4} = \sum\limits_{i=1}^{4} x_{i4} = 5 + 5 + 5 + 0 = 15.$

So far as the general properties of a compound summation are concerned, the preceding discussion should have suggested the following to the reader:

(7.1.5) (*Properties of Compound Summation*). **THEOREM**

(1) $\sum\limits_{i=1}^{r} \sum\limits_{j=1}^{c} x_{ij} = \sum\limits_{j=1}^{c} \sum\limits_{i=1}^{r} x_{ij}$

(2) $\sum\limits_{i=1}^{r} \sum\limits_{j=1}^{c} (ax_{ij} + b) = a \sum\limits_{i=1}^{r} \sum\limits_{j=1}^{c} x_{ij} + rcb$

(3) $\sum\limits_{i=1}^{r} x_{.j} = rx_{.j}, \quad \sum\limits_{j=1}^{c} x_{i.} = cx_{i}$

Note: An inductive proof is used here operating on the index i. This involves no loss of generality because the proof would be identical if the index j were used instead. *Proof* (1)

Let $r = 1$. Then:

(1) $\sum\limits_{i=1}^{r} \sum\limits_{j=1}^{c} x_{ij} = \sum\limits_{j=1}^{c} x_{1j} = \sum\limits_{j=1}^{c} \sum\limits_{i=1}^{1} x_{1j}.$ (7.1.1)

(2) Assume that

$$\sum\limits_{i=1}^{r-1} \left(\sum\limits_{j=1}^{c} x_{ij} \right) = \sum\limits_{j=1}^{c} \left(\sum\limits_{i=1}^{r-1} x_{ij} \right). \quad \text{(Inductive assumption)}$$

(3) $\sum\limits_{i=1}^{r} \sum\limits_{j=1}^{c} x_{ij} = \sum\limits_{i=1}^{r-1} \left(\sum\limits_{j=1}^{c} x_{ij} \right) + \sum\limits_{j=1}^{c} x_{rj},$ (7.1.1)

(4) $= \sum\limits_{j=1}^{c} \left(\sum\limits_{i=1}^{r-1} x_{ij} \right) + \sum\limits_{j=1}^{c} x_{rj},$ (Steps 2 and 3)

(5) $= \sum\limits_{j=1}^{c} \left(\sum\limits_{i=1}^{r-1} x_{ij} + x_{rj} \right),$ (7.1.2.1)

(6) $= \sum\limits_{j=1}^{c} \sum\limits_{i=1}^{r} x_{ij}.$ (7.1.1)

In Step 2, the term $\sum\limits_{j=1}^{c} x_{ij}$ might have been written $x_{i.}$ as in 7.1.4. This is a simple variable in i, so the appeal to 7.1.1 is appropriate. The remaining proofs are left as exercises.

This proof demonstrates the generality of a commonplace fact that reflects the commutative property of addition: So long as all values in a table such as 7.1 are summed, the result is independent of the order of summation. Note that Part 1 of the theorem also implies that the sum of the row marginals must be the same as the sum of the column marginals.

Exercises

7.1. Express each of the following using the $\sum$ operator:

(a) $x_1 + x_2 + x_3 + x_4$
(b) $X_2 + X_3 + X_4$
(c) $X_2 + X_4 + X_6$
(d) $Z_4^2 + Z_6^3 + Z_8^4$
(e) $B_{n_1} + B_{n_2} + B_{n_3}$
(f) $ab_1c_2 + ab_2c_4 + ab_3c_6$

7.2. Write out the full summation of the following:

(a) $\sum_{i=0}^{4} x_i$

(b) $a \sum_{i=1}^{4} x_i$

(c) $\sum_{i=0}^{4} (x_i + y_i)$

(d) $n \sum_{i=0}^{3} (x_i + y_i)$

(e) $\sum_{i=3}^{5} x_i y_i$

(f) $\sum_{i=6}^{8} a_i^2$

(g) $\sum_{i=1}^{4} (y_i + 1)$

(h) $\sum_{i=0}^{5} \alpha$

7.3. Prove 7.1.2, parts 2 and 3.

7.4. Prove 7.1.5, parts 2 and 3.

7.5. Let $a_1 = 3$, $a_2 = 4$, $a_3 = 4$, $a_4 = 5$, $a_5 = 5$, $a_6 = 5$, $a_7 = 6$, $a_8 = 7$, $a_9 = 8$, $a_{10} = 8$, $a_{11} = 9$, $a_{12} = 11$. Find each of the following:

(a) $\displaystyle\sum_{i=1}^{12} a_i$

(b) $\displaystyle\sum_{i=1}^{6} a_{2i}$

(c) $\displaystyle\sum_{i=1}^{10} ka_i$ where $k = 2$

(d) $\displaystyle\sum_{i=6}^{12} (a_i + 5)$

(e) $\displaystyle\sum_{i=1}^{6} (a_i)^2$

(f) $\displaystyle\left(\sum_{i=1}^{6} a_i\right)^2$ (Compare this with [e].)

7.6. A proportion, P, is a rational number $\dfrac{x}{n}$ in which the denominator is the total number of elements in a set and the numerator is the number of elements in the set with a particular attribute—that is, the numerator gives the number of elements in some subset of the original set. Prove that $0 \leq P \leq 1$. (HINT: Use 7.1.2, parts 2 and 3.)

7.7. Use the notation of 7.1.4 and interpret the following proportions:

(a) $\dfrac{x_{ij}}{x_{i\cdot}}$

(b) $\dfrac{x_{ij}}{x_{\cdot j}}$

(c) $\dfrac{x_{ij\cdot}}{\displaystyle\sum_i x_{i\cdot}}$

(d) $\dfrac{x_{i\cdot}}{\displaystyle\sum_j x_{\cdot j}}$

(e) $\dfrac{x_{\cdot i}}{\displaystyle\sum_i x_{i\cdot}}$

7.8. In Table 7.1, compute and interpret:

(a) $\displaystyle\sum_j (x_{3j} + x_{4j})$

(b) $\displaystyle\sum_i (x_{i1} - x_{i5})$

(c) $\dfrac{1}{c} \displaystyle\sum_j (x_{3j})$

(d) $\displaystyle\sum_j \dfrac{(x_{4j} + x_{1j})}{x_{\cdot j}}$

7.2 Exponents and Radicals

As is the case with addition, multiplication can be extended from an operation on a pair of numbers to an operation on any set of numbers. When it is applied to more than two numbers, the operation usually is called *repeated* or *serial multiplication*. In repeated addition the Σ operator is a useful shorthand device. In serial multiplication, a similar operator, Π, the Greek letter pi, is used:

(7.2.1) If x_i $(i = 1, 2, \cdots, n)$ are n numbers, then: **Definition**

$$\prod_{i=1}^{n} x_i = \begin{cases} x_1 \text{ if } n = 1 \\ \left(\prod_{i=1}^{n-1} x_i\right)(x_n) \text{ if } n > 1, \, n \in I^+. \end{cases}$$

The reader should recognize this for what it is: an inductive definition of an operator that instructs one to multiply serially any string of numbers, x_i.

A special and uniquely important case of serial multiplication is given by letting $x_1 = x_2 = \cdots x_n = x$, that is, the repeated multiplication of a number x *by itself*, n times.

(7.2.2) The number $\prod_{i=1}^{n} x$ is noted x^n (read "x to the nth   **Definition**
power), for n a nonnegative integer, and is subject to

$$x^n = \begin{cases} 1 \text{ if } n = 0 \text{ and } x \neq 0 \\ x(x^{n-1}) \text{ if } n > 0 \end{cases}$$

and n is called the exponent or power of the base number, x.

The reason for permitting a number of the form x^0 (which must equal one, so long as $x \neq 0$) will become clear as the properties of powers are investigated. For the present, note that 0^0 is an undefined number. Positive integral exponents represent repeated multiplication (of a constant number) and, thus, are subject to the rules of multiplication already considered. With the definition and these rules, the following can be demonstrated (again by mathematical induction):

(7.2.3) (*Properties of positive integral exponents*). For any real numbers, a and b, and for any nonnegative integers, m and n, the following are true:

(1) $(ab)^n = a^n b^n$.
(2) $a^m a^n = a^{(m+n)}$.
(3) $(a^m)^n = a^{mn}$.
(4) $x = y \leftrightarrow x^n = y^n$, $(xy) \geq 0$, $n > 0$.

THEOREM

Proof (1)
(By induction)

(1) $(ab)^0 = 1 = a^0 b^0$.   (7.2.1)
(2) Assume $(ab)^{n-1} = a^{(n-1)} b^{(n-1)}$.   (Inductive assumption)
(3) $(ab)^n = (ab)(ab)^{n-1}$,   (7.2.2)
(4) $= (ab)(a^{(n-1)} b^{(n-1)})$,   (Step 2)
(5) $= (a)(a^{(n-1)})(b)(b^{(n-1)})$,   (M3 and M4)
(6) $= a^n b^n$.   (7.2.2)

Proof (2)
(By induction)

(1) $a^m a^0 = a^m(1) = a^m = a^{(m+0)}$.   (7.2.2)
(2) Assume
       $a^m a^{n-1} = a^{m+n-1}$ for all $n \geq 1$.   (Inductive assumption)
(3) $a^m a^n = a^m(a^{n-1})a$,   (7.2.2)
(4) $= (a^{m+n-1})a$,   (Step 2)
(5) $= a^{m+n-1+1}$,   (7.2.2)
(6) $= a^{m+n}$.   (A6 and A3)

Proofs of parts 3 and 4 proceed along similar lines and are left as exercises. The reader would do well to restate the four properties of 7.2.3 in more prosaic terms. For example, the first property says that a power of the product of two numbers is the product of the two numbers each raised to that power.

To complete this survey of the powers, it is necessary to extend the definition of an exponent to the negative integers, then to the rational, and finally to the real numbers.

(7.2.4) If x is any real number such that $x \neq 0$, and if n is any nonnegative integer, then:

Notation

$$x^{-n} = 1/x^n.$$

This notation adds to the versatility of exponents, because it permits us to consider the inverse of any positive integral power of any real number. With this the following added properties of exponents can be derived:

(7.2.5) (*Further Properties of Exponents*) For all integers, n:

(1) $x^{-n} = (1/x)^n$, $x \neq 0$.

(2) $\left(\dfrac{a}{b}\right)^n = \dfrac{a^n}{b^n}$, $b \neq 0$.

(3) $\dfrac{a^m}{a^n} = a^{m-n}$, $a \neq 0$.

Proofs are left as exercises.

For instance, $\left(\dfrac{2}{3}\right)^2 = \left(\dfrac{2}{3}\right)\left(\dfrac{2}{3}\right) = \dfrac{4}{9} = \dfrac{2^2}{3^2}$. Also, $\dfrac{2^4}{2^2} = \dfrac{16}{4} = 4 = 2^2 = 2^{4-2}$.

The final job of this section consists of extending exponents from the set of integers to the set of rational numbers. Any rational number can be formed simply by multiplying the integer a by the inverse of b. For this reason, only those exponents need be considered that are inverses of positive integers, say $1/n$ where n is greater than 1. Consider first the way in which an exponent of the form $x^{1/n}$ ought to behave. Surely its behavior must be consistent with other properties of exponents. In particular, $(x^{1/n})^m$ according to 7.2.3.3 ought to equal $x^{m/n}$. Now, suppose that $m = n$ so that $x^{m/n} = x^1 = x$. Then $x^{1/n}$ must be some number that, when multiplied by itself n times, gives the original number, x. Since x is a real number, we know that such a number exists in the set R. This reasoning leads to the following definition:

(7.2.6) If a is any nonnegative number and n is any positive integer then $a^{1/n}$ is a number, k, such that $k^n = a$, and k is called the nth root of a. The number $a^{1/2}$ may be written $\sqrt{a}$ and $a^{1/n}$ may be written $\sqrt[n]{a}$.

Suppose that one wishes to compute the "one-third" power of a number, say, a. This would have to be a number that, when multiplied by itself three times, would give as a final product the original number a. This number would be denoted by $a^{1/3}$ or $\sqrt[3]{a}$ (which in this case is called the *cube root* of a). This number, of course, is the greatest lower bound of a sequence of rational numbers.

From this definition, it follows that the number $a^{m/n}$ is just the nth root of a^m. For example, the number $4^{3/2}$ can be expressed as the square root of the third power of the number 4, that is, $\sqrt{4^3}$. Synonymously, the number can be written as the third power of the square root of the number 4, that is $(\sqrt{4})^3$. These two numbers are equal, of course, since $4^3 = 64$ and $\sqrt{64} = 8$. At the same time, $\sqrt{4} = 2$ and $2^3 = 8$.

Time will not be spent working with numerical methods for computing roots of numbers, for two reasons. First, tables of square roots are readily available; and, second, logarithms, which are discussed later in this chapter, are used in most work with roots.

Exercises

7.9. Express the following products with the $\prod$ operator:

(a) $a_1 \cdot a_2 \cdot a_3 \cdot a_4$
(b) $S_{12} \cdot S_{13} \cdot S_{14} \cdot S_{16}$
(c) $(a_1 x_1)(a_2 x_2)(a_3 x_3)$
(d) $(x_2 + y_2)(x_2 + y_3)(x_2 + y_4)$

7.10. Compute the following products:

(a) $\displaystyle\prod_{i=0}^{6} x_i$

(b) $\displaystyle\prod_{i=1}^{6} a$

(c) $\displaystyle\prod_{i=1}^{5} 5$

(d) $\displaystyle\prod_{i=0}^{4} i$

(e) $\displaystyle\prod_{i=1}^{4} an_i$

(f) $\dfrac{\prod\limits_{i=1}^{7} x_i}{\prod\limits_{i=1}^{5} x_i}$

7.11. Simplify $(a > 0)$:

(a) $(a^3)^2$
(b) $(a^n)^p$
(c) $a^2 \cdot a^3 \cdot a^4$
(d) $a^\alpha \cdot a^{\beta\alpha}.$
(e) a^7/a^2
(f) α^2/α^{-2}
(g) $(a^m)^{m+1}$
(h) $(a^{2/4})^{1/2}$
(i) $(a^{m/p})^{1/m}$
(j) $[(a^n)^2][(a^{-n})^2]$

7.12. Write in exponential form $(x, y, a > 0)$:

(a) $\sqrt{x}$
(b) $\sqrt[4]{xy}$
(c) $\sqrt{x/y}$
(d) $\sqrt[3]{x}\,\sqrt[5]{x}$
(e) $\sqrt{\sqrt{a}}$
(f) $\sqrt[3]{2}$

7.13. Using the laws of exponents, prove the following $(a, b > 0)$:

(a) $\sqrt[n]{ab} = \sqrt[n]{a}\,\sqrt[n]{b}.$
(b) $\sqrt[n]{\sqrt[m]{a}} = \sqrt[nm]{a}.$
(c) $\sqrt[an]{b^{am}} = \sqrt[n]{b^m}.$

7.14. Find the numerical value of the following, where $a = 3, b = 2, c = 5$:

(a) $a^2 + a^3$
(b) $a^2 + b^2$
(c) $(a + b)^2$
(d) $b^2 \cdot b^3$
(e) $(b^0)^2$
(f) $c^{-1}(b^4 + a^2)^{1/2}$
(g) $(-c)^2 + (-a)^3$
(h) $6b^2$
(i) $(6b)^2$
(j) $6b^{-1}$
(k) $(a^4)^{1/2}$
(l) $(a^{-1} + b^{-1})^{-1}(c)$
(m) $(4a^2)^{1/2}$

(n) $\left[\dfrac{(a+c)^2}{b+c^2}\right]^{2/3}$

7.15. Prove 7.2.3.3.

7.16. Prove 7.2.3.4.

7.17. Prove 7.2.5.1.

7.18. Re-prove the four parts of 7.2.3, allowing m and n to be *rational* numbers.

7.3 Logarithms

In the preceding section, equations of the form $x = k^r$ were investigated. In such an equation, k could be any (positive) real number, but until this point r has been restricted to the rational numbers. Under these restrictions it was seen that x is a real number because all such terms as $2^{1/2}(= \sqrt{2})$ are included in R. The final task in this section is that of investigating exponential equations, $x = k^r$, in which r is not merely a rational number but is any real number. Thus, a typical identity might be $x = \sqrt{2}^{\sqrt{2}}$ and the question is immediately raised whether x itself is still a real number. If indeed it is, then how might one interpret it? Answers to these questions provide an introduction to *logarithms*, a particularly useful tool for analysis.

The following shows that, whether an exponent is a rational or an irrational number, any positive real number to that exponent is itself a real number.

(7.3.1) For any two real numbers, k and r, such that $k > 0$, there exists a unique positive real number, x, such that:

THEOREM

$$x = k^r.$$

This theorem will not be proved here. The theorem says that any positive real number, k, when raised to *any* real valued power, r, remains a real number. Thus, numbers such as $5^{\sqrt{2}}$ are real numbers in good standing. Such a number can be interpreted, as can any other real number, as the greatest lower bound of a sequence of rational numbers. We have seen that $\sqrt{2}$ is the greatest lower bound of a sequence of rationals, 2, 1.5, 1.42, 1.415, $\cdots$. Then, $5^{\sqrt{2}}$ is the greatest lower bound of a related sequence of rational numbers: 5^2; $5^{1.5}$; $5^{1.42}$; $5^{1.45}$; $\cdots$.

The reader should observe carefully that Theorem 7.3.1 contains an important restriction. Notice that the base numbers, k, must be positive. Thus, this theorem does not say that such a number as $(-1)^{1/2}$ is a real number. Suppose, in fact, that there existed a number, i, such that $i = \sqrt{-1}$. Then it would be the case that $i^2 = -1 < 0$. But we know that the square of any nonzero (real) number is greater than zero. The real numbers, then, do not contain all powers of all negative numbers. (However, a number such as $\sqrt[3]{-1}$ is a real number. Why?) This fact leads to the development of the set of complex or imaginary numbers, a set containing an element, i, with the property described above. If $i = \sqrt{-1}$, then numbers of the form $a + bi$, where a, $b \in R$, are called *complex* numbers. The addition of complex numbers to R brings us full circle in that R, when augmented in this way, is closed under all algebraic operations, including the taking of roots of negative numbers. However, it will not be necessary for us to consider the set of complex numbers (see Allendoerfer and Oakley, *Principles* [1], Chapter 5, for an analysis of this set).

Theorem 7.3.1 can be turned about in such a way that the exponent, r, rather than the number k, becomes the subject.

(7.3.2) If x is any positive real number and k is any positive real number such that $k \neq 1$, then there exists one and only one real number r, such that:

$$x = k^r.$$

THEOREM

Thus, each positive real number, x, can be uniquely related to a second positive real number, k, by the identity $x = k^r$. For our purposes, the chief interest of this theorem, which also remains unproven here, is that it leads immediately to the concept of logarithm.

(7.3.3) If real numbers x, k, and r, as in Theorem 7.3.2,   **Definition**
are such that $x = k^r$, then r is called the *logarithm* (or
simply the log) of x to the base k and is noted:

$r = \log_k (x)$ (read "r equals the log to the base k of x").

Verbally, the log of a number, x, to the base, k, is the unique
exponent to which k must be raised in order to equal the
original number, x. The two sentences "$x = k^r$" and
"$r = \log_k (x)$" are equivalent. Theorem 7.3.2 assures us
that, for any ordered pair of real numbers, $\langle k, x \rangle$, $\log_k (x)$
is a unique real number so long as $0 < k \neq 1$ and $x > 0$.
For the present, the reader should think of the logarithm as
a binary operation on ordered pairs $\langle k, x \rangle$ to the elements r.
In succeeding chapters, this relation will also be viewed as
a function. If the reader has mastered the definition of the
logarithm, he should recognize, for example, that $\log_2 (8) =$
$\log_3 (27) = \log_4 (64) = \log_5 (125) = 3$.

This topic would perhaps remain too specialized for our
purposes were it not that logarithms are exceedingly useful
in numerical computations. Familiarity with logarithms,
together with a table of logarithmic values, takes much of
the tedium from computations involving serial multiplications, powers, and quotients. Logarithms have this usefulness because of the following properties:

(7.3.4) (*Properties of Logarithms*). For each of the posi-   **THEOREM**
tive real numbers, $x_i (i = 1, 2, \cdots, n)$, u, and v, and for
each positive real number $k \neq 1$, the following hold:

(1) $\log_k \left(\prod_{i=1}^{n} x_i \right) = \sum_{i=1}^{n} \log_k (x_i)$.

(2) $\log_k (u/v) = \log_k (u) - \log_k (v)$.

(3) $\log_k (u^v) = v \log_k (u)$.

(4) $\log_k (u) = \log_k (v) \leftrightarrow u = v$.

(5) $\log_k (u) < \log_k (v) \leftrightarrow u < v$.

(6) $k^{\log_k (x)} = x$.

(7) $\log_k (x) = 0 \leftrightarrow x = 1$.

(8) $\log_k (x) = 1 \leftrightarrow x = k$.

All proofs are left as exercises. Parts 1–3 of this theorem are
especially useful in computational work. Part 1 assures us

that the log of the serial product of n numbers is the sum of their separate logs. Thus, if each number can be converted into a log and these numbers added, the sum is the log of the desired result. Then, if a number can be located whose log is this sum, that number is the serial product. This number is called the *antilog of the sum*:

(7.3.5) If $\log_k (x)$ is defined, then the number x is called the antilog of $\log_k (x)$.   **Definition**

In each part of Theorem 7.3.4, one would be interested in the antilog of, for example, $\log_k (u/v)$.

Part 2 of the theorem says that the log of a quotient is the log of the numerator minus the log of the denominator. Once this difference is obtained, its antilog is the desired quotient.

Clearly, logs are useful devices in computation only insofar as the value of the log (and antilog) of a number can be obtained readily. This, of course, requires tables of values. Such tables have been constructed for many different base numbers. By all odds, the most common of these are the two known as Briggsian or *common logs*, which use the base number 10, and Naperian or *natural logs*, which use an irrational number $e = 2.71828\cdots$. For the present, only the common log system will be used.

The simple proposition that follows serves to make logs both understandable as mathematical entities and useful in numerical computations.

(7.3.6) If x is any positive rational number, then there exist two numbers, $k \,\epsilon\, I$ and $\beta \,\epsilon\, R'$ such that $1 \le \beta < 10$, such that: **PROPOSITION**

$$x = \beta(10)^k.$$

This states that any positive rational number can be converted into the product of a rational number between one and ten and an integral-valued power of 10, such as 10^{-2} or 10^3. The number 1238.47, for instance, when multiplied by $1/1,000 = 10^{-3}$, is the number 1.23847, which certainly is a rational number between one and ten. Similarly,

.002371 $= 2.371(10)^{-3}$ and $12.345 = 1.2345(10)^{-1}$. Now consider $\log_{10}(x)$, where x is as in 7.3.6. Part 1 of Theorem 7.3.4 tells us at once that $\log_{10}(x) = \log_{10}(\beta) + \log_{10}(10)^k$. But Parts 3 and 8 of this same theorem assure us that $\log_{10}(10)^k = k\log_{10}(10) = k$. Thus, $\log_{10}(x) = \log_{10}(\beta) + k$ where β is a rational number between 1 and 10 and k is an integer. Tables of logs to the base 10 are constructed only for numbers between 1 and 10 because of this property. Such tables do not, therefore, provide the number k, but k is easily computed. (The reader should construct a rule for evaluating k as a function of the decimal point location.)

Before we actually evaluate the logs of several numbers, one point must be clear: Proposition 7.3.6 concerns only rational numbers. The exclusion of irrationals represents a temporary shift from an emphasis on mathematical theory to one on working with numbers. In computation of this sort, one deals with rational numbers only. An irrational number must be approximated by a rational number, whose decimal expansion can be carried out to any arbitrary length but which must stop at some point. Thus, for example, $\sqrt{2}$ might be approximated by 1.4, 1.41, 1.414, 1.4142, or even a much longer and, hence, more accurate (why?) approximation.

By virtue of 7.3.6, it is clear that the evaluation of the log of a positive number, x, requires only the log of a number between 1 and 10, together with the value of k such that $10^k \leq x < 10^{k+1}$. Tables of $\log_{10}(\beta)$ are readily available in sources such as Arkin and Colton, *Tables for Statisticians* [2], Table 5. Such tables usually carry the decimal expansion of $\log_{10}(\beta)$ to 3, 4, or 5 places. A typical logarithm table contains such entries as:

Table 7.1

β	0	1	2	3	4	5	6	7	8	9
$\cdots$										
159	20 140	167	194	222	249	276	303	330	358	385
160	412	439	466	493	520	548	575	602	629	656
161	683	710	737	763	790	817	844	871	898	925
$\cdots$										
$\cdots$										
$\cdots$										

The numerals in the left column of this table represent the first three digits of x, and the numeral in the column head represents its fourth digit. To find $\log_{10}(1613)$, one would move across the row with marginal entry 161 until it intersects the column headed by the numeral 3. In Table 7.1 this cell is seen to contain the number 763. This represents the *final three digits* of the decimal expansion of the log. The first two digits are printed only once, in the column headed 0, to avoid unnecessary duplication. Thus, the complete 5-place log is 20763. This is not the log of 1613; it is instead the log of $\beta = 1.613$. Since $1613 = 1.613(10)^3$, $\log_{10}(1613) = \log_{10}(1.613) + 3$. All that remains is to locate a decimal point in the number 20763. Since $1 \leq \beta < 10$, it follows that $0 \leq \log_{10}(\beta) < 1$. (Why?) In general, each entry in a log table is a decimal number of the form .xxxxx. Finally, we see that $\log_{10}(1613) = \log_{10}(1.613) + 3 = .20763 + 3 = 3.20763$. It must be re-emphasized that common log tables conventionally do not contain any decimals, and it should be understood that the original numbers are between 1 and 10, while the log values are between 0 and 1.

In summary, the procedure for locating the common log of a number, x, consists of four steps. First, locate an integer k such that $10^k \leq x < 10^{k+1}$. Second, evaluate the number β such that $x = \beta(10)^k$. This is a number between one and ten. These first steps represent nothing more than the operation of shifting the decimal point k places (to the left if k is positive and to the right if it is negative). Third, use a common log table to evaluate $\log_{10}(\beta)$, recognizing that this must be a number between 0 and 1 written in decimal form. Finally, evaluate $\log_{10}(x)$ from the identity $\log_{10}(x) = \log_{10}(\beta) + k$.

With Theorem 7.3.4 and the procedure for evaluating logs, we are now in a position to use logarithms as labor-saving devices in computation. As a first application, we have:

(7.3.7) Evaluate the following expression: **Problem**

$$x = \frac{(1.59)^3(17.13)^{3/2}}{(.015)^{1/2}(37.8)}.$$

(1) $\begin{cases} 1.59 = 1.590(10)^0. \\ 17.13 = 1.713(10)^1. \\ .015 = 1.500(10)^{-2}. \\ 37.8 = 3.780(10)^1. \end{cases}$ (Evaluate k and β in $x = \beta(10)^k$)

(2) $\begin{cases} \log_{10}(1.59) = .20140. \\ \log_{10}(1.713) = .23376. \\ \log_{10}(1.500) = .17609. \\ \log_{10}(3.780) = .57749. \end{cases}$ (Use table of logs to evaluate $\log_{10}(\beta)$)

(3) $\begin{cases} \log_{10}(1.59) = 0.20140. \\ \log_{10}(17.13) = 1.23376. \\ \log_{10}(.015) = -1.82391. \\ \log_{10}(37.8) = 1.57749. \end{cases}$ (Steps 1 and 2 and 7.3.6)

(4) $\log_{10}(x) = \log_{10}\{(1.59)^3(17.13)^{3/2}\},$
$\qquad - \log_{10}\{(.015)^{1/2}(37.8)\}.$ (7.3.4.2)

(5) $\log_{10}\{(1.59)^3(17.13)^{3/2}\},$
$\qquad = \log_{10}(1.59)^3 + \log_{10}(17.13)^{3/2},$ (7.3.4.1)

(6) $\qquad = 3\log_{10}(1.59) + (\frac{3}{2})\log_{10}(17.13),$ (7.3.4.3)

(7) $\qquad = 3(0.20140) + \frac{3}{2}(1.23376).$ (Step 3)

(8) $\log_{10}\{(.015)^{1/2}(37.8)\},$ (7.3.4.1, 7.3.4.3,
$\qquad = \frac{1}{2}(-1.82391) + 1.57749.$ and Step 3)

(9) $\log_{10}(x) = 3(0.20140) + \frac{3}{2}(1.23376),$
$\qquad - \frac{1}{2}(-1.82391) - 1.57749,$ (Steps 7, 8)

(10) $\qquad\qquad = 1.78931.$

(11) $x = 61.56.$ (Locate antilog of 1.7893)

The reader should follow the solution of this problem through in careful detail. Steps 1–3 of the solution should present no problems if the reader obtains a table of 5-place logs of 4-place numbers.

There exists one potential trap in this exercise that has caught many who would use logarithms. This involves numbers between zero and one. In 7.3.7 the term $(.015)^{1/2}$ must be converted to a logarithm. In 7.3.7.2 we find that $\log_{10}(1.500)$ is equal to .17609. But in 7.3.7.3 we see that $\log_{10}(.015) = -1.82391$. The connection between these facts is vague at best, unless 7.3.6 is carefully reconsidered. From that proposition we see that $\log_{10}(x) = \log_{10}(\beta) + k$.

It should be clear that $\log_{10}(\beta)$ is a *positive* number for any positive rational number, x (why?). However, k, in the case of $0 < x < 1$, must be a negative number (again, why?). In this example it is true that $.015 = 1.5(10)^{-2}$ and that $\log_{10}(.015) = -2 + .17609$. But this number clearly is $\log_{10}(.015) = -1.82391$ (consider the number $-(2 - .17609)$). The common pitfall when dealing with numbers between zero and one consists of adding the absolute value of k to the value of β. The correct rule, instead, is to add the value of β (necessarily positive) to the *algebraic* value of k and proceed from there. If $0 < x < 1$, $\log_{10}(x) < 0$, and in all such cases $\log_{10}(x)$ is obtained by subtracting a positive number ($\log_{10}(\beta)$) from a negative number (k), yielding a negative remainder $\log_{10}(x)$.

Steps 4–10 of this solution represent a straightforward application of portions of Theorem 7.3.4. The final step, 11, requires more careful consideration. Step 10 yielded $\log_{10}(x) = 1.78916$. We know that this can be re-expressed as $\log_{10}(x) = \log_{10}(\beta)10^1$, in which $\log_{10}(\beta) = 0.78916$. In searching through the log values of a table, it becomes apparent that $\text{antilog}_{10}(0.78916) = 6.154$ so that $x = 6.154(10)^1 = 61.54$. If the exact solution is not contained in the table, the best approximation can be obtained by using a solution by interpolation (for a discussion, see Arkin and Colton [2], page 6).

Exercises

7.19. Write the following in logarithmic form:

(a) $3^3 = 27$.
(b) $10^0 = 1$.
(c) $p^k = 6$.
(d) $10^1 = 10$.

7.20. For what number k are the following identities true?

(a) $\log_k 8 = 2$.
(b) $\log_3 27 = k$.
(c) $\log_2 32 = k$.
(d) $\log_k 100 = 2$.
(e) $\log_k 3.14 = 1$.
(f) $\log_2 k = 6$.

7.21. Given that $\log_k 2 = .33$, $\log_k 3 = .56$, $\log_k 5 = 1.10$, $\log_k 7 = 1.61$, find the following:

(a) $\log_k (45)$

(b) $\log_k 2/\log_k 5$

(c) $\log_k (15)$

(d) $(\log_k 2)^2$

(e) $\log_k (2)^2$

(f) $\log_k (27)$

(g) $\log_k (\sqrt{2}/5)$

(h) $\log_k (1/7)$

(i) $\log_k 7/\log_k 1$ (Careful!)

(j) $\log_k (7k)$

7.22. Why are logarithmic bases never set equal to 1?

7.23. Use logs to solve the following inequality in n:

$(4)^n > 32$. (HINT: Use 7.3.4.3 and choose the log base, k, carefully with respect to the numbers 4 and 32.)

7.24. Use 7.3.4 and a table of common logs to simplify each of the following:

(a) $(\frac{1}{2}) (\frac{1}{3}) (\frac{1}{4}) (\frac{1}{5})$

(b) $(\frac{1}{2})^2 (\frac{1}{3})^3 (\frac{1}{4})^4 (\frac{1}{5})^5$

(c) $\prod\limits_{i=1}^{5} \left(\prod\limits_{k=1}^{i} k \right)$

(d) $\dfrac{(3.721)^{1/2}(4.278)^{3/2}}{(1.414)(2)^{1/2}}$

7.25. Prove 7.3.4.6. (HINT: You need appeal only to 7.3.3, which might be restated to say $x = k^r \leftrightarrow r = \log_k (x)$.)

7.26. Prove $\log_k (u) = x \leftrightarrow k^{vx} = u^v$, $v \neq 0$.

7.27. Prove 7.3.4.3. (HINT: Take logs to the base k in the preceding exercise, use 7.3.4.6, and assume the truth of 7.3.4.8.)

7.28. Assume that for any *real* numbers, m and n, $a^m a^n = a^{(m+n)}$. Then let $\log_k x_1 = y_1$ and $\log_k x_2 = y_2$. Use these identities to prove

$$\log_k (x_1 x_2) = \log_k x_1 + \log_k x_2.$$

7.29. Use the results of Exercise 7.28 to prove 7.3.4.1 by induction on n.

7.30. Prove $-\log_k (v) = \log_k (1/v)$.

7.31. Use Exercises 7.28 and 7.30 to prove 7.3.4.2.

7.32. Prove 7.3.4.4, implication and converse, by indirection.

7.33. Use Theorem 7.3.4 to extend the four parts of Theorem 7.2.3 to include all nonnegative *real* numbers, m and n.

Selected References

1. Allendoerfer, C. B., and Oakley, C. O. *Principles of Mathematics*. New York: The McGraw-Hill Book Company, Inc., 1955. Chapter 9.
2. Arkin, Herbert, and Colton, Raymond R. *Tables for Statisticians*. New York: Barnes and Noble, Inc., 1950.
3. Richardson, Moses. *Fundamentals of Mathematics* (Revised Edition). New York: The Macmillan Company, 1958.
4. Walker, Helen M. *Mathematics Essential for Elementary Statistics* (Revised Edition). New York: Holt, Rinehart and Winston, Inc., 1951. Chapters 16 and 17.

Matrices of Numbers

In one sense, this chapter contains nothing new. In another, it deals with a subject that is entirely novel in relation to what has gone before. This chapter, and indeed the rest of this book, will deal with numbers, a subject with which the reader ought to be on a familiar footing by this point. Here, however, numbers will be put together in an unusual manner, the result being called a *matrix*. Although matrices are built up out of numbers, in some respects they behave quite differently from ordinary numbers as we now know them. In the two sections following, the necessary foundation of axioms and definitions will be constructed. In the remaining sections, some of the more elementary but nonetheless useful properties of matrices will be investigated.

8.1 Matrices in Social Analysis

There are limitless instances in the social sciences in which an investigator finds himself confronted by an array of numbers that seem to "hang together" in a peculiar way. To illustrate this, let us suppose that a psychologist who is interested in mental tests is confronted with four separate tests, each of which purportedly measures a subject's intelligence level. Suppose that each of these tests consists of three sub-batteries of items that tap (1) verbal skills; (2) quantitative facility; and (3) capacity to manipulate spatial relations. It might be that each test turns out to have reasonably high test validity, as measured by some independent criterion, but that the best test intelligence measures can be obtained by giving unequal weights to the three component scores. Moreover, it may be that the systems of weights vary among the four tests. Suppose that for test T_1 the weights are 2, 3, 1 for the three respective components, that for T_2 they are 1, 1, 4, that for T_3 they are 1, 2, 3, and that for T_4 they are 1, 5, 5. Now each set of weights can be considered as an *ordered triple* of numbers.

These four sets of ordered triples have more in common than their structure. In addition to the fact that each is an ordered triple, it should be clear by their construction that

8

each ordered component (that is, each number in a specified position) has something in common with the number
in the corresponding position of each other triple. The four
numbers in the second position, for instance, are all weights
of a common subtest, in this case quantitative facility. This
property of the sequences suggests a yet more convenient
representation of the sets of weights. If the ordered triples
are themselves ordered into four rows, the following 4 × 3
(read "four by three"—the first number always gives the
number of rows; the second, the number of columns) array
results:

(8.1.1)

$$T = \begin{bmatrix} 2 & 3 & 1 \\ 1 & 1 & 4 \\ 1 & 2 & 3 \\ 1 & 5 & 5 \end{bmatrix}.$$

Each row represents a test, and each column represents a
subtest weight. This array of numbers is called a matrix,
a set of numbers whose elements are doubly ordered: hori-
zontally (by rows) and vertically (by columns).

Suppose that these four tests were divided into two parts
in such a way that each of the three components was represented in each part, although not necessarily by an equal
number of items. Suppose, moreover, that T is the set of
weights for Part I of the test and that the weights for Part II
are given by:

(8.1.2)

$$U = \begin{bmatrix} 4 & 6 & 2 \\ 2 & 2 & 8 \\ 2 & 4 & 6 \\ 2 & 10 & 10 \end{bmatrix}.$$

Given these two matrices, one should immediately ask: Does
it make sense to combine them in a manner that somehow
reflects addition of numbers? Clearly, it does make sense,
since their "sum" would be the weights of the combined
tests. What about something on the order of multiplication?
In this case, the operation does not appear to carry substantive meaning, but in some cases, as we shall see, it does.
The careful reader should already have observed, however,
that the identity $T = \alpha U$, where α is a number and αU

means that each element of U is multiplied by α, makes some sort of sense.

Suppose that n countries export commodities to other countries in the set and to none outside the set, thus forming a trade bloc. The entire complex can be represented by a matrix of n rows and n columns such as:

(8.1.3)

$$
A = \begin{array}{c} \textit{Exports by} \\ \textit{Country} \end{array}
\begin{array}{c}
\overset{\textit{Imports by Country}}{\underline{\begin{array}{cccccc} 1 & 2 & 3 \cdots & j & \cdots & n \end{array}}}
\end{array}
$$

$$
A = \begin{array}{c} 1 \\ 2 \\ \vdots \\ i \\ \vdots \\ n \end{array}
\begin{bmatrix}
a_{11} & a_{12} & \cdots & a_{1j} & \cdots & a_{1n} \\
 & & & & & \\
 & & & & & \\
a_{i1} & a_{i2} & & a_{ij} & \cdots & a_{in} \\
 & & & & & \\
a_{n1} & a_{n2} & \cdots & a_{nj} & \cdots & a_{nn}
\end{bmatrix},
$$

in which the number a_{ij} represents the volume of goods exported from country i to country j. The reader should consider carefully this matrix and its contents in order to gain some familiarity both with the notation and with some of the properties of matrices. Suppose, for instance, that $a_{ij} = 0$. What does this mean? Does it follow from this that $a_{ji} = 0$? Not necessarily, but it could. In fact, it is possible that $a_{ij} = a_{ji}$, for all i and j, giving a sort of symmetry to the matrix. What sort of trading bloc might this represent?

The matrix of 8.1.3 presents a particularly interesting conceptual problem in the case of the diagonal entries, a_{ii}. If the notation used to this point has been digested, then it should be clear that a_{ii} is the volume of commodities which country i "exports" to itself. By the usual definition of export, it follows that $a_{ii} = 0$, all i. On the other hand, if a_{ij} simply represents a disposition of goods, then clearly $a_{ii} > 0$ so long as country i consumes some of its own products.

Now let us consider a different sort of matrix in the sphere of international trade economics. Suppose that m countries are engaged in export to one another of n different commodities altogether. The export picture of specific commodities could be summarized in matrix form by:

(8.1.4)

$$B = $$

	Commodity					
Exports by Country	1	2	$\cdots$	j	$\cdots$	n
1	b_{11}	b_{12}	$\cdots$	b_{1j}	$\cdots$	b_{1n}
2						
$\vdots$						
i	b_{i1}	b_{i2}	$\cdots$	b_{ij}	$\cdots$	b_{in}
$\vdots$						
m	b_{m1}	b_{m2}	$\cdots$	b_{mj}	$\cdots$	b_{mn}

Although the matrix of 8.1.4 resembles the matrix of 8.1.3 superficially, the reader should contrast the two carefully. One difference is that 8.1.3 represents a "square" matrix, that is, one in which the number of columns is the same as the number of rows. On the other hand, that of 8.1.4 is rectangular but not necessarily square. Moreover, the row numbers, $i = 1, 2, \cdots, m$, stand for entirely different things than do the column numbers, $j = 1, 2, \cdots, n$ (countries and commodities, respectively). In this matrix the diagonal values, b_{ii}, present no interpretational problem: b_{ii} is just the volume of export of commodity i by country i.

Now consider two particularly important matrices with dimensions $n \times 1$ and $1 \times m$ respectively:

$$(8.1.5) \quad C = \begin{bmatrix} c_1 \\ c_2 \\ \cdot \\ \cdot \\ \cdot \\ c_i \\ \cdot \\ \cdot \\ \cdot \\ c_n \end{bmatrix}, \quad D = [d_1 \quad d_2 \quad \cdots \quad d_j \quad \cdots \quad d_m].$$

Matrix C is called a *column vector*, and D is called a *row vector*. Suppose that C is a matrix whose entries represent the unit cost of commodities, so that c_n is the unit cost of commodity n. Let the components of D, d_j, represent export duties levied by country j. Then, if they could be multiplied together properly, both the "matrix products" BC and DB might be capable of interpretation, the first representing *total* export revenue earned by each country and the second representing total export tariffs associated with each commodity. The dimension of the two product matrices should be $1 \times n$ and $m \times 1$ respectively. The reason for not calling the latter $1 \times m$ will be made clear below.

Social psychologists make frequent use of the mathematics of matrices. The study of patterns of interaction in small groups requires that each communication from one member to another member of an experimental group be recorded. Matrices provide a convenient form for the recording and analysis of data such as these. The typical entry of an interactional matrix, say a_{ij}, is the frequency (or relative frequency) of acts directed from actor i to actor j. With this, the reader should be able to list several necessary properties of interactional matrices. What about the number of rows and columns, the integers m and n respectively? What does the cell a_{ii} represent? Why might the social psychologist's convention that $a_{ii} = 0$ be anticipated?

Suppose that a social psychologist observes a relation, C, on a set of elements, A, to A. Let us interpret C as communication. To help structure his observation, suppose that the observer assumes C to be irreflexive, symmetrical, and nontransitive. (The reader should consider carefully what these conditions on C require. Under what form of communication might symmetry be an unrealistic requirement? What is necessary in the communication process to make the assumption of nontransitivity reasonable?) Let C be:

$$(8.1.6) \quad C = \left\{ c_{ij} : \begin{array}{l} c_{ij} = 1 \text{ if } a_i \text{ communicates with } a_j \\ c_{ij} = 0 \text{ otherwise; } a_i, a_j \in A \end{array} \right\}.$$

Assume that A is a five-element set, which could contain individuals or social groups. Suppose that, on this five-element set, C is represented by:

$$(8.1.7) \qquad C = \begin{bmatrix} 0 & 1 & 1 & 0 & 0 \\ 1 & 0 & 1 & 1 & 0 \\ 1 & 1 & 0 & 1 & 0 \\ 0 & 1 & 1 & 0 & 0 \\ 0 & 0 & 0 & 0 & 0 \end{bmatrix}.$$

This simple table represents with vast efficiency a segment of social behavior. Clearly, it fails to convey many of the subtleties of human dialogue, but in it one can see represented behavior suggested by such terms as "popular," "gossip," "isolate." Before we proceed, the reader would do well to study 8.1.7 carefully, to determine, for example, which actors, a_i, are most and least talkative. Again, what implicit condition does the major diagonal represent? How might such a matrix look if the elements of A were a set of schizophrenics? What might be the situation if a single column contains 1's, with zeros in all other cells?

Now consider a different order of question. Suppose that a_4 must transmit a message to a_1. The reader should recognize from 8.1.7 that he cannot do this, at least not directly, because the two elements do not communicate. The task can be accomplished, however, in either of two ways. Either a_4 can communicate the message to a_3 with instructions to pass it on, or he can give it to a_2. Note that both a_3 and a_2 do communicate with a_1. To determine in exactly how many ways a_i can get a message to a_j using a "middle-man," we must anticipate an operation that later will be called *matrix multiplication*.

In how many ways can actor a_3 communicate with a_2 using an intervening actor? To answer this, consider first the row vector that represents the elements with whom a_3 communicates and then the column vector that gives the elements that communicate with a_2. These are:

$$(8.1.8) \qquad a_{3\cdot} = \langle 1, 1, 0, 1, 0 \rangle \qquad a_{\cdot 2} = \begin{matrix} 1 \\ 0 \\ 1 \\ 1 \\ 0 \end{matrix}.$$

Now let us multiply *in order* the elements of the row vector by the elements of the column vector and add the products. This odd operation gives $(1 \cdot 1) + (1 \cdot 0) + (0 \cdot 1) + (1 \cdot 1) + (0 \cdot 0) = 2$. If one considers this procedure carefully, he should recognize that the sum of products is just the number of ways in which a_3 can get a message to a_2 through a "middle-man." The first product, $(1 \cdot 1)$, represents a connection of a_3 to a_2 through a_1. This product is one only because both a_3Ca_1 and a_1Ca_2. The second product, $(1 \cdot 0)$, is zero and represents the fact that, although a_3Ca_2, that is a_3 does communicate with a_2 directly, a_2 cannot be a middle-man for himself.

In a similar way, it is possible to multiply ordered elements of each row vector of C by those of each of its column vectors and to sum the products, thus obtaining a single number. Each number can be entered in a new matrix in a systematic way, giving a new matrix. Call the new matrix C^2 and form it by entering the sum of elements in the ith row and jth column in the ijth cell. Thus, the number 2 would be entered in the third row, 2nd column of C^2. The reader should verify that this new matrix is:

$$(8.1.9) \qquad C^2 = \begin{bmatrix} 2 & 1 & 1 & 2 & 0 \\ 1 & 3 & 2 & 1 & 0 \\ 1 & 2 & 3 & 1 & 0 \\ 2 & 1 & 1 & 2 & 0 \\ 0 & 0 & 0 & 0 & 0 \end{bmatrix}.$$

What does the major diagonal of this new matrix represent? Why are the fifth row and column still filled with zeros? If C^2 is represented in matrix symbols by $C \cdot C$ (note that this is *not* a product of numbers, but of matrices), then what might be represented by $C^2 \cdot C^2$?

These few illustrations should suffice to give the reader an idea of the value of a matrix as a system for ordering data. Moreover, they should suggest intuitively that a sort of arithmetic of matrices might be highly useful in the sense that such operations can often be interpreted substantively. The rudiments of this new arithmetic will be considered in the next section.

Exercises

8.1. Let B be a *country* $\times$ *commodity* export distribution as in 8.1.4. Let C be a similar *country by commodity* import distribution.

(a) What might $(C - B)$ represent?

(b) If B is an $m \times n$ matrix, what must be the size of C?

(c) If b_{ij} and c_{ij} are typical components of B and C respectively, what is a typical component of $C - B$?

8.2. Let A_1, A_2, and A_3 represent interactional matrices of n experimental subjects at times t_1, t_2, and t_3, respectively.

(a) What might $A_1 + A_2 + A_3$ represent?

(b) Should $(A_1 + A_2) + A_3 = A_1 + (A_2 + A_3)$?

(c) Construct a definition of $+$ on matrices on the basis of these considerations.

(d) By your definition of $+$, is this operation commutative?

8.3. Let

$$A = [1 \quad 2 \quad 3 \quad 1], \quad B = \begin{bmatrix} 2 & 0 & 5 \\ 3 & 2 & 0 \\ 0 & 6 & 3 \\ 1 & 0 & 2 \end{bmatrix}, \quad C = \begin{bmatrix} 0 & 7 & 0 \\ 0 & 0 & 5 \\ 9 & 0 & 0 \\ 0 & 3 & 0 \end{bmatrix}, \quad D = \begin{bmatrix} 4 \\ 1 \\ 6 \end{bmatrix},$$

where A = (uniform) import tariff on all goods by country i,
B = amount of commodity j exported by country i ($i = 1, \cdots, 4, j = 1, 2, 3$),
C = amount of commodity j imported by country i,
D = unit cost of commodity j.

(a) Using addition as constructed in Exercise 8.2, compute and interpret $B - C$.

(b) Compute a 4×1 matrix (call it BD) such that the first entry represents gross revenue earned by the first country, $\cdots$, the fourth entry represents gross revenue earned by the fourth country. (HINT: The first component of BD is 38.)

(c) Construct a second 4×1 matrix, call it CD, in which component j represents import costs in country j.

(d) Construct a 1×3 matrix, call it AC, in which the jth entry represents the total import tariff created by the flow of commodity j.

8.4. Carefully reconsider your constructions in Exercise 8.3.

(a) Construct a definition of multiplication on matrices that reflects these operations. (HINT: An element of a product matrix must contain a *sum* of products of elements from a row of one matrix and a column of the other.)

(b) If two matrices with dimensions $m \times n$ and $n \times q$ are multiplied, what must be the size of the product matrix?

(c) Does your definition of matrix multiplication cover the product of two matrices of dimensions $m \times n$ and $p \times q$ respectively? Why or why not?

8.5. In Exercise 8.3, construct $(B - C)D$ and $(BD - CD)$. What does this suggest about a distributive rule of matrix multiplication?

8.6. Suppose that a sociometric choice function is given by:

$$a_{ij} = \begin{cases} 1 \text{ if person } i \text{ chooses person } j \\ 0 \text{ otherwise} \end{cases} \quad (i, j = 1, 2, \cdots, n).$$

(a) Construct a matrix, A, with arbitrary numbers, on a four-person group, and interpret it.
(b) What should be the uniform value of a_{ii}? Why?
(c) Describe what is represented by the condition $a_{ij} = a_{ji}$, all i, j. Is this realistic?
(d) Construct a second 4×4 matrix, call it B, the matrix of choice perception, in which

$$b_{ij} = \begin{cases} 2 \text{ if person } i \text{ thinks that person } j \text{ chose him} \\ 0 \text{ otherwise} \end{cases}$$

(e) Compute $A + B$ and interpret it.
(f) Compute AB and interpret it.

8.7. Consider matrices T and U of 8.1.1 and 8.1.2.

(a) Identify α (a real number, *not* a matrix) in the identity $T = \alpha U$.
(b) This identity illustrates what will be called *scalar multiplication*. Construct a definition of scalar multiplication of any number α and any matrix A.

8.2 Operations on Matrices

By now the reader should be able to anticipate the progression of events in this section. The formalization of any notion requires one or more definitions, then the construction of a set of axioms, and, finally, an investigation of the consequences of the definitions and axioms. So far as the definition is concerned, it may contain any properties of constructs developed to this point. The exercises should suggest that considerable use will be made of our work with sums and of the general properties of real numbers.

(8.2.1) If a set of mn real numbers, a_{ij} $i = 1, 2, \cdots, m$, **Definition**
$j = 1, 2, \cdots, n$, is arranged into n ordered $m$tuples, and if the $m$tuples are arranged into an ordered $n$tuple, then the resulting element is called an $m \times n$ *matrix*. The number a_{ij} is called the ith component of the jth column (or equivalently, the jth component of the ith row). In particular, a $1 \times n$ matrix is called an *n-component* row vector, and an

$m \times 1$ matrix is called an *m-component* column vector. Thus, in Exercise 8.3, A is a 4-component row vector, B and C are 4×3 matrices, and D is a 3-component column vector. Note carefully that in a matrix system, the first item of information about location or dimension always concerns rows, and the second always concerns columns.

(8.2.2) If the dimensions of a matrix, A, are $m \times n$, the matrix will be denoted $A_{m,n}$ except where the context makes the dimensionality clear. A matrix such that $A_{m,n} = [a_{ij}]$ implies that $i = 1, 2, \cdots, m$ and $j = 1, 2, \cdots, n$. **Notation**

With this notational machinery, the basic properties of numbers, and especially those of compound summation, some mathematical structure can be imposed on the entity called a matrix. As with the case of rational numbers, what we need are axioms on equality, addition, and multiplication. The preceding exercises should have provided broad hints as to their form:

Axioms on Matrices

(8.2.3) If $A_{m,n}$ and $B_{p,q}$ are two matrices, then:

(1) $A_{m,n} = B_{p,q} \leftrightarrow m = p$, $n = q$ and $a_{ij} = b_{ij}$, all $a_{ij} \in A$ and $b_{ij} \in B$.

If $m = p$, $n = q$, and $A_{m,n} = [a_{ij}]$, $B_{p,q} = [b_{ij}]$, then:

(2) $A + B = [(a_{ij} + b_{ij})]$, which may be written $[(a + b)_{ij}]$.

If $A_{m,n} = [a_{ik}]$ and $B_{n,q} = [b_{kj}]$, $k = 1, 2, \cdots, n$, then:

(3) $(AB)_{m,q} = [(ab)_{ij}]$, where $(ab)_{ij} = \sum_{k=1}^{n} a_{ik}b_{kj}$.

These axioms must be perfectly understood if anything that follows is to make sense to the reader. The first axiom states that if two matrices are equal, they must contain the same number of rows and columns and each pair of components in corresponding positions must consist of identical numbers.

The second axiom states that addition is defined only with respect to matrices whose dimensions are identical.

The third axiom carries with it a certain sense of the

notion of transitivity. Recall that a relation is transitive if and only if existence of the pairs $\langle a, b \rangle$ and $\langle b, c \rangle$ in the relation implies that the pair $\langle a, c \rangle$ also is in the relation. Matrix multiplication requires that the two matrices to be multiplied be related by *dimension* in that the second dimension of the first matrix must be the same as the first dimension of the second matrix. When this is the case, the product matrix turns out to have dimensions given respectively by the first dimension of the first matrix and by the second dimension of the second matrix. Thus, $A_{m,n} \cdot B_{n,q} = AB_{m,q}$. The careful reader ought to suspect already that multiplication of matrices may well have some different properties from those inherent in multiplication of real numbers.

These axioms, of course, generate a rich variety of consequences, several of which already have been suggested in exercises or in the text. Let us consider first the consequences of the axiom on addition.

THEOREM

(8.2.4) (*On Addition of Matrices*). If A, B, and C are matrices each of dimension $m \times n$, then:

(1) $A + B = B + A$.
(2) $(A + B) + C = A + (B + C)$.
(3) There exists an $m \times n$ matrix, Z, such that $A + Z = A$, and Z is called the zero matrix, in which $z_{ij} = 0$, all i, j.
(4) For each $m \times n$ matrix, A, there exists an $m \times n$ matrix, $-A$, such that $A + (-A) = Z$, in which $-A = [(-a)_{ij}]$.

Proof (2)

Let A, B, and C be of dimension $m \times n$. Then:

(1) $(A + B) = [a_{ij} + b_{ij}]$.   (8.2.3.2)
(2) $(A + B) + C = [(a_{ij} + b_{ij}) + c_{ij}]$,   (8.2.3.2)
(3) $= [a_{ij} + b_{ij} + c_{ij}]$.   (5.2.1-A5)
(4) $(B + C) = [b_{ij} + c_{ij}]$.   (8.2.3.2)
(5) $A + (B + C) = [a_{ij} + (b_{ij} + c_{ij})]$,   (8.2.3.2)
(6) $= [a_{ij} + b_{ij} + c_{ij}]$.   (Same as Step 3)
(7) $(A + B) + C = A + (B + C)$.   (Steps 3 and 6)

Proof (3)

Let $Z_{m,n} = [z_{ij}]$ and $z_{ij} = 0$, all i, j. Then:

(1) $A + Z = [a_{ij} + z_{ij}]$,   (8.2.3.2)

(2) $= [a_{ij} + 0]$,   (Hypothesis about z_{ij})
(3) $= [a_{ij}]$,   (5.2.1-A3 and 8.2.3.1)
(4) $= A$.

The proofs of Parts 1 and 4 are left as exercises. None of these results is especially startling. So far as addition is concerned, quantities that are matrices behave exactly as do quantities that are real numbers. Such is not quite the case, however, insofar as multiplication is concerned.

THEOREM

(8.2.5) (*On Multiplication of Matrices*). Let matrices A, B, and C be such that AB, BA, BC and CA are defined. Then:

(1) There exist matrices A and B such that $AB \neq BA$.
(2) $A(BC) = (AB)C$.
(3) $A(B + C) = AB + AC$ and $(B + C)A = BA + CA$.
(4) If A is a square matrix, say $A_{n,n}$, there exists a second square matrix, $I_{n,n}$ such that:

$$(AI)_{n,n} = (IA)_{n,n} = A_{n,n},$$

$$I_{n,n} = [\delta_{ij}], \text{ where } \delta_{ij} = \begin{cases} 1 \text{ if } i = j \\ 0 \text{ otherwise} \end{cases}$$

Proof (1)

For matrices $A_{m,n}$ and $B_{n,q}$ it is clear that AB is defined but that BA is defined only if $m = q$. Moreover, let:

$$A = \begin{bmatrix} 1 & 1 & 1 \\ 0 & 0 & 0 \\ 0 & 0 & 0 \end{bmatrix}, \quad B = \begin{bmatrix} 0 & -1 & -1 \\ -1 & 0 & 1 \\ 1 & 1 & 0 \end{bmatrix}.$$

Then $AB \neq BA$.

Proof (2)

Consider the matrices $A_{m,n}$, $B_{n,p}$, and $C_{p,q}$. Clearly, AB, BC, $A(BC)$, and $(AB)C$ are defined.

(1) $(AB)_{m,p} = [ab_{ik}] = \left[\sum_{j=1}^{n} a_{ij}b_{jk} \right]$,   (8.2.3.3)

$$\begin{pmatrix} i = 1, 2, \cdots, m \\ j = 1, 2, \cdots, n \\ k = 1, 2, \cdots, p \end{pmatrix}.$$

(2) $(BC)_{n,q} = [bc_{jg}] = \left[\sum_{k=1}^{p} b_{jk}c_{kg} \right]$,   (8.2.3.3)

$g = 1, 2, \cdots, q$.

(3) $(A(BC))_{m,q} = [(a(bc))_{iq}] = \sum_{j=1}^{n} a_{ij}(bc)_{jq},$ (8.2.3.3)

(4) $= \sum_{j=1}^{n} a_{ij} \sum_{k=1}^{p} b_{jk}c_{kq},$ (Step 2)

(5) $= \sum_{j=1}^{n} \sum_{k=1}^{p} a_{ij}b_{jk}c_{kq}.$ (7.1.5.2)

(6) $((AB)C)_{m,q} = [((ab)c)_{iq}] = \sum_{k=1}^{n} (ab)_{ik}c_{kq},$ (8.2.3.3)

(7) $= \sum_{k=1}^{p} \left(\sum_{j=1}^{n} a_{ij}b_{jk} \right) c_{kq},$ (Step 1)

(8) $= \sum_{j=1}^{n} \sum_{k=1}^{p} a_{ij}b_{jk}c_{kq},$ (7.1.5.1)

(9) $= A(BC).$ (Steps 5 and 8)

Proofs of Parts 3 and 4 are left as exercises. The first part of this theorem says that the commutative rule of multiplication sometimes fails to apply in matrix multiplication. This is an irritating kind of assertion; it fails to indicate when the rule does or does not obtain. Nonetheless, its proof is simple enough, requiring only that a single example, usually called a *counterexample*, be displayed. In this case, the counterexample also demonstrates another curious feature of matrix multiplication, which the reader should recognize after he forms the product AB. The reader should verify that $AB = Z$, the zero matrix, (and that $BA \neq Z$). We know that the real number, 0, is such that if $ab = 0$ either $a = 0$, $b = 0$, or both a and b are equal to zero. It is clear, however, that this is not the case with matrices. Despite the fact that neither $A = Z$ nor $B = Z$, the product $AB = Z$.

The importance of these differences of matrices from real numbers under the operation of multiplication cannot be overemphasized. It is extremely easy to make serious formal errors when manipulating matrices. Such mistakes are usually caused by the incorrect assumption that matrix multiplication behaves like multiplication of real numbers. Part 1 of this theorem, which says that matrix multiplication is not commutative, possibly is the chief single cause of formal errors in algebraic manipulations of matrices.

Parts 2 and 3 of the theorem say that the associative and

distributive rules of multiplication, with which we are familiar from working with real numbers, are true also with respect to matrices. The fourth part of the theorem introduces a square matrix, I, that has the familiar properties of the number 1 under multiplication. The various matrices $I_{n,n}$ (different for each value of n) are called *identity matrices*. Notice that $I_{n,n}$ is just a square matrix with zeros in each cell except for those along the principal diagonal (those for which $i = j$), which contain ones. The δ_{ij} that was defined in 8.2.5.4 is sometimes called "Kronecker's Delta."

These axioms and theorems should be reviewed slowly and carefully until the reader is certain that he recognizes exactly what is said by each. The following are representative questions that the reader should be able to answer before he proceeds: Under what conditions are the sum and product matrices defined? If $A + B$ and AB are defined, does it follow that $B + A$ and BA are defined? If not, under what special circumstances does this follow? Just why was step 5 of the second part of the proof of 8.2.5 justified (this cannot be answered without reference to the various subscripts and indices of summation)?

If two matrices are to be multiplied together, the number of columns of the first matrix must be the same as the number of rows of the second. This is so important, and at the same time so peculiar a property, that it merits a name of its own:

(8.2.6) If $A_{m,n}$ and $B_{p,q}$ are two matrices, then: **Definition**

$\qquad$ B is said to be conformable to $A \leftrightarrow n = p$,

and $\quad$ A is said to be conformable to $B \leftrightarrow m = q$.

Thus, the product AB is defined only if B is conformable to A, and the product BA is defined only if A is conformable to B. If both AB and BA are defined, does it necessarily follow that both A and B are square matrices?

In Exercise 8.7, a sort of multiplication was suggested that is altogether different from matrix multiplication as it has been defined here. Recall that the matrices T and U, of 8.1.1 and 8.1.2 respectively, were related by the identity

$T = \alpha U$. The reader who won his gold star for Exercise 8.7 recognized that a reasonable guess was $\alpha = \frac{1}{2}$. That is, each component of T is just half the size of the corresponding component of U. All this suggests a frequently useful method of transforming matrices by what is known as scalar multiplication.

(8.2.7) If $A_{m,n}$ is a matrix and α is any real number, then in the matrix given by:

$$\alpha A = [\alpha a_{ij}],$$

α is called the *scalar* of A.

Definition

In other words, multiplication by a scalar effects a uniform shift in the components of a matrix because each of them is multiplied by the value of the scalar. For example, if $\alpha = 3$,

(8.2.8)

Illustration

$$3\begin{bmatrix} 2 & 1 & 3 \\ 1 & 1 & 2 \\ 0 & 2 & 3 \end{bmatrix} = \begin{bmatrix} 6 & 3 & 9 \\ 3 & 3 & 6 \\ 0 & 6 & 9 \end{bmatrix}.$$

Consider what a scalar transformation accomplishes. If an economist's *country* $\times$ *export* matrix contains components representing millions of units exported, a suitable scalar transformation could convert it into a matrix whose components are, say, hundreds or tens of units exported. (What should the value of α be in each case?)

Scalar multiplication has several obvious and useful properties that the reader ought to be able both to anticipate and to demonstrate to his own satisfaction.

(8.2.9) (*On Scalar Multiplication*). Let α and β be any scalars, and let $A_{m,n}$ and $B_{n,p}$ be matrices (so that AB is defined). Then:

THEOREM

(1) $\alpha A = A\alpha$.
(2) $\alpha(AB) = (\alpha A)B = A(\alpha B)$.
(3) $(\alpha + \beta)A = A(\alpha + \beta) = \alpha A + \beta A$.

(4) If m, n, and p are such that $A + B$ is defined, then
$$\alpha(A + B) = \alpha A + \alpha B.$$
(5) $\alpha\beta A = \alpha(\beta A) = \beta(\alpha A).$

All proofs of this theorem are left as exercises. They should offer no problem so long as it is remembered that each component of a matrix and each scalar are real numbers and are subject to all properties of real numbers.

To illustrate these matrix operations, consider the following matrices:

$$A = \begin{bmatrix} 2 & 1 \\ 3 & 0 \end{bmatrix}, \quad B = \begin{bmatrix} 3 & 4 \\ 1 & 2 \end{bmatrix}, \quad C = \begin{bmatrix} 0 & 1 \\ 3 & 4 \end{bmatrix}.$$

To obtain the new matrix, $A + B$, elements in similar positions are added together according to 8.2.3.2. Thus $(a + b)_{11} = a_{11} + b_{11} = 2 + 3 = 5$. When this is done for each of the four cells, we have:

$$A + B = \begin{bmatrix} 5 & 5 \\ 4 & 2 \end{bmatrix}.$$

The reader may satisfy himself that $A + B = B + A$. The matrix $(A + B) + C$ is obtained by adding elements in similar position of $(A + B)$ and C. The element $((a + b) + c)_{11} = (a + b)_{11} + c_{11} = 5 + 0 = 5$. By continuing in this way, we obtain:

$$(A + B) + C = \begin{bmatrix} 5 & 6 \\ 7 & 6 \end{bmatrix}.$$

Once again, the reader should convince himself that the identity $(A + B) + C = A + (B + C)$ is satisfied by these matrices. Now let us transform A by multiplying it by a scalar, say, $\alpha = 2$. Then, according to 8.2.7, $2A = [2a_{ij}]$ so that $2a_{11} = 2 \cdot 2 = 4$ and:

$$2A = \begin{bmatrix} 4 & 2 \\ 6 & 0 \end{bmatrix}.$$

Finally, the product matrix AB is formed by summing products, working across rows of A and columns of B. Definition 8.2.3.3 tells us that $(ab)_{11} = a_{11}b_{11} + a_{12}b_{21} = 2 \cdot 3 + 1 \cdot 1 = 7$. In the same way, $(ab)_{21} = a_{21}b_{11} + a_{22}b_{21} = 3 \cdot 3 + 0 \cdot 1 = 9$. After this is repeated for the remaining matrices, the result is:

$$AB = \begin{bmatrix} 7 & 10 \\ 9 & 12 \end{bmatrix}.$$

The reader should verify that:

$$BA = \begin{bmatrix} 18 & 3 \\ 8 & 1 \end{bmatrix},$$

which looks nothing at all like AB. Finally, these illustrative matrices should be used to check the identities $A(B + C) = AB + AC$ and $(B + C)A = BA + CA$.

Exercises

8.8. Construct each of the following, using appropriately subscripted letters for the components:

(a) $A_{2,3}$
(b) $B_{3,2}$
(c) $C_{2,1}$
(d) $D_{1,2}$
(e) $E_{3,5}$
(f) $F_{4,3}$

8.9. Let

$$A = \begin{bmatrix} 2 & 1 \\ 1 & 2 \\ 2 & 3 \end{bmatrix}, \quad B = \begin{bmatrix} 2 & 3 & 2 \\ 4 & 1 & 3 \\ -2 & 4 & 0 \end{bmatrix}.$$

8.10. For each of the following pairs of matrices indicate whether either the product matrix AB or BA is defined. If either is defined, give its dimension.

(a) $A_{1,3}, B_{3,3}$
(b) $A_{1,3}, B_{3,1}$
(c) $A_{1,3}, B_{1,3}$
(d) $A_{2,2}, B_{2,2}$
(e) $A_{3,1}, B_{1,3}$
(f) $A_{3,1}, B_{1,4}$

8.11. Prove 8.2.4.1. (HINT: Recall that a_{ij} and b_{ij} are real numbers.)

8.12. Prove 8.2.4.4.

8.13.

$$A = \begin{bmatrix} 2.5 & 0 & -3 \\ 1 & 4.6 & 2 \\ -2 & 3 & 1 \end{bmatrix}, \quad B = \begin{bmatrix} 1 & 3 & 5 \\ 1.5 & -2 & 3 \\ 2 & 4 & -3.3 \end{bmatrix}, \quad C = \begin{bmatrix} 1 & -1 & 1 \\ 2.5 & -3.4 & 2 \\ 0 & 1.6 & 3 \end{bmatrix}.$$

(a) Construct the matrix $-A$ such that $A - A = Z$.
(b) Construct $Z_{3,3}$ and obtain $A + Z$.
(c) Demonstrate that matrix addition is commutative for matrices A and B.
(d) Demonstrate that matrix addition is associative for matrices A, B, and C.

8.14. Use the matrices of Exercise 8.13 to obtain:

(a) AB
(b) BA
(c) BC
(d) $(AB)C$
(e) $A(BC)$

8.15. Use the matrices of 8.13 to demonstrate the distributive rule of 8.2.5.3.

8.16. Evaluate the two matrix products, AB and BA, offered as counterexamples of the commutative rule of matrix multiplication (proof of 8.2.5.1).

8.17. Use the matrices of Exercise 8.13 and construct $I_{3,3}$ (see 8.2.5.4) to obtain:

(a) $(IA)B$
(b) $(AI)B$
(c) $A(IB)$
(d) $A(BI)$

8.18. Let $\alpha = 2$. Use the data of Exercise 8.17 to construct:

(a) αI
(b) $\alpha I(AB)$
(c) $\alpha(AB)$
(d) $A(\alpha B)$
(e) $A(I\alpha B)$

8.19. Prove 8.2.5.3.

8.20. Prove 8.2.5.4.

8.21. Prove Theorem 8.2.9:

(a) Part 1
(b) Part 3
(c) Part 4

8.3 Some Special Matrices

In social analysis, a few particular matrix forms appear regularly enough to merit special consideration. The first of these is an operator matrix of which the various forms of I, the identity matrices, are a special case. A member of the class of *permutation* matrices can be used to interchange rows and columns of a given matrix in any way that might be required for a particular analysis.

(8.3.1) A permutation matrix is any $n \times n$ matrix such that each row and each column contains a single component 1, the remaining components being 0.   **Definition**

The reader should convince himself that a permutation matrix with n rows and columns contains exactly n ones and $n(n-1)$ zeroes. Which of the following are permutation matrices?

$$(8.3.2) \quad A = [1], \qquad B = \begin{bmatrix} 0 & 1 & 0 \\ 1 & 0 & 0 \\ 0 & 0 & 1 \end{bmatrix},$$

$$C = \begin{bmatrix} 0 & 0 & 1 & 0 \\ 0 & 0 & 0 & 1 \\ 0 & 0 & 1 & 0 \\ 1 & 0 & 0 & 0 \end{bmatrix}, \quad I = \begin{bmatrix} 1 & 0 & 0 \\ 0 & 1 & 0 \\ 0 & 0 & 1 \end{bmatrix}.$$

The reader should recognize that A, B, and I are permutation matrices but C is not. How could C be rearranged into a permutation matrix?

We have seen that an identity matrix does not change a second matrix under multiplication. That is $AI = A$. This can be thought of as an identity mapping of each column vector and of each row vector into itself. But what happens when a permutation matrix other than I is used? An example should provide the necessary clue.

(8.3.3) Let:

$$A = \begin{bmatrix} 2 & 3 & 1 \\ 0 & 1 & 2 \\ 2 & 1 & 1 \end{bmatrix}, \qquad T = \begin{bmatrix} 0 & 1 & 0 \\ 0 & 0 & 1 \\ 1 & 0 & 0 \end{bmatrix}.$$

Then

$$AT = \begin{bmatrix} 1 & 2 & 3 \\ 2 & 0 & 1 \\ 1 & 2 & 1 \end{bmatrix}, \quad \text{and} \quad TA = \begin{bmatrix} 0 & 1 & 2 \\ 2 & 1 & 1 \\ 2 & 3 & 1 \end{bmatrix}.$$

These results should be considered most carefully. A notational convention might help in this consideration.

(8.3.4) In the matrix product AB, B is said to be pre-multiplied by A, and A is said to be postmultiplied by B.

Notation

As a brief aside, the reader might ask himself why such terms as these have not crept into the vocabulary of multiplication of ordinary numbers. Notice in 8.3.3 that postmultiplication of A by T permutes (changes the order of) *column* vectors but leaves the components of each unaltered. For example, column 3 of A is column 1 of AT, with its ordered elements unaffected. Premultiplication of A by T has rather a different consequence. In this case, *row* vectors are permuted with components unchanged. Row 1 of A, for instance, is row 3 of TA. To show that these results are quite general, we have the following:

(8.3.5) If $A_{m,n}$ is a matrix and $T_{m,m}$ and $T_{n,n}$ are permutation matrices, then $(TA)_{m,n}$ is a reordering of row vectors of A, and $(AT)_{m,n}$ is a reordering of column vectors of A, subject to:

$$t_{pq} = 1 \longrightarrow \begin{cases} ta_{pj} = a_{qj} \\ at_{iq} = a_{ip} \end{cases}.$$

(Do not despair. This makes sense after a careful reading.)

Let T be a permutation matrix such that A is conformable to T, and let $t_{pq} = 1$.

(1) $(ta_{pj}) = \left(\sum_{i=1}^{m} t_{pi}a_{ij} \right)$, $i, p = 1, 2, \cdots, m,$ (8.2.3.3)

$$j = 1, 2, \cdots, n,$$

(2) $\qquad = a_{qj}$. (Since $t_{pq} = 1$ and $t_{pi} = 0$, all $i \neq q$.)

Now let T be conformable to A with $t_{pq} = 1$.

(3) $at_{iq} = \sum_{j=1}^{n} a_{ij}t_{jq}$, $j, q = 1, 2, \cdots, n,$ (8.2.3.3)

(4) $\qquad = a_{ip}$. (Since $t_{pq} = 1$ and $t_{jq} = 0$, all $j \neq p$.)

It will help to compare this theorem with the illustration of 8.3.3. Consider the permutation matrix as a premultiplier in that illustration. Notice that $t_{12} = 1$. Then the theorem tells us that $ta_{1j} = a_{2j}$. Since the column index, j, is unaffected, this amounts to saying that the first row of TA is identical to the second row of A. Similarly, $t_{23} = 1$ tells us that the second row of TA is the same as the third row of A. In general, $t_{pq} = 1$ tells us that row p of TA equals row q of A.

Another particularly useful kind of matrix, called a *transpose*, is one that is generated from a matrix by inverting columns and rows. That is,

(8.3.6) The transpose, $A'_{n,m}$, of a matrix, $A_{m,n} = [a_{ij}]$, is **Definition**
given by:

$$A'_{n,m} = [a'_{ij}], \text{ where } a'_{ij} = a_{ji}.$$

Thus, a transposition can be thought of as flipping a matrix over on its back and then turning it over on its side. For example,

(8.3.7) if $A = \begin{bmatrix} 0 & 1 \\ 2 & 3 \\ 4 & 5 \end{bmatrix}$, $A' = \begin{bmatrix} 0 & 2 & 4 \\ 1 & 3 & 5 \end{bmatrix}$.

Before looking at some elementary properties of transposition matrices, it will be convenient to use this definition to construct another definition.

(8.3.8) If a square matrix, A, is such that $A = A'$, then **Definition**
A is said to be symmetric.

Why is symmetry defined only with respect to square matrices? (HINT: Consult 8.2.3.1.)

A particularly useful matrix in social research is called the *correlation* matrix. A correlation coefficient is a measure of "association" between two variables. If $R_{n,n}$ is a correlation matrix, each row represents a variable, and the jth column represents the same variable as does the jth row. The typical component, r_{ij}, is the measure of correlation between variables i and j, but this must be the same number as r_{ji}. Thus, a correlation matrix is symmetric.

(8.3.9) (*Properties of Transposition Matrices*). **THEOREM**

(1) For any matrix A, $(A')' = A$.
(2) A is conformable to A' and A' is conformable to A.
(3) AA' and $A'A$ are both symmetric.
(4) If α and β are scalars and if A and B are matrices of identical dimension, then $(\alpha A + \beta B)' = \alpha A' + \beta B'$.
(5) If B is conformable with respect to A then A' is conformable with respect to B' and $(AB)' = B'A'$.
(6) If A is square then $(A + A')$ is symmetric.

All proofs are left as exercises. They involve little more than making direct use of the appropriate definitions.

Another special and highly useful matrix is the product of a square matrix multiplied by itself. In fact, since the dimension of the product is the same as that of the original matrix (does the reader agree?), there is nothing to prevent one's repeating the multiplicative operation a third, fourth, or, in general, an nth time. All of this of course is reminiscent of the powers of real numbers (see Definition 7.2.2 and Theorem 7.2.3) and suggests the following:

(8.3.10) If $A_{k,k}$ is any square matrix and n is any non-negative integer, then: **Definition**

$$A^n = \begin{cases} I_{k,k} & \text{if } n = 0 \\ A & \text{if } n = 1 \\ A \cdot A^{n-1} & \text{if } n > 1 \end{cases}.$$

One should recognize this as an inductive definition of the powers of square matrices, analogous to that for real numbers. Despite the similarity of definitions, it does not follow that the properties of powers of matrices are the same as those of powers of numbers. Recall that multiplication is commutative on numbers but not necessarily on matrices. The following theorem, however, makes matters more orderly than one might have hoped.

(8.3.11) If A is any square matrix and m and n are non-negative integers, then: **THEOREM**

(1) $A^m A^n = A^{m+n}$.
(2) $(A^m)^n = A^{mn}$.

(Part 1—by induction). Let A be a square matrix and **Proof** n a nonnegative integer. Then:

(1) $A^0 A^n = I A^n = A^n = A^{n+0}$.   (8.3.10, 8.2.5.4)
(2) $A^1 A^n = A A^n = A^{n+1}$.   (8.3.10)
(3) Assume $A^{m-1} A^n = A^{m+n-1}$.   (Inductive assumption
                                           for $m > 1$)

(4) $A^m A^n = (A A^{m-1}) A^n$,   (8.3.10)
(5) $= A(A^{m-1} A^n)$,   (8.2.5.2)
(6) $= A A^{m+n-1}$,   (Step 3)
(7) $= A^{m+n}$.   (8.3.10)

The proof of Part 1 of this theorem is left as an exercise. Note that Part 2 of the theorem provides a special case in which products of matrices *are* commutative. That is, $A^m A^n = A^n A^m$ since both are equal to A^{m+n}.

Although the properties of powers of matrices are more similar to those of powers of real numbers than might have been expected, they are not identical. Remember that for real numbers a, b, and n it is true that $a^n b^n = (ab)^n$. The reader should try to prove the (false) theorem $A^n B^n = (AB)^n$ for n, a real number, and A and B matrices, in order to discover where matters go amiss.

Exercises

8.22. Let:

$$T = \begin{bmatrix} 0 & 1 \\ 1 & 0 \end{bmatrix}, \quad U = \begin{bmatrix} 0 & 1 & 0 \\ 1 & 0 & 0 \\ 0 & 0 & 1 \end{bmatrix}, \quad V = \begin{bmatrix} 0 & 0 & 1 \\ 1 & 0 & 0 \\ 0 & 1 & 0 \end{bmatrix}, \quad W = \begin{bmatrix} 0 & 0 & 1 & 0 \\ 1 & 0 & 0 & 0 \\ 0 & 0 & 0 & 1 \\ 0 & 1 & 0 & 0 \end{bmatrix}.$$

(a) Evaluate T^2.
(b) Evaluate U^2, U^3.
(c) Evaluate W^2, W^3, W^4.
(d) Use this exercise to make an inference about powers of permutation matrices.

8.23. Let:

$$A = \begin{bmatrix} 1 & 3 & -2 \\ 2 & -1 & 3 \\ 4 & 2 & -2 \end{bmatrix}, \quad B = \begin{bmatrix} 0 & 3 & 0 \\ 1 & -1 & 2 \\ 5 & 1 & 4 \end{bmatrix}, \quad C = \begin{bmatrix} 1 & 2 & 3 & 4 \\ 4 & 3 & 2 & 1 \\ 2 & 4 & 1 & 3 \\ 3 & 1 & 4 & 2 \end{bmatrix}.$$

Then use the permutation matrices of Exercise 8.22 to obtain each of the following:

(a) UA
(b) AU
(c) $U(AB)$
(d) $(AU)B$
(e) UAV
(f) VAU
(g) WC
(h) CW

8.24. Construct a permutation matrix that puts the first column of matrix C in Exercise 8.23 into the same order as its first row.

8.25. Let a matrix, $I_{n,n} = (\delta_{ij}^*)$ be given by $\delta_{ij} = \begin{cases} 1 & \text{if } n + 1 - i = j \\ 0 & \text{otherwise} \end{cases}$.

(a) Verbally contrast this matrix with I_n.

(b) In Exercise 8.23, construct I^*A and BI^*.

(c) Compute $(I_{3,3}^*)^2$ and $(I_{3,3}^*)^3$.

8.26. A square matrix, A, is said to be *skew symmetric* if $(-A)' = A$.

(a) Show that $A - A'$ is skew symmetric, for the case of $n = 3$.

(b) Prove that a 3×3 matrix can be written as the sum of a symmetric matrix and a skew symmetric matrix.

(c) Prove that the diagonal elements of a skew symmetric matrix are uniformly equal to zero.

8.27. Prove that if $T_{n,n}$ and $U_{n,n}$ are permutation matrices, $(TU)_{n,n}$ also is a permutation matrix.

8.28. Construct A', B', and C' using the matrices of Exercise 8.23.

8.29. Define a matrix in your own area of interest that must always be symmetric. Define a second matrix for which symmetry would represent a special circumstance.

8.30. Prove Theorem 8.3.9:

(a) Part 1

(b) Part 2

(c) Part 4

8.4 Matrices and Linear Equations

In many instances, social analysis requires the manipulation of a set of equations in which real numbers are coefficients to the first power only. Such a set of equations is called a *system of linear equations*. Such a system is indispensable to factor analysis, for example. Suppose that one has a test, such as an intelligence test, that bears on several different factors, say n, such as arithmetic ability and verbal ability. Let s_i represent the standard score of individual i on the test. Suppose that the subject's standard scores on each of the n factors are the known numbers p_{ik}, $k = 1, 2, \cdots, n$. Then the basic assumption of factor analysis is:

$$(8.4.1) \quad s_i = \sum_{k=1}^{n} L_k p_{ik} \ (= L_1 p_{i1} + L_2 p_{i2} + \cdots + L_n p_{in}),$$

where L_k is the factor loading of the test on factor k.

This is called a linear equation (the reasons for the term "linear" will become clear in Section 10.5). The assumption is that individual i has a certain level of facility with

respect to each factor, that these facility levels have nothing
to do with one another and, hence, that these levels are additive. Thus, the test score, s_i, is just the sum of these facili-
ties, each weighted by the extent to which the test taps it,
that is, the term L_k. Suppose that a set of n individuals takes
the test and that each factor score, p_{ik}, is known for each
individual. Then, the only unknowns are the n numbers,
L_k, the factor loading of the test on each factor. This situation yields a set of n linear equations with n unknown terms.

$$
\begin{aligned}
(8.4.2) \quad L_1 p_{11} + L_2 p_{12} + \cdots + L_n p_{1n} &= s_1. \\
L_1 p_{21} + L_2 p_{22} + \cdots + L_n p_{2n} &= s_2.
\end{aligned}
$$

$$
\vdots
$$

$$
L_1 p_{n1} + L_2 p_{n2} + \cdots + L_n p_{nn} = s_n.
$$

The reader should recognize that the definition of matrix
multiplication permits a simple restatement of these equations in matrix form. That is,

(8.4.3) Let $A_{n,n} = [p_{ij}]$, $B_{n,1} = [L_i]$ and $C_{n,1} = [s_i]$, **PROPOSITION**
where p_{ij}, L_i and s_i are as in 8.4.1. Then the n equations of
8.4.2 can be expressed as the matrix product

$$
AB = C.
$$

The proof is immediate by virtue of the definition of matrix
multiplication. One advantage of this expression is that it
sets out the unknowns as a single entity, the column vector,
$B_{n,1}$. Moreover, since both the matrices A and C are known,
it would seem that the vector B is soluble by the identity
$B = C/A$. The rub, of course, is that here vectors were
treated like real numbers under the assumption that there
exists a multiplicative inverse of the matrix A. The location
of such inverses is often a difficult job. Indeed, it is sometimes impossible, for there are cases in which the inverses
do not exist. Before a procedure for locating solutions is
undertaken, the reader must be clear as to what the components of a system of linear equations are and what constitutes a solution.

(8.4.4) Any identity of the form

$$A_{n,n} B_{n,1} = C_{n,1},$$

in which A is a square matrix and B and C are column vectors, is called a system of n *simultaneous linear equations*. A is called the *coefficient matrix* and C, the *right member*. The vector B that makes the equation an identity is called the *solution set* of the system.

Generally B is given variable components. With matrices A and C given, the problem consists of locating a constant vector B such that $AB = C$.

To get a first grasp of the problem, consider the following pair of linear equations with two unknowns:

(8.4.5)

$$
\begin{array}{ll}
\text{I} & x_1 + 2x_2 = 3 \\
\text{II} & 3x_1 + x_2 = -6
\end{array}
\leftrightarrow
\begin{bmatrix} 1 & 2 \\ 3 & 1 \end{bmatrix} \cdot \begin{bmatrix} x_1 \\ x_2 \end{bmatrix} = \begin{bmatrix} 3 \\ -6 \end{bmatrix}.
$$

The reader may have encountered a procedure for evaluating the solution set. First, multiply equation I by 3, giving I $\times$ 3: $3x_1 + 6x_2 = 9$. (What property of real numbers makes this procedure permissible?) Then, subtract equation II from I $\times$ 3, giving $(3x_1 + 6x_2) - (3x_1 + x_2) = 9 - (-6)$, which reduces to $x_2 = 3$. With this information, the value of x_2 can be substituted in either equation to determine that $x_1 = -3$.

Now let us consider a solution in the more general case, in which values of the coefficient matrix and the right member are not specified but are assumed to be known.

(8.4.6)

$$
\begin{array}{ll}
\text{I} & a_{11}x_1 + a_{12}x_2 = y_1 \\
\text{II} & a_{21}x_1 + a_{22}x_2 = y_2
\end{array}
\leftrightarrow
\begin{bmatrix} a_{11} & a_{12} \\ a_{21} & a_{22} \end{bmatrix} \cdot \begin{bmatrix} x_1 \\ x_2 \end{bmatrix} = \begin{bmatrix} y_1 \\ y_2 \end{bmatrix}.
$$

In order to eliminate the unknown x_2, let us multiply I by the coefficient a_{22} and II by a_{12}. The reader should verify that when the second equation is subtracted from the first, that is, (I)a_{22} − (II)a_{12}, the resulting identity is $(a_{11}a_{22} - a_{12}a_{21})x_1 = a_{22}y_1 - a_{12}y_2$. In a similar manner, if I is multiplied by a_{21} and II by a_{11} and if the former is subtracted from the latter, the result is $(a_{11}a_{22} - a_{12}a_{21})x_2 = a_{11}y_2 - a_{21}y_1$. These labors yield the following general solution set:

$$(8.4.7) \qquad \begin{bmatrix} x_1 \\ x_2 \end{bmatrix} = \begin{bmatrix} \dfrac{a_{22}y_1 - a_{12}y_2}{a_{11}a_{22} - a_{12}a_{21}} \\[2em] \dfrac{a_{11}y_2 - a_{21}y_1}{a_{11}a_{22} - a_{12}a_{21}} \end{bmatrix}.$$

Several facts about 8.4.7 must be considered carefully. First, notice that the solutions for x_1 and x_2 have a common denominator. Second—and this is critically important—observe that the solutions are defined *only* if $a_{11}a_{22} \neq a_{12}a_{21}$. Finally, consider the form of the solutions. The process of cross-multiplication and subtraction has produced a certain symmetry. This regularity suggests the following definition:

(8.4.8) If A is any 2 × 2 matrix given by: **Definition**

$$A = \begin{bmatrix} a_{11} & a_{12} \\ a_{21} & a_{22} \end{bmatrix},$$

then the *determinant* of A, noted $|A|$, or $\left| \begin{bmatrix} a_{11} & a_{12} \\ a_{21} & a_{22} \end{bmatrix} \right|$, or

sometimes Det (A), is the real number

$$|A| = a_{11}a_{22} - a_{12}a_{21}.$$

Thus, the determinant is a real number obtained from a two-rowed square matrix by subtracting from the product of the two diagonal elements, $a_{11}a_{22}$, the product of the two off-diagonal elements, $a_{12}a_{21}$.

Look once again at 8.4.7 in light of this definition. First, it should be clear that a solution set is defined if and only if $|A| \neq 0$. Moreover, the numerators of the solutions are themselves determinants of two-rowed matrices. The reader should write these matrices and attempt to determine what they represent before continuing. As a starter, the numerator of x_1 is $\left| \begin{bmatrix} y_1 & a_{12} \\ y_2 & a_{22} \end{bmatrix} \right|.$

If two linear equations are such that the determinant of the coefficient matrix is zero, what must be true of the equations? A careful comparison of the definition of a determinant with that of equality of rational numbers 6.2.1.1 should convince one that $|A| = 0$ implies that the two ordered pairs $\langle a_{11}, a_{12} \rangle$ and $\langle a_{21}, a_{22} \rangle$ are equal in the sense of congruence. This in turn suggests that the two equations are either dependent or inconsistent. For instance, the pair of linear equations:

(8.4.9)
$$x_1 + 3x_2 = 5,$$
$$2x_1 + 6x_2 = 9,$$

is inconsistent. The reader should satisfy himself that the determinant of the coefficient matrix is zero. This reflects the fact that the first pair of coefficients is congruent to the second. Notice that, if the first equation is multiplied by 2, the result is $2x_1 + 6x_2 = 10$, which contradicts the second equation. On the other hand, if the right term of the first equation were 4.5 rather than 5, then when multiplied by two the first equation would be identical to the second and a single solution could not be obtained.

It might appear that the next job would be to investigate properties of determinants and solutions of linear equations. It will be more efficient, however, to put off this task until the procedure has been generalized to systems of more than two linear equations.

Exercises

8.31. In 8.4.7, express the solutions, x_1 and x_2, as ratios of determinants. In each case, how is the numerator related to the denominator?

8.32. In the case of 2×2 matrices, prove the following:

(a) $|A| = |A'|$.

(b) If rows or columns are inverted, the sign of $|A|$ is reversed but the absolute value is unchanged.

(c) If each element of a row or column is multiplied by a constant, k, the determinant is multiplied by k.

8.33. Suppose that a market consists of only two commodities, with prices p_1 and p_2. The demand for either product might be expected to reflect both these prices. Suppose that the demands are given by the following:

$$D_1 = \alpha + a_{11}p_1 + a_{12}p_2.$$
$$D_2 = \beta + a_{21}p_1 + a_{22}p_2.$$

(a) Interpret the numbers α and β. (HINT: Let the commodities be free of price.)

(b) For a fixed demand vector and coefficient matrix, what are the prices of the two commodities?

(c) Let $K = \begin{bmatrix} \alpha \\ \beta \end{bmatrix}$. Then express these linear equations in matrix form.

8.34. In each of the following, evaluate the solution vector if a solution exists. If no solution exists, explain why.

(a) $\begin{bmatrix} -1 & 2 \\ 2 & -1 \end{bmatrix} \begin{bmatrix} x_1 \\ x_2 \end{bmatrix} = \begin{bmatrix} 3 \\ 5 \end{bmatrix}$

(b) $\begin{bmatrix} 2 & 3 \\ 3 & 5 \end{bmatrix} \begin{bmatrix} x_1 \\ x_2 \end{bmatrix} = \begin{bmatrix} 0 \\ 4 \end{bmatrix}$

(c) $\begin{bmatrix} 1 & 2 \\ 3 & -4 \end{bmatrix} \begin{bmatrix} x_1 \\ x_2 \end{bmatrix} = \begin{bmatrix} 0 \\ 0 \end{bmatrix}$

(d) $\begin{bmatrix} 0 & 1 \\ 2 & 3 \end{bmatrix} \begin{bmatrix} x_1 \\ x_2 \end{bmatrix} = \begin{bmatrix} y_1 \\ y_2 \end{bmatrix}$

8.5 The General Case

Suppose that, rather than having a pair of linear equations, we are faced with four, five, or, in general, n such equations. In such a case the developments of the preceding section are clearly inadequate. Since in social analysis one is just as likely to encounter ten or a dozen linear equations as a pair, some new and more general procedures are required. The first step in this direction must consist of broadening the definition of the determinant of a matrix. Unfortunately, this becomes rather a complicated business. It first requires a pair of auxiliary definitions.

(8.5.1) Let A be any n-rowed square matrix. Let B_{ij} be an **Definition** $(n-1)$-rowed square submatrix of A formed by removing row i and column j of A. Then the *minor* of A associated with cell ij is the real number M_{ij}, given by:

$$M_{ij} = |B_{ij}|,$$

where $|B_{ij}|$ is a determinant as defined in 8.5.5 below.

Thus, each cell of a square matrix has associated with it a number called the minor. This number is the determinant of the matrix formed by eliminating the row and column that intersect the given cell. For example,

(8.5.2) Let $A = \begin{bmatrix} 3 & 1 & 2 \\ -1 & 4 & 0 \\ 0 & 3 & 7 \end{bmatrix}.$

To evaluate M_{11}, the matrix B_{11} is constructed by removing the first row and column of A:

$$B_{11} = \begin{bmatrix} 4 & 0 \\ 3 & 7 \end{bmatrix},$$

for which the determinant is $M_{11} = 28$, which the reader should verify. Similarly,

$$B_{22} = \begin{bmatrix} 3 & 2 \\ 0 & 7 \end{bmatrix},$$

for which the determinant is $M_{22} = 21$. The reader should evaluate the remainder of the matrix of minors of A.

The careful reader will recognize that 8.5.1 appears to be an entirely unsatisfactory definition because it falls flat in the case of $n > 3$. For instance,

(8.5.3) Let:

$$B = \begin{bmatrix} 1 & 2 & 0 & 2 \\ 2 & 1 & -1 & 2 \\ 1 & 2 & -1 & 3 \\ 0 & -1 & 1 & 0 \end{bmatrix}, \quad M_{11} = \begin{vmatrix} 1 & -1 & 2 \\ 2 & -1 & 3 \\ -1 & 1 & 0 \end{vmatrix},$$

$$M_{12} = \begin{vmatrix} 2 & -1 & 2 \\ 1 & -1 & 3 \\ 0 & 1 & 0 \end{vmatrix}, \quad M_{14} = \begin{vmatrix} 2 & 1 & -1 \\ 1 & 2 & -1 \\ 0 & -1 & 1 \end{vmatrix}.$$

Each of the minors is the determinant of a 3×3 matrix, which we cannot evaluate—at least, not thus far. With patience and the aid of yet another definition, matters will begin to clear up.

(8.5.4) If A is a square n-rowed matrix, then the *cofactor* of cell ij is the real number, C_{ij}, given by:

Definition

$$C_{ij} = (-1)^{i+j} M_{ij},$$

which is an odd-looking contraption but a useful one, as we shall soon see. Notice that the cofactor of cell ij is either M_{ij} or $-M_{ij}$, depending upon whether $(i + j)$ is an even integer or an odd one. In the example of 8.5.2 the reader should verify that $C_{11} = (-1)^2 M_{11} = 28$ and that $C_{23} = (-1)^5 M_{23} = (-1)(9) = -9$.

Despite these elaborate definitions, we are still helpless in any general sense. With only these definitions, a minor cannot be evaluated for $n > 3$, nor can a determinant be evaluated if $n > 2$. However, one final definition clears up these problems:

(8.5.5) If A is any square n-rowed matrix, then the determinant of A, written $|A|$, is given by:

$$|A| = \begin{cases} a_{11} & \text{if } n = 1 \\ \displaystyle\sum_{j=1}^{n} a_{ij}C_{ij} & \text{if } n > 1, \text{ any } i = 1, 2, \cdots, n. \end{cases}$$

If A contains only a single component, then the component is said to be the determinant of A. If $n > 1$, then the determinant is evaluated by picking a row quite arbitrarily and summing (across columns) the product of cell value and cofactor. This is an entirely different definition in its appearance of something that already has been defined for the case of $n = 2$. The reader certainly should satisfy himself that the two are consistent.

Consider once again the illustration of 8.5.2. To evaluate A in this case, let us operate on row 1 so that:

(8.5.6) If A is as given in 8.5.2, then: **Definition**

$$|A| = 3(-1)^2(28) + 1(-1)^3(-7) + 2(-1)^4(-3),$$
$$= \quad 84 \quad + \quad 7 \quad - \quad 6 \quad = 85.$$

This evaluation should be repeated, using, for instance, the second row, in order to see that the determinant is invariant in choice of row. If $i = 2$ had been selected, then we would have $|A| = -1(-1)^3(1) + 4(-1)^4(21) + 0 = 85$. The curious reader certainly will try to find out whether the determinant can be evaluated by substituting column operations for row operations. That is, is the same value given for $|A|$ in 8.5.5 if the following is substituted: $|A| = \displaystyle\sum_{i=1}^{n} a_{ij}C_{ij}$ for an arbitrarily selected column, j? (HINT: The answer is yes, but why?)

To see how this latest definition yields a solution in the case of $n > 3$, look once again at 8.5.3. There we found that minors M_{ij} turned out to be 3×3 matrices. With definition 8.5.5 at hand, each of these minors and cofactors can now be evaluated.

(8.5.7) If B is as given in 8.5.3, then:

M_{11} (by row 3) $= -1(-1)^4(-1) + 1(-1)^5(-1) + 0 = 2.$
M_{12} (by row 3) $= 0 + 1(-1)^5(4) + 0 = -4.$
M_{14} (by row 3) $= 0 + (-1)(-1)^5(-1) + 1(-1)^6(3) = 2.$

With this information and with definition 8.5.5 reapplied, the determinant of B in 8.5.3 is given by:

(8.5.8) If the matrix B is as given in 8.5.3, then:

$$|B| = 1(-1)^2(2) + 2(-1)^3(-4) + 0 + 2(-1)^5(2) = 6.$$

Notice that M_{13} was not evaluated in anticipation of the fact that it would not be used. (Why?)

Before the determinant is used to solve a system of linear equations, something of its characteristics should be known. The following theorem, whose proofs are provided in Beaumont and Ball, *Modern Algebra* [1], Section 19, provides some modern important information about this real number that characterizes a matrix:

(8.5.9) (*On Properties of Determinants*). If A and B are   **THEOREM**
any square n-rowed matrices with $A = [a_{ij}]$, $B = [b_{ij}]$,

(1) $|AB| = |BA| = |A|\,|B|.$
(2) $|A| = |A'|.$
(3) Let $p \neq q$. Then for all $i \neq p, q$, and all j, if $b_{ij} = a_{ij}$ and if $b_{pj} = a_{qj}$, then:

$$|B| = -|A|.$$

(4) If $p \neq q$ and for all $j \neq p, q$, $b_{ij} = a_{ij}$ and if $b_{ip} = a_{iq}$, $b_{iq} = a_{ip}$, then:

$$|B| = -|A|.$$

(5) $|A| = 0 \leftrightarrow$ for all j, some i, k such that $i \neq k$, and α any real number, $a_{ij} = \alpha a_{kj}$. If $|A| = 0$, A is called *singular*; otherwise, it is called *nonsingular*.

Thus, (1) the determinant of a product of matrices is the product of their determinants, regardless of the order of multiplication; (2) the determinant of the transpose of a matrix is identical to the determinant of the matrix; (3) if any two rows or (4) columns of a matrix are inverted, the determinant of the resultant matrix is the negative of that of the original; (5) the necessary and sufficient (that is, the *only*) condition of $|A| = 0$ is that the elements of some row must be similarly proportional to the elements of another row. Thus, for example, if the *i*th row of A is $\langle 1, 3, 4 \rangle$, this theorem tells us that if any other row of A is a scalar of this vector, for instance $\langle 0, 0, 0 \rangle$, $\langle 1, 3, 4 \rangle$, $\langle 1.5, 4.5, 6.0 \rangle$ and so on, then $|A| = 0$. The conditions of 8.5.9.5 are sometimes called the *conditions of linear dependence*.

With this, after so many elaborate new definitions, a determinant finally has been evaluated in the case of $n > 3$. The joy occasioned by this great leap forward should not cause the reader to forget our main objective: the solution of n linear equations with n unknown terms. The following theorem, which will not be proved here (see Beaumont and Ball [1], Theorem 11.6), fills the final gap:

(8.5.10) If $AX = C$ is a system of linear equations such that $|A| \neq 0$, then the typical member of the solution set X, say x_i, is given by: **THEOREM**

$$x_i = |K_i|/|A|,$$

where the matrix K_i is the matrix A with column i replaced by the vector C.

Thus, a solution element, x_i, is the ratio of two determinants, the denominator being the determinant of A, the coefficient matrix, and the numerator being the determinant of K_i, which looks exactly like A except for column i.

With a last look at 8.5.2, let us consider a system of equations given by:

$$(8.5.11) \quad \begin{bmatrix} 3 & 1 & 2 \\ -1 & 4 & 0 \\ 0 & 3 & 7 \end{bmatrix} \begin{bmatrix} x_1 \\ x_2 \\ x_3 \end{bmatrix} = \begin{bmatrix} 2 \\ 1 \\ 3 \end{bmatrix},$$

in which A, the coefficient matrix, is as in 8.5.2. It was seen in 8.5.6 that $|A| = 85$. All that remains, then, is to evaluate K_i and $|K_i|$ in order to locate a solution set for 8.5.11. The reader should satisfy himself that:

(8.5.12)

$$K_1 = \begin{bmatrix} 2 & 1 & 2 \\ 1 & 4 & 0 \\ 3 & 3 & 7 \end{bmatrix}, \ K_2 = \begin{bmatrix} 3 & 2 & 2 \\ -1 & 1 & 0 \\ 0 & 3 & 7 \end{bmatrix}, \ K_3 = \begin{bmatrix} 3 & 1 & 2 \\ -1 & 4 & 1 \\ 0 & 3 & 3 \end{bmatrix},$$

so that $|K_1| = 31$, $|K_2| = 29$, $|K_3| = 24$. This gives the final solution of 8.5.11:

$$(8.5.13) \qquad X = \begin{bmatrix} \dfrac{31}{85} \\[2mm] \dfrac{29}{85} \\[2mm] \dfrac{24}{85} \end{bmatrix} = \begin{bmatrix} .364 \\[2mm] .340 \\[2mm] .283 \end{bmatrix},$$

which the reader should certainly check by doing the appropriate matrix multiplication in 8.5.11.

It must be clear that, even with these rudiments of matrix algebra, the solution of simultaneous equations often remains an awkward business. Solutions of even six or seven simultaneous equations involves a monumental amount of computing labor. Fortunately, electronic computers can eliminate much of this tedium. But a computer is no more capable of doing matrix algebra than is its instructor, and it can never be made to "understand" the basic language of matrices as the reader now should.

Exercises

8.35. Write out the general form of solutions for three linear equations.

8.36. Prove each proposition of exercise 8.32 in the case of $n = 3$.

8.37. Prove that Definition 8.4.8 is consistent with 8.5.5.

8.38. Determine the solution set, if it exists, for each of the following:

(a) $\begin{bmatrix} -1 & -2 & 1 \\ 0 & 1 & 0 \\ 2 & 1 & 1 \end{bmatrix} \cdot \begin{bmatrix} x_1 \\ x_2 \\ x_3 \end{bmatrix} = \begin{bmatrix} 1 \\ 3 \\ 5 \end{bmatrix}$.

(b) $\begin{bmatrix} 1 & 2 & 3 \\ 3 & 6 & 9 \\ 2 & 4 & 1 \end{bmatrix} \cdot \begin{bmatrix} x_1 \\ x_2 \\ x_3 \end{bmatrix} = \begin{bmatrix} 2 \\ 4 \\ -1 \end{bmatrix}$.

(c) $\begin{bmatrix} 1 & 2 & 3 \\ 2 & 1 & 3 \\ 3 & 2 & 1 \end{bmatrix} \cdot \begin{bmatrix} x \\ x \\ x \end{bmatrix} = \begin{bmatrix} 2 \\ 0 \\ -1 \end{bmatrix}$.

(d) $\begin{bmatrix} 0 & 1 & 0 \\ -1 & 1 & 1 \\ 2 & 3 & 1 \end{bmatrix} \cdot \begin{bmatrix} x_1 \\ x_2 \\ x_3 \end{bmatrix} = \begin{bmatrix} 1 \\ 0 \\ 0 \end{bmatrix}$.

(e) $\begin{bmatrix} 0 & 1 & 0 \\ -1 & 1 & 1 \\ 2 & 3 & 1 \end{bmatrix} \cdot \begin{bmatrix} x_1 \\ x_2 \\ x_3 \end{bmatrix} = \begin{bmatrix} 0 \\ 0 \\ 0 \end{bmatrix}.$

(f) $\begin{bmatrix} 1 & 2 & 0 \\ 2 & 3 & 2 \\ 3 & 4 & 2 \end{bmatrix} \cdot \begin{bmatrix} x_1 \\ x_2 \\ x_3 \end{bmatrix} = \begin{bmatrix} 2 \\ 3 \\ 2 \end{bmatrix}.$

8.39. In Exercise 8.38, call the coefficient matrix of part (a) A and that of part (c) B. Evaluate:

(a) AB
(b) BA
(c) $|AB|$
(d) $|BA|$
(e) $|A|$

8.40. Let $A^* = \begin{bmatrix} -1 & 4 & 0 \\ 3 & 1 & 2 \\ 0 & 3 & 7 \end{bmatrix}$. Evaluate $|A^*|$ and compare it with 8.5.10 and 8.5.9.3.

8.41. Give an interpretation of 8.5.9.5 in relation to 8.5.9.

8.6 The Inverse of a Matrix

In the preceding section, matrix algebra was used to locate the solution of the equation $AX = C$. This is a new and exciting result only in that A, X, and C are matrices rather than mere numbers. If this fact were overlooked, one might attempt to check his results by noting that $AX = C \leftrightarrow X = A^{-1}C$, where $A^{-1}C$ could just as readily be written as C/A. However, the fact that we are dealing with sometimes slippery matrices should provide sufficient warning that the thing A^{-1} has not been defined thus far for A, a matrix. Could such an entity as A^{-1} be useful, and what properties should it possess? This paragraph provides its own answer to any thoughtful reader.

For any nonzero real number, a, a^{-1} is characterized by the fact that $a \cdot a^{-1} = 1$. This multiplicative inverse is useful in exploiting the cancellation rule of multiplication. For instance, if one must locate a number x such that $ax = c$, the obvious step consists of dividing c by a—that is, of locating the product $a^{-1}c$. This represents multiplying both sides of the equation as follows:

(8.6.1) $ax = c$ $\rightarrow$,

$a^{-1}ax = a^{-1}c \rightarrow$,

$x = a^{-1}c.$ $(a^{-1}a = 1$ and $1x = x)$

The real number a^{-1} is extremely important, then, because $(a^{-1}a)x = 1x$ and because of the identity property of 1 under multiplication.

All this should suggest that, for a matrix A, A^{-1} should be such that the product $A^{-1}A$ gives a multiplicative identity. But in matrix algebra, we know that this identity element is the square matrix I. This suggests the following:

(8.6.2) If A is any square matrix of size $n \times n$, then if there exists a matrix X of size $n \times n$, such that: **Definition**

$$AX = XA = I,$$

then X is called the inverse of A and is written A^{-1}.

The definition, of course, does not assure us that A^{-1} necessarily or ever exists, but it should be enough to spur one's curiosity as to what it looks like when, if ever, it is defined. If not, the following properties of inverses may further stimulate curiosity about this new matrix.

(8.6.3) If A^{-1} is defined, then: **THEOREM**

(1) $(A^{-1})^{-1} = A$.
(2) $(AB)^{-1} = B^{-1}A^{-1}$.
(3) $(A')^{-1} = (A^{-1})'$.

Let A^{-1} be defined.   *Proof (1)*

(1) $A^{-1}(A^{-1})^{-1} = I$.   (8.6.2)
(2) $A[A^{-1}(A^{-1})^{-1}] = AI = A$. (Step 1 and 8.2.5.4)
(3) $(AA^{-1})(A^{-1})^{-1} = A$.   (Step 2 and 8.2.5.2)
(4) $I(A^{-1})^{-1} = (A^{-1})^{-1} = A$. (Step 3, 8.6.2, and 8.2.5.4)

The proofs of parts 2 and 3 are left as exercises. Clearly, A^{-1} is a useful tool, theoretically; but the same could be said of leprechauns or the fountain of youth, neither of which has been shown to exist. In the case of matrix inverses, however, we can determine that A^{-1} is at least a sometimes thing. To do this, the following lemma, proven in Beaumont and Ball [1], Section 11.4, is needed:

(8.6.4) If A is any square n-rowed matrix, then:

$$AC'_A = C'_A A = |A|I,$$

where C'_A is the transpose of the matrix of cofactors, C_{ij}, defined in 8.5.4.

Thus, for the matrix of A of 8.5.2, we have:

(8.6.5) $C_A = \begin{bmatrix} 28 & 7 & -3 \\ -1 & 21 & -9 \\ -8 & -2 & 13 \end{bmatrix}$.

By carrying through the multiplications, the reader should check the following assertion and compare it carefully with 8.6.4.

(8.6.6)

$$\begin{bmatrix} 3 & 1 & 2 \\ -1 & 4 & 0 \\ 0 & 3 & 7 \end{bmatrix} \begin{bmatrix} 28 & -1 & -8 \\ 7 & 21 & -2 \\ -3 & -9 & 13 \end{bmatrix} = \begin{bmatrix} 85 & 0 & 0 \\ 0 & 85 & 0 \\ 0 & 0 & 85 \end{bmatrix}.$$

With this, it follows that:

(8.6.7) If A is a nonsingular (if $|A| \neq 0$) square n-rowed matrix, then A^{-1} is a unique n-rowed matrix given by:

$$A^{-1} = |A|^{-1}C'_A,$$

where C'_A is as in 8.6.4.

Let $|A| \neq 0$ and $X = |A|^{-1}C'_A$:

(1) $AX = A|A|^{-1}C'_A$,
(2) $= |A|^{-1}AC'_A$,   (8.2.9.2, since $|A|^{-1}$ is a scalar)
(3) $= |A|^{-1}|A|I$,   (8.6.4)
(4) $= 1I = I$.

The proof for XA is similar, so that X is an inverse of A according to 8.6.2. To show uniqueness, suppose that A has a second inverse, Y. Then:

(5) $Y = IY = (XA)Y$,   (Since X is an inverse)
(6) $= X(AY)$,   (8.2.5.2)
(7) $= XI = X$,   (Hypothesis about Y and 8.2.5.4)

so that $X = A^{-1}$ is unique.

At long last, we are in a position to check the solution of the linear equations in 8.5.13. In the equation $AX = C$, where A and C were given by 8.5.11, we evaluated X by using Theorem 8.5.9. If these results were correct, they should check against the identity $X = A^{-1}C$. To make this check, we must locate A^{-1}, which we now know to be $|A|^{-1}C'_A$. It was found that $|A| = 85$ and C'_A is just the transpose of 8.6.5, all of which gives:

(8.6.8)

$$A^{-1} = |A|^{-1}C'_A,$$

$$= \frac{1}{85}\begin{bmatrix} 28 & -1 & -8 \\ 7 & 21 & -2 \\ -3 & -9 & 13 \end{bmatrix}, = \begin{bmatrix} .329 & -.012 & -.094 \\ .082 & .247 & -.024 \\ -.035 & -.106 & .153 \end{bmatrix}.$$

The final step, then, consists of evaluating $A^{-1}C$:

(8.6.9)

$$A^{-1}C = \begin{bmatrix} .329 & -.012 & -.094 \\ .082 & .247 & -.024 \\ -.035 & -.106 & .153 \end{bmatrix}\begin{bmatrix} 2 \\ 1 \\ 3 \end{bmatrix}, = \begin{bmatrix} .364 \\ .340 \\ .283 \end{bmatrix} = X.$$

When this result is checked against that of 8.5.13, we see that a sigh of relief is in order. Not only do we now know when a matrix has an inverse (when it is nonsingular), but we also know how to evaluate it.

Exercises

8.42. Verify your solution in each system of Exercises 8.38 by computing A^{-1} in those cases where it is defined.

8.43. Prove 8.6.3.2. (HINT: Premultiply $(B^{-1}A^{-1})$ by a strategic matrix product.)

8.44. Prove $I^{-1} = I$.

8.45. Assume that $C'_{A'} = C_A$ and prove 8.3.3.3.

Selected References

1. Beaumont, Ross A., and Ball, Richard W. *Introduction to Modern Algebra and Matrix Theory.* New York: Rinehart and Co., Inc., 1954. Chapter 1.
2. Birkhoff, Garrett, and Mac Lane, Saunders. *A Survey of Modern Algebra* (Revised Edition). New York: The Macmillan Company, 1953. Chapters 7 and 8.
3. Halmos, P. R. *Finite Dimensional Vector Spaces.* Princeton, New Jersey: Princeton University Press, 1942.

4. Horst, Paul. *Matrix Algebra for Social Scientists*. New York: Holt, Rinehart and Winston, Inc., 1963.

5. Kemeny, J. G., Mirkil, H., Snell, J. L., and Thompson, G. L. *Finite Mathematical Structures*. Englewood Cliffs, New Jersey: Prentice-Hall, Inc., 1959. Chapter 4.

6. MacDuffee, C. C. *The Theory of Matrices* (Second Edition). New York: Chelsea Publishing Co., 1946.

FUNCTIONS
ON
NUMBERS

III

Functions on Integers

Two critically important mathematical ideas, that of number and that of function, have been explored already. In this chapter these two ideas will be fused, and we shall begin to investigate mechanisms, called *real* (or real-valued) *functions*, that map numbers into new numbers. A function whose domain and range consist of sets of numbers is a highly powerful and sophisticated entity. Its power is invested by the properties of the sets themselves. For example, because of the order property of numbers (see Section 5.4), it is natural to speak of numerical functions as becoming "large" or "small," even though this is not at all sensible in referring to functions on unordered sets, such as the function of marriage on sets of people. In this sense the ensuing investigation of real functions will rely heavily on the theory developed in the preceding sections. The reader should be aware of this reliance constantly and, upon encountering a new property of real functions, should ask himself whether the property might be expected to hold for nonnumeric functions as well.

As we have seen, numbers fall into several different sets, such as positive integers, integers, and rationals. Thus, a rather complicated system for classifying real functions could be developed. For instance, functions on irrationals to positive integers could be distinguished from those on rationals to integers. Our purpose will be satisfied, however, by a much more elementary classification. In fact, we need be concerned with just two broad classes of numerical functions, distinguished from one another by their domains. The first of these classes consists of functions whose domains include only the positive integers. Functions of this sort are called *sequences*. The second class consists of functions whose domains contain complete intervals of real numbers. This class will be considered in Chapter 10.

9

9.1 Sequences

As it is used in daily language, the term sequence sometimes means a set of events that occur in succession. In other contexts, it refers to the order rather than to the events themselves. Both these senses are denoted by the term as it is used in mathematics:

Definition

(9.1.1) A sequence is any function whose domain is a subset of the positive integers.

Thus, a sequence is a relation that is ordered (well-ordered, in fact) by virtue of the order properties of its domain. In nearly every case the domain of a sequence contains the initial set of positive integers, 1, 2, 3, $\cdots$, but this is not a necessary condition of the definition. It will be convenient at times to add zero to the domain set.

If the primitive notion of an ordered $n$tuple is recalled from Section 3.3, it should be clear that such an ordered set is itself a sequence. The ordered $n$tuple $\langle 1, 2, 3, \cdots, n \rangle$, for instance, can be rewritten as the function $\{\langle 1, 1 \rangle, \langle 2, 2 \rangle, \langle 3, 3 \rangle, \cdots, \langle n, n \rangle\}$, in which the first member of each ordered pair gives the position of the second element in the ordered set. Similarly, the $n$tuple $\langle 1, \frac{1}{2}, \frac{1}{3}, \cdots, 1/n \rangle$ can be expressed as the function $\{\langle 1, 1 \rangle, \langle 2, \frac{1}{2} \rangle, \langle 3, \frac{1}{3} \rangle, \langle n, 1/n \rangle\}$. In this sense, an $n$tuple is an implicitly expressed function and is usually called a *finite* sequence because, no matter how large n is, the domain is finite. Of course, a sequence need not be finite at all by Definition 9.1.1. For example, the function $\{\langle 1, 1 \rangle, \langle 2, \frac{1}{2} \rangle, \langle 3, \frac{1}{3} \rangle, \cdots\}$ contains no stopping point, no upper domain value, n. Thus, according to 6.6.3, its domain is countably infinite. Conventionally, such a function is itself called *countable* or countably infinite.

Because of the ordered domain of a sequence, it is often unnecessary to write out the entire set of ordered pairs that it defines. Instead, a *general term* that gives the range value for any element in the domain can be represented. Rather than writing out a function such as $f(k) = \{\langle 1, 2 \rangle, \langle 2, 4 \rangle, \langle 3, 6 \rangle, \cdots\}$, it is much simpler to write $f(k) = \{\langle k, 2k \rangle : k \in I^+\}$ or the yet more abbreviated form $f(k) = 2k$, which is read "the range-correspondent of any element, k, in the domain of the sequence, f, is the element $2k$." Often the letter s is reserved for a function that is a sequence. That is,

(9.1.2) A function that is a sequence (whose domain consists of a subset of the positive integers) is noted s. The functional correspondent of any positive integer k is noted s_k.

Thus, in the above sequence we would write $s_k = 2k$. Here are several other sequences, for which the reader should supply general terms:

(9.1.3)

(1) $1, 2, 3, \cdots$

(2) $1, \dfrac{1}{2^2}, \dfrac{1}{3^2}, \cdots$

(3) $(1 + 1)^2, (1 + 2)^2, (1 + 3)^2, \cdots$

(4) $1, \dfrac{1}{2^2}, \dfrac{1}{2^3}, \dfrac{1}{2^4}, \cdots$

(5) $1/(1)(2), 1/(2)(3), 1/(3)(4), \cdots$

(6) $-1, 1, -1, 1, \cdots$

(7) $1, -1, 1, -1, \cdots$

For example, the general term of 9.1.3.6 is $s_k = (-1)^k$.

The general terms of a wide variety of sequences are so similar that they can be analyzed together as a *class of progressions*:

(9.1.4) Any sequence for which the kth term is given by some combination of the first term, s_1, a number, c, in which s_1 and c are called constants or *parameters* and the value of k is called the variable term, is called a *progression*. In particular,

(1) Any sequence of the form

$$s_k = s_1 + (k - 1)c$$

is called an *arithmetic* progression.

(2) Any sequence of the form

$$s_k = s_1 c^{(k-1)}$$

is called a *geometric* progression.

(3) If s is any arithmetic progression with term s_k, subject to $s_k \neq 0$, then a sequence with general term $\dfrac{1}{s_k}$ is called a *harmonic* progression.

Before continuing, the reader would do well to return to the above illustrative sequences in an effort to determine what examples of these three types of progressions they contain. For example, 9.1.3.4 is a geometric sequence with $s_1 = 1$ and $c = \frac{1}{2}$. In order to get some idea of the manner in which progressions behave, let us set $s_1 = 3$, $c = 2$ and examine the resulting progressions. The reader should verify that the arithmetic progression with these constants is just the infinite sequence $\langle 3, 5, 7, 9, 11, \cdots \rangle$, and that the harmonic progression thus is $\langle \frac{1}{3}, \frac{1}{5}, \frac{1}{7}, \frac{1}{9}, \cdots \rangle$. Note that the former *builds up* in a regular fashion and really never stops building, while the latter *decreases* in a fairly rapid fashion, moving closer and closer to zero. Contrast these with the geometric progression with the same parameters $\langle 3, 6, 12, 24, 48, \cdots \rangle$, and note especially that the acceleration of this sequence is considerably greater than is the case with the arithmetic progression. The increasing gap between range values of the arithmetic and geometric progressions could itself be accelerated by increasing the value of the constant, c. The reader should repeat this investigation, using other values of s_1 and c. In particular, he should discover what happens to each type of progression as c becomes smaller than 1 and then smaller than 0.

Many of the regular patterns of man's life assume the form of progressions. One of the more painful of these patterns is the professional lender's practice of charging compound interest rates at regular intervals on any sum that is lent. Suppose that some amount, say s_1, is borrowed at time t_1 with interest rate i, $0 < i < 1$. Then, after the first interval the amount owed, say s_2, is the principal, s_1, plus a fraction, $s_1 i$, which represents the interest. After another interval, at time t_3, an amount s_3 is owed that consists of the amount s_2 plus interest on it. That is, $s_3 = s_2 + s_2 i$. It is convenient to let $c = (i + 1)$, so that:

(9.1.5) $\quad s_2 = s_1 + (s_1)i = cs_1.$

$\qquad\quad s_3 = s_2 + (s_2)i = cs_2 = c^2 s_1.$

$\qquad\quad s_4 = s_3 + (s_3)i = cs_3 = c^3 s_1.$

By continuing this process one should be able to convince himself that:

(9.1.6) The principal and compound interest on an **PROPOSITION**
amount, s_1, at time t_k (after $k - 1$ intervals) is

$$s_k = s_1 c^{k-1},$$

where c is one plus the interest rate.

This assertion could, of course, be proven more formally
than was done in 9.1.5 by appealing to the principle of finite
induction (see Section 5.5).

It has been observed that human populations appear to
increase in roughly geometric progressions, for short-run pe-
riods of time at least. The gap between the production of
humans and the production of goods with which to feed and
clothe them is at the heart of the notion of "over-popula-
tion." A recognition of the accelerating difference between
arithmetic and geometric sequences with similar constants
gave rise to the gloomy Malthusian view of the future:
"Means of subsistence increase arithmetically while population increases geometrically."

Exercises

9.1. Write the first five terms of the following progressions:

(a) $s_k = 4 + (k - 1)2$.
(b) $s_k = 4 + (k - 1)(-2)$.
(c) $s_k = 4 + (k - 1)0$.
(d) $s_k = (4)(2^{k-1})$.
(e) $s_k = (4)(-2^{k-1})$.
(f) $s_k = (4)(0^{k-1})$. (Careful!)

9.2. Interpret k, s_1, and c if:

(a) the number of votes cast for President of the United States is given by $s_1 + (k - 1)c$.
(b) the number of votes cast for the President of the Lapin Republic is given by
$s_k = s_1 c^{(k-1)}$.
(c) the number of infant deaths per thousand live births in Cuba from 1900 to 1909
is given by $1/s_k$, where $k = 1, 2, \cdots, 10$ and $s_k = s_1 + (k - 1)c$.
(d) the number of infant deaths per thousand live births in the United States from
1900 to 1909 is given by $1/s_k$, where $k = 1, 2, \cdots, 10$, and $s_k = s_1 c^{(k-1)}$.

9.3. In Exercise 9.2,

(a) contrast the growth in number of voters in the United States and the Lapin Republic from their respective initial Presidential elections.
(b) contrast the hypothetical medical situation in the United States and Cuba, 1900–
1909.

9.4. Suppose that a candidate for office wins five million votes of the 22 million cast in his first campaign and wins seven million of 23 million votes cast on his second trial. "Prove" that the candidate will be elected on his fifth trial for office. (HINT: Set his proportion of the vote in the form of a ratio of two progressions, equal to $\frac{1}{2}$.)

9.5. By induction, prove 9.1.6. (HINT: Note that $s_k = s_{k-1} + is_{k-1}$, where i is the interest rate.)

9.2 Partial Sums

A new and important class of sequences can be constructed from progressions as follows: Let the kth term of a sequence consist of the sum of the first k terms of any progression. Such a sequence is sensibly enough named a sequence of partial sums.

(9.2.1) If s is any progression with kth term s_k, then the related *sequence of partial sums* is the sequence, **S**, with nth term:

Definition

$$\mathbf{S}_n = \sum_{k=1}^{n} s_k.$$

For convenience, **S** will sometimes be referred to as a partial sum, but it must be remembered that $\mathbf{S}_n$, the nth term of **S**, is the partial sum, that **S** itself is a sequence of partial sums.

Consider once again the illustrative sequences of 9.1.3. The general term of 9.1.3.3 is $s_k = (1 + k)^2$, and the nth term of the sequence of partial sums generated by this progression is $\mathbf{S}_n = \sum_{k=1}^{n} (1 + k)^2$. For example, $\mathbf{S}_3 = (1 + 1)^2 + (1 + 2)^2 + (1 + 3)^2 = 29$.

At least one important partial sum was encountered in Chapter 5 (see 5.5.4) in connection with the principle of finite induction. It was discovered there that the simple arithmetic progression, $s_k = k$, converts into a rather elegant partial sum. If $\mathbf{S}_n = \sum_{k=1}^{n} k (= 1 + 2 + 3 + \cdots + n)$, then this partial sum was seen to reduce to $\mathbf{S}_n = \dfrac{n(n + 1)}{2}$.

When this result came to light, there was no particular reason to attempt to generalize it. Now, however, there is a good reason to attempt such a generalization. The sum of the first n integers is just one of a large class of partial sums of arithmetic progressions. If a labor-saving result can be found for one member of this class, then perhaps it might work for all of them. It happens that the job is simplicity itself, requiring only a bit of juggling of summational operators.

(9.2.2) If $S_n = \sum_{k=1}^{n} [s_1 + (k - 1)c]$, that is, if S_n is the   **THEOREM**

nth partial sum of any arithmetic progression, then:

$$S_n = ns_1 + \frac{n(n - 1)c}{2}.$$

Let $S_n = \sum_{k=1}^{n} [s_1 + (k - 1)c]$.   *Proof*

(1) $S_n = \sum_{k=1}^{n} s_1 + \sum_{k=1}^{n} ck - \sum_{k=1}^{n} c,$ (by 7.1.2.1)

(2) $= ns_1 + c \sum_{k=1}^{n} k - nc,$ (by 7.1.2, parts 2 and 3)

(3) $= ns_1 + c \left(\frac{n[n + 1]}{2} \right) - nc,$ $\left(\text{by } 5.5.4 \right.$

$$\sum_{k=1}^{n} k = \frac{n(n + 1)}{2} \bigg)$$

(4) $= ns_1 + \frac{n(n - 1)c}{2}.$ (by factoring c and constructing a common denominator in Step 3)

As an illustration of the way in which this theorem works, consider the phenomenon of acquaintance formation among individuals in a finite set of strangers. Such a set might be represented by a group of new inductees at a military training center or by a freshman class of a university. The problem consists of assessing the number of acquaintanceships that an individual acquires as a function of intervals of time, such as weeks or semesters. It is reasonable to hypothesize that acquaintanceships increase as a progression through time, since the set of acquaintances at time t can serve as sources of introduction to new acquaintances at time $(t + 1)$. Suppose that an individual's acquaintance pattern is an arithmetic progression with $s_1 = 10$ and growth parameter $c = 13$. The subject's set of acquaintances at the end of the first period then consists of just 10 people. Thanks, however, to the growth parameter and the eight-semester period of exposure, it follows that, during the final semester, the subject acquired 101 new acquaintances, since $s_8 = 10 + (7)(13)$ according to 9.1.4.1. Theorem 9.2.2 tells us that the *total* set of acquaintances acquired by the subject during an eight-semester period is $S_8 (= s_1 + s_2 + \cdots + s_8) = 8(10) + (8)(7)(13)/2 = 444$.

Of course, Theorem 9.2.2 serves no purpose at all in the case of a partial sum generated by a *geometric* progression. Once again, however, the location of a general formula is a simple matter:

(9.2.3) If $S_n = \sum\limits_{k=1}^{n} [s_1 c^{(k-1)}]$, that is, if S_n is the partial sum of any geometric progression, then:

THEOREM

$$S_n = \begin{cases} \dfrac{s_1(c^n - 1)}{c - 1} & \text{if } c \neq 1 \\ ns_1 & \text{if } c = 1 \end{cases}.$$

Let $S_n = \sum\limits_{k=1}^{n} [s_1 c^{(k-1)}]$. If $c = 1$ then $S_n = \sum\limits_{k=1}^{n} s_1$, since

Proof
(*By induction*)

$1_n = 1$ and $\sum\limits_{k=1}^{n} s_1 = ns_1$ by 7.1.2.2. Let $c \neq 1$.

(1) If $n = 1$,

$$\sum\limits_{k=1}^{n} [s_1 c^{k-1}] = s_1 = \frac{s_1(c^n - 1)}{c - 1}.$$

$\left(\text{Since} \quad \frac{(c^1 - 1)}{c - 1} = 1 \right)$

(2) Assume $S_{n-1} = \dfrac{s_1(c^{n-1} - 1)}{c - 1}$.

(Inductive
assumption)

(3) $S_n = S_{n-1} + s_1 c^{(n-1)}$,   (Hypothesis,

$$s_n = s_1 c^{(n-1)})$$

(4) $= \dfrac{s_1(c^{n-1} - 1) + s_1 c^{(n-1)}(c - 1)}{c - 1}$,   (Steps 2 and 3 and constructing a common denominator)

(5) $= \dfrac{s_1 c^{n-1} - s_1 + s_1 c^n - s_1 c^{(n-1)}}{c - 1}$,   (M7 and 7.2.2,

$$s_1 c^{(n-1)} c = s_1 c^n)$$

(6) $= \dfrac{s_1(c^n - 1)}{c - 1}$.   (Cancelling and factoring in Step 5)

Suppose that a second subject had a growth parameter, c, smaller than that of the first, say $c = 3$, and the same number of first-semester acquaintances, $s_1 = 10$. But suppose that the pattern of the second followed a geometric rather than an arithmetic progression during the eight semesters of residence. Then, as the reader should verify, subject number two should have acquired an astounding total number of acquaintances, since $S_8 = \dfrac{10(3^8 - 1)}{3 - 1} = 32{,}800$.

Exercises

9.6. Compute each partial sum:

(a) S_5 if $s_k = 3 - .1(k - 1)$.
(b) S_5 if $s_k = (3)(.1^{k-1})$.
(c) S_5 if $s_k = (-1)^k$.
(d) S_5 if $s_k = (-1)^{k+1}$.
(e) S_5 if $s_k = (-1)^k + (-1)^{k+1}$.
(f) S_5 if $s_k = [(-1)^k][(-1)^{k+1}]$.

9.7. Consider two production units, say A and B, which could be anything so diverse as cows producing milk, discussional groups talking, a cohort of mothers bearing children, firms producing goods, or nations stockpiling thermonuclear weapons. Suppose that the production of the two units during the kth interval are:

$$S_{k_A} = 100 + 10(k - 1).$$
$$S_{k_B} = 10(2^{k-1}).$$

(a) Compare production during the first interval; the fifth; the tenth.
(b) Construct an equation that compares annual production of the two units.
(c) Compare gross production during the first five intervals; the first ten.
(d) Construct an equation that compares gross production of A and B over an n-interval period.

9.8. The proofs of Theorems 9.2.2 and 9.2.3 appear to be quite different. Carefully contrast the two proofs and show that the appearance is deceiving. (HINT: How was Theorem 7.1.2 proved?)

9.3 Equivalence Classes and Partitions

A particularly important function whose domain and, in this case, whose range are subsets of the nonnegative integers, permits us to count things in a more elaborate way than one might have imagined possible. In order to develop what is called the *factorial function* and to explore it fully, the remainder of this chapter will be given over to a discussion of counting the number of elements in sets. Although this may sound like a particularly juiceless and simpleminded subject, it will become apparent that the task of counting elements is anything but a routine one. This is the case, at least, when sets are divided into a class of subsets. Let us deal first with the process of carving up sets under the headings of equivalence classes and partitions.

A primordial order of business in scientific research consists of dividing a set of elements into subsets in which each element is like every other element in the subset with respect to some property. For instance, in any given human population one can place each element in exactly one of two classes with respect to the "sex" variable. In one subset, labeled females, are to be found elements of almost infinite variation. There are tall ones, short ones, women of overwhelming beauty, and others. In partitioning by sex, however, these variations are disregarded and only similarities in certain relevant characteristics are considered. The elements of such a set clearly are not identical in the sense that each is the *same thing* as the next. We say instead that they are *equivalent* in terms of the properties under consideration. This process of partitioning can be formalized by noting that in defining a set of equivalent elements we have, in fact, defined a particular sort of relation. Consider the relation "is the same as" on the set of all elements in such a class. Call this relation E. Notice that for every element, a, in the set, aEa, that is, each element "is the same as" itself. Moreover, for every pair of elements, a and b, in the set, both aEb and bEa. Finally, it should be clear that if aEb and bEc then it must be true that aEc. More formally, we have the following:

(9.3.1) Any relation that is reflexive, symmetric, and transitive in a set A is called an *equivalence relation* in A. **Definition**

It should be clear that the relations of equality and congruence are equivalence relations and that the strict inequality is an example of a relation that is not an equivalence relation. It was suggested in Section 5.1 that an equivalence relation serves to carve a set into a class of equivalent subsets. This class of subsets is called a partition in the language of mathematics. We have used this term earlier; it now requires a formal definition.

(9.3.2) A partition of any set A is a class of sets $A = \{A_i\}$ $(i = 1, 2, 3, \cdots)$ subject to: **Definition**

(1) $\bigcup A_i = A,$
(2) $A_i \cap A_j = \emptyset$, all A_i, $A_j \epsilon_i$ for which $i \neq j$.

By condition 1 of this definition, each element $a \epsilon A$ must be contained in at least one subset, A_i. By condition 2, no element can be contained in more than one subset. It should be intuitively evident to the reader that each equivalence relation on a set A generates a partition on A and that each partition of a set represents an equivalence relation.

The idea of partitioning a set into exhaustive and mutually exclusive subsets (by conditions 1 and 2 of 9.3.2 respectively) raises an interesting question. If the parent set is finite, then in how many distinct ways can it be partitioned? The remainder of this chapter will be given over to a search for answers to this and related questions.

Exercises

9.9. Consider the following:

i	Nationality	Age	Religion
1	U. S. A.	24	Protestant
2	France	32	Protestant
3	England	61	Catholic
4	U. S. A.	50	Catholic
5	U. S. A.	26	Buddhist
6	France	28	Catholic
7	England	34	Protestant
8	U. S. A.	41	Jewish
9	U. S. A.	33	Jewish
10	Austria	44	Protestant
11	U. S. A.	46	Protestant
12	U. S. A.	48	Jewish

(a) Which i's are equivalent when the criterion is citizenship in the U. S. A.? in Austria? in France?

(b) Which i's are equivalent when the criterion is Judaism?

(c) Which i's are equivalent when the criteria are citizenship in the U. S. A. and age between 30 and 35 years?

(d) Which i's are equivalent when the criteria are citizenship in the U. S. A., Protestant faith, and age between 20 and 25 years?

(e) Show that, if religion is used as the criterion for partitioning, the above table can be partitioned into mutually exclusive and exhaustive sets.

(f) Is the following set a partition on *ages?*

$$A_1 = \{x: 20 \le x \le 25\}, A_2 = \{x: 25 \le x \le 30\}, A_3 = \{x: 30 \le x \le 60\}.$$

9.10. A sociologist decides to partition the respondents in his sample into three socio-economic statuses—low, middle, and high. Some of the data he has gathered on the respondents are listed below.

Sample I. D.	Age	Occupation	Value of home	Value of auto	Income (per year)	Years of education	Hours worked per week
1	33	Mechanic	$10,000	$2,700	$6,000	11	48
2	36	V. P. of huge electronics firm	30,000	5,500	32,000	16	32
3	21	High school teacher	7,500	2,000	4,200	16	40
4	55	Barber	11,000	2,500	6,500	9	40
5	46	Pipe fitter	14,000	4,000	8,000	8	40
6	38	Bank teller	16,000	6,000	7,200	14	36
7	45	Chemical engineer	11,000	4,300	6,800	18	40
8	62	Garbage collector	7,000	1,200	3,800	4	40
9	23	Professional musician	9,000	No auto	5,800	14	28
10	34	College professor	17,000	1,700	9,000	21	30
11	48	Manager of grocery chain	18,000	4,300	10,000	16	60
12	57	Foreign agent	16,500	4,800	8,500	16	65
13	60	Gas station attendant	8,500	2,400	4,000	9	40
14	30	Doctor	24,000	8,000	40,000	22	50
15	26	Pharmacist	19,000	6,000	12,000	17	50
16	32	Cashier at food store	7,500	450	3,200	12	40
17	44	Farmer	14,000	1,200	4,200	12	80
18	64	High school teacher	13,500	1,100	5,800	16	38

(a) Partition the set into the following equivalence classes by listing the members (I. D. numbers) of each:

$H = \{x: x$ has home valued at more than $15,000\}$.
$M = \{x: x$ has home valued at $12,000$ to $14,999\}$.
$L = \{x: x$ has home valued at less than $12,000\}$.

(b) List the elements of the following partition:

$H = \{x: x$ has at least 17 years of education$\}$.
$M = \{x: x$ has 13–16 years of education$\}$.
$L = \{x: x$ has less than 13 years of education$\}$.

(c) Analyze the partition of part (a) in terms of hours worked per week. Interpret.
(d) Analyze the partition of part (b) in terms of annual income. Interpret.
(e) Construct a partition that utilizes jointly value of automobile and value of home.

9.4 Permutations of Sets

In attempting to discuss the number of possible ways of partitioning a set, it is useful first to consider the number of distinct ways in which a set of objects can be *arranged*. This consideration yields a most useful mathematical operation called the *factorial*.

"Arrangement" in this context means little more than it does ordinarily, although it sometimes carries the more impressive label of *permutation*. To the mathematician, an arrangement is any conversion of an *n*-element set into an ordered *n*tuple (only finite sets are considered here). That is,

(9.4.1) An ordered *n*tuple, α, is a permutation of an *n*-element set, A, if and only if: **Definition**

$$a \in \alpha \leftrightarrow a \in A.$$

The question now arises as to how many permutations there are of a set, A. In order to reach an answer, we must first consider a theorem called the Principle of Counting or the Multiplication Principle.

(9.4.2) (*Principle of Counting*). Let a sequence of actions, $A_1, A_2, \cdots, A_r$ be such that A_1 can occur in n_1 different ways; that after A_1 has occurred, A_2 can occur in n_2 ways; and, in general, that after A_{i-1} has occurred, A_i can occur in n_i different ways. Then the number of ways in which the event $\langle A_1, A_2, \cdots, A_r \rangle$ can occur, say N, is given by: **THEOREM**

$$N = \prod_{i=1}^{r} n_i.$$

If $r = 2$, then the number of outcomes is just the number of ordered pairs $\langle x, y \rangle \in A_1 \times A_2$. For each of the n_1 elements in A_1 there are n_2 possible ordered pairs. Thus there are $\sum_{i=1}^{n_1} n_2 = n_1 n_2$ ordered pairs $\langle x, y \rangle \in A_1 \times A_2$. If $r = 3$, then the number of possible outcomes is the number of triples **Proof**

$\langle x, y, z \rangle \epsilon A_1 \times A_2 \times A_3$. But this is the number of elements in $(A_1 \times A_2) \times A_3$. From the case of $r = 2$ this is seen to be $(n_1 n_2) n_3$. Proceeding by induction, the theorem is true of every integer $r > 1$.

If this theorem is thought through carefully, it should become clear that it squares well with one's informal knowledge of counting. It says, as an example, that if a woman has two coats, three dresses, and four hats (and if she has only one each of all other essentials), her wardrobe can be selected in any of $24(= (2)(3)(4))$ different combinations. It says also that she has eight $(= (4)(2))$ possible combinations of hats and coats. The sense of this theorem, in the case of the lady's hat-coat-dress possibilities, is shown in Figure 9.1.

The preceding example can be generalized so that it will cover a richer variety of problems in this way: Given n objects, in how many different ways can one *arrange* or *order* them? Let us reason out the answer. Suppose that the objects are to be lined up in a row so that a number can be assigned to each (beginning, say, at the left with 1). Pick any of the n objects for the first spot, thus giving n different possibilities. To fill the second spot, choose any of the remaining $(n - 1)$ objects. For *each* of the n choices for first spot, there are $(n - 1)$ for the second. Thus, for the first two spots *together* there are by the Principle of Counting $n(n - 1)$ possibilities. For the third spot, choose any of the remaining $(n - 2)$ objects, so that for the first three spots there is a total number of possibilities of $n(n - 1)(n - 2)$. This reasoning can be continued in exactly the same manner until only one spot remains. Since, for the final choice, only one object remains, there is only one possible placement. This suggests a general definition:

(9.4.3) To any nonnegative integer, n, another integer is associated which is called n factorial and is written $n!$ (or sometimes $\lfloor n$) and is given by:

Definition

$$n! = \begin{cases} 1 & \text{if } n = 0 \\ n(n - 1)! & \text{if } n > 0 \end{cases}$$

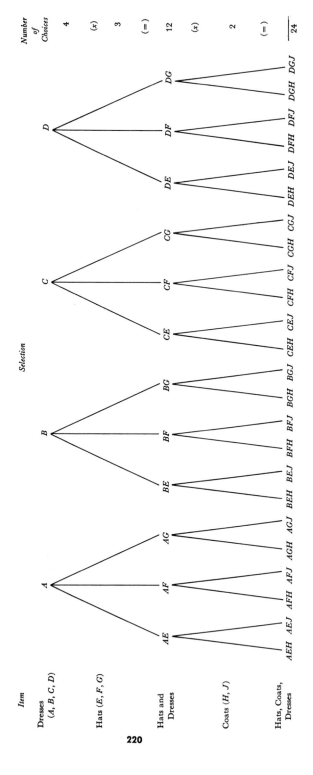

Figure 9.1   COUNTING A WARDROBE

The reasoning that was used suggests a clear interpretation of the function defined by $n!$. This function yields the number of possible permutations that can be made of n objects. The following lemma is required to prove this assertion:

(9.4.4) If a set containing $n - 1$ elements can be arranged in k different ways (generate k permutations) for k a positive integer, then an n-element set generates nk different arrangements, all $n \geq 2$.

LEMMA

Let an $(n - 1)$ element set generate k permutations. The first member of an ordered $n$tuple can be chosen from an n-element set in n different ways, one for each different element in the set. This choice made, there remain $(n - 1)$ elements that, by hypothesis, can be arranged in k different ways. By 9.4.2, the n-element set thus generates nk different arrangements.

Proof

The following important theorem stems immediately by induction from 9.4.1 and from this lemma:

(9.4.5) The number of possible arrangements of n objects is $n!$.

THEOREM

The proof is left as an exercise in inductive proof. The theorem says, for instance, that three experimental subjects can be arranged in $3! = 6$ distinct ways. The reader should verify this by listing the permutations of a 3-element set, say $A = \{a, b, c\}$. Notice that a relatively small increment in n yields a disproportionately large increase in the number of permutations. For example, $3! = 6$ but $6! = 720$, so that adding only three elements to a three-element set increases the number of possible permutations by 714.

Suppose that an experimenter wishes to select k subjects from a pool of n volunteers, $k \leq n$, and order them in an experimental arrangement. In how many ways can this be done? For instance, if an experimenter wished to select three subjects from a set of five and arrange them as an ordered triple, in how many ways could he do it? Before attempting to answer this question, some new notation is needed:

(9.4.6) The number of permutations of a subset of k elements selected from a set of size n, $k \leq n$, is noted $\mathbf{P}\begin{pmatrix} n \\ k \end{pmatrix}$ (read "the permutations of n elements taken k at a time").

Thus, the experimenter's problem consists of evaluating $\mathbf{P}\begin{pmatrix} 5 \\ 3 \end{pmatrix}$. To do this, we must recognize that the first element in the ordered triple can consist of any of the five members of the set. Once the first element is chosen, the second element can be chosen from among the four remaining. The third element can be chosen in three different ways from the three elements still in the set. The Principle of Counting tells us then that $\mathbf{P}\begin{pmatrix} 5 \\ 3 \end{pmatrix} = 5 \cdot 4 \cdot 3 = 60$. That is, there are 60 different patterns by means of which a five-element set can be converted into an ordered triple.

How is this related to $n!$? The careful reader should recognize from 9.4.4 that $\mathbf{P}\begin{pmatrix} n \\ n \end{pmatrix} = n!$ Now, in the more general case, $\mathbf{P}\begin{pmatrix} n \\ k \end{pmatrix}$, the number $n!$ is too big by just the number of permutations generated by the unselected set of elements whose size is $(n - k)$. This implies that $n!$ is too large by a factor of $(n - k)!$, which can be trimmed out simply by canceling. The reader should verify, for example, that $\mathbf{P}\begin{pmatrix} 5 \\ 3 \end{pmatrix} = 5!/(5 - 3)!$. In general

$$(9.4.7) \quad \mathbf{P}\begin{pmatrix} n \\ k \end{pmatrix} = \frac{n!}{(n - k)!}.$$

Partition a set of size n into two ordered sets of size k and $(n - k)$, respectively. The number of ways of selecting and ordering the first set is the unknown number $\mathbf{P}\begin{pmatrix} n \\ k \end{pmatrix}$. Once the first subset is selected and ordered, the remaining set can be arranged in $(n - k)!$ ways. But, when this has been done, all possible arrangements have been constructed. That is:

(1) $\mathbf{P}\begin{pmatrix} n \\ n \end{pmatrix} = \mathbf{P}\begin{pmatrix} n \\ k \end{pmatrix}(n-k)!$.

(2) $\mathbf{P}\begin{pmatrix} n \\ k \end{pmatrix} = \dfrac{n!}{(n-k)!}.$ $\left(\text{since } \mathbf{P}\begin{pmatrix} n \\ n \end{pmatrix} = n!\right)$

Exercises

9.11. Compute the following factorials:

(a) 4!
(b) 2!
(c) 5!
(d) 8!

9.12. Simplify the following:

(a) $\dfrac{10!}{9!}$

(b) $\dfrac{7!}{5!}$

(c) $\dfrac{6!+7!}{5!+6!}$

(d) $\dfrac{8!-6!}{9!-7!}$

(e) $\dfrac{n!}{(n-1)!}$

(f) $\dfrac{(n!)^2}{(n-1)!\,(n+1)!}$

9.13. Simplify:

(a) $\dfrac{(n+1)!+n!}{n!}$

(b) $\dfrac{n!+(n-1)!}{(n-1)!}$

9.14. If two dice are tossed, in how many combinations can they turn up? If three dice are thrown?

9.15. Show that Definition 9.4.2 is "complete" by using it to prove the following:

(a) $1! = 1$.
(b) $3! = 6$.
(c) $5! = 120$.
(d) $7! = 40,320$.
(e) $9! = 362,880$.

(Note: These exercises should be worked in order. Why?)

9.16. Consider a *circular* rather than a linear arrangement.

(a) Construct a function to represent the reduction in the number of arrangements of n elements by this substitution.

(b) How many possible arrangements would be eliminated in this manner if $n = 3$? If $n = 6$?

9.17. How many six-letter code words can be formed from the first ten letters of the alphabet?

9.18. How many three-letter code words can be formed from the alphabet if no letter is used more than once?

9.19. A psychologist has six rats to run through a maze. In how many ways can he pick the first rat to run the maze? What is the number of distinct orders in which he can run the six rats through the maze?

9.20. If a social psychologist has a sample of 12 students and wishes to pick three of the 12 for a small group experiment, in how many ways can he pick the first person? After he has picked the first, in how many ways can he pick the second? In how many ways can he pick all three persons for the experiment?

9.21. Suppose that the twelve students of the preceding exercise can be represented by the following joint partition:

Academic Major

Sex	PSYCHOLOGY	BATON-TWIRLING	
MALE	3	1	4
FEMALE	4	4	8
	7	5	12

In how many ways could the experimenter assemble a small group to consist of:

(a) 3 males?
(b) Two female psychology majors?
(c) Two male baton-twirling majors? (Careful!)
(d) Two psychology majors and two baton-twirling majors? (HINT: The answer to this exercise depends on the use of the Principle of Counting as well as on permutation theory.)
(e) Two females and two baton-twirling majors?

9.22. An anthropologist studying the dance movements of a certain North American Indian tribe finds that the dancers use 7 different movements. Suppose that a total of 5 movements constitutes one dance; if a dancer can use no movement twice in the same dance, how many different dances are possible? If the dancer is permitted to use the same movement as many times as he wishes in a dance, how many different dances are possible? Suppose that the dancer cannot follow a given movement by the same movement. How many dances are now possible?

9.5 Combinations

In the last section it was noted in an offhand way that $\mathbf{P}\begin{pmatrix} n \\ k \end{pmatrix}$ accounts for order in the sense that a permutation maps a set into an ordered $k$tuple. For instance, let a set consist of three elements, say $\{a, b, c\}$. Permutation theory tells us that six distinct ordered pairs can be constructed from this set since $\mathbf{P}\begin{pmatrix} 3 \\ 2 \end{pmatrix} = 3!/(3 - 2)! = 6$. It will help in developing a new idea to list these 6 ordered pairs.

(9.5.1) *Ordered pairs from the set* $\{a, b, c\}$:

(1) $\langle a, b \rangle$,	(4) $\langle b, a \rangle$,
(2) $\langle a, c \rangle$,	(5) $\langle c, a \rangle$,
(3) $\langle b, c \rangle$,	(6) $\langle c, b \rangle$.

Now suppose that one were interested not in the number of *ordered pairs* but, rather in the number of *subsets* of size two that could be constructed from the set $\{a, b, c\}$. The reader should recall from Section 3.1 that $\{a, b\} = \{b, a\}$ and that $\langle a, b \rangle \neq \langle b, a \rangle$, where $\{a, b\}$ is a set of two elements and $\langle a, b \rangle$ is an ordered pair of elements. In the case of 9.5.1 the answer is altogether obvious: There are just three possible sets of size two generated by the set $\{a, b, c\}$. These are $\{\{a, b\}, \{a, c\}, \{b, c\}\}$. In order to move toward a more general solution, we should review carefully the reasoning by means of which the answer was found. First, however, a definition is needed.

(9.5.2) A combination of n things taken k at a time is any subset of size k of a given set of n elements. The number of possible combinations of n things taken k at a time is noted $\begin{pmatrix} n \\ k \end{pmatrix}$ (or, in some texts $\mathbf{C}\begin{pmatrix} n \\ k \end{pmatrix}$ or $_n\mathbf{C}_k$).

Definition

From a set of size n, construct all $\mathbf{P}\begin{pmatrix} n \\ k \end{pmatrix}$ ordered $k$tuples. Construct a partition by means of the equivalence relation "contains the same elements as, disregarding order." Thus, the distinct ordered triples $\langle 1, 2, 3 \rangle$ and $\langle 3, 2, 1 \rangle$ are equivalent by this relation. Then the number of combinations of n things taken k at a time, $\binom{n}{k}$, is the same as the number of partitions of the $\mathbf{P}\binom{n}{k}$ ordered $k$tuples by this equivalence relation. The only added information required now is the *number* of $k$tuples in each partition. It is clear, however, that this can only be the number $k!$ since each partition contains all possible arrangements of k elements. Thus, $\mathbf{P}\binom{n}{k}$ contains $k!$ times as many elements as are contained in $\binom{n}{k}$. All this proves the following:

$$(9.5.3) \qquad \binom{n}{k} = \frac{\mathbf{P}\binom{n}{k}}{k!} = \frac{n!}{k!(n-k)!}. \qquad \text{THEOREM}$$

The reader would do well to construct some sets with reasonably small n and check the way in which the theorem works by actually listing the possible combinations of size k.

Although $n!$ becomes a number of horrendous size as n becomes only moderately large, the number $\binom{n}{k}$ can be computed fairly easily by judicious use of cancellation. As an example, suppose that one had to select a list of six participants from an initial list of 12 eligibles. This could be done in $\binom{12}{6}$ different ways. To compute this number, we have:

$$(9.5.4) \qquad\qquad\qquad \text{Illustration}$$

$$(1) \quad \binom{12}{6} =$$

$$\frac{12!}{6!(12-6)!}, \qquad \text{(By 9.5.3)}$$

$$(2) \quad = \frac{12 \cdot 11 \cdot 10 \cdot 9 \cdot 8 \cdot 7 \cdot 6 \cdot 5 \cdot 4 \cdot 3 \cdot 2 \cdot 1}{6 \cdot 5 \cdot 4 \cdot 3 \cdot 2 \cdot 1 \cdot 6 \cdot 5 \cdot 4 \cdot 3 \cdot 2 \cdot 1}, \qquad \begin{array}{l}\text{(A mess, thanks to}\\ \text{9.4.3)}\end{array}$$

$$(3) \quad = \frac{12 \cdot 11 \cdot 10 \cdot 9 \cdot 8 \cdot 7}{6 \cdot 5 \cdot 4 \cdot 3 \cdot 2 \cdot 1},$$

$$\left(\text{Since} \right.$$

$$\left. \frac{6 \cdot 5 \cdot 4 \cdot 3 \cdot 2 \cdot 1}{6 \cdot 5 \cdot 4 \cdot 3 \cdot 2 \cdot 1} = 1 \right)$$

$$(4) \quad = \frac{12}{4 \cdot 3} \cdot \frac{10}{5 \cdot 2} \cdot \frac{11 \cdot 9 \cdot 8 \cdot 7}{6},$$

(Cancel as indicated)

$$(5) \quad = \frac{5544}{6} = 924.$$

Thus, although one could have selected a final list of six from many more than 600,000 *ordered* lists of six persons, less than 1,000 possibilities exist if order is disregarded.

One can look in vain for complete tables of values of factorials. Since for even so small a number as 15, 15! contains 13 digits, it is not difficult to imagine the space that would be required to table the factorials of even the first hundred integers. There is, however, a convenient computing device that is available in any of several sets of mathematical tables. When used with a table of common logs of factorials and with a knowledge of the properties of logarithms, combinatorial work can be ground out with no overwhelming effort. For instance, to compute $\binom{47}{12}$ would be a terrible chore on a desk calculator. However, if one has mastered Section 7.3, he should recognize that

$$\log \binom{47}{12} = \log (47!) - [\log (12!) + \log (35!)],$$ which re-

quires only a bit of table-hunting, an addition, and a subtraction.

The combinatorial, $\binom{n}{k}$, turns out to have some fascinating general properties that can be useful both theoretically and in computing work. To get at some of these properties, let us look first at the *sequence* of range values of $\binom{n}{k}$, allowing k to vary from 0 through n, for several values of n. Thus, for example, $\binom{3}{k}$ generates a sequence of numbers, $\langle 1, 3, 3, 1 \rangle$, by allowing k to take on successively each value from 0 through 3. As n is varied from 0 through 4, the following sequences result: $\langle 1 \rangle$, $\langle 1, 1 \rangle$, $\langle 1, 2, 1 \rangle$, $\langle 1, 3, 3, 1 \rangle$, $\langle 1, 4, 6, 4, 1 \rangle$.

These observations should be sufficient to suggest several properties of the combinatorial. If not, then an examination of Table 9.1 should help. This table reflects a number of

Table 9.1   VALUES OF $\binom{n}{k}$ FOR $n = 0, 1, \cdots, 10$.

N	k											$\sum_{k=0}^{n}\binom{n}{k}$
	0	1	2	3	4	5	6	7	8	9	10	
0	1											1
1	1	1										2
2	1	2	1									4
3	1	3	3	1								8
4	1	4	6	4	1							16
5	1	5	10	10	5	1						32
6	1	6	15	20	15	6	1					64
7	1	7	21	35	35	21	7	1				128
8	1	8	28	56	70	56	28	8	1			256
9	1	9	36	84	126	126	84	36	9	1		512
10	1	10	45	120	210	252	210	120	45	10	1	1024

useful properties of $\binom{n}{k}$. Among the less obvious of these is the fact that any number except $\binom{0}{0}$ in the table is the sum of the number directly above it in the table and the number to the left of the latter. That is,

(9.5.5) $$\binom{n}{k} = \binom{n-1}{k} + \binom{n-1}{k-1},$$ **THEOREM**

the proof of which is left as an exercise.

Another property of the numbers $\binom{n}{k}$ is illustrated in the final column of Table 9.1. After a bit of contemplation, the reader should recognize that a functional relation exists between the numbers n and $\sum_{k=0}^{n}\binom{n}{k}$. The relation is given by:

(9.5.6) $$\sum_{k=0}^{n}\binom{n}{k} = 2^n.$$ **THEOREM**

The proof will be put off until the next section. Before dismissing the theorem, notice that it has something important to say. Theorem 9.5.6 says that there are exactly 2^n possible *partitions* of any set of size n into two classes of size k, and $(n - k)$ where k takes each value from 0 to n.

If appropriate rows and columns of Table 9.1 are traced, a pair of minor but useful facts should become apparent. The first of these is:

(9.5.7) $$\binom{n}{n} = \binom{n}{0} = 1.$$

PROPOSITION

Once this is proved (again, a worthwhile exercise), the proof of a much more general statement is suggested. See if the next assertion does not appear to be a more or less direct consequence of the last.

(9.5.8) $$\binom{n}{k} = \binom{n}{n - k}.$$

THEOREM

Before it is filed away, Table 9.1 should be examined for yet another apparent regularity. Notice that, in each row with a sufficient number of entries, the values increase in a regular fashion and then begin to move resolutely downward. This raises quite a general question: For any given n, what is the value of k such that $\binom{n}{k}$ is a maximum? To put it somewhat differently, is there a number (or numbers), say k_0, such that, for all $k \neq k_0$, $\binom{n}{k} \leq \binom{n}{k_0}$? This requires that two conditions be true of k_0: $\binom{n}{k_0} \geq \binom{n}{k_0-1}$; and also $\binom{n}{k_0} \geq \binom{n}{k_0+1}$. This statement makes a hidden assumption about the sequence in k generated by $\binom{n}{k}$. Can the reader ferret it out? It is necessary then, to determine what must be true of k_0 for these two weak inequalities to obtain:

(9.5.9)

$$\binom{n}{k} \geq \binom{n}{k - 1}, \quad \binom{n}{k + 1} \to \frac{n - 1}{2} \leq k \leq \frac{n + 1}{2}.$$

THEOREM

Let $\binom{n}{k} \geq \binom{n}{k-1}$. Then:

(1) $\dfrac{n!}{k!(n-k)!} \geq \dfrac{n!}{(k-1)!(n-k+1)!}$,

$$= \dfrac{kn!}{k!(n-k+1)(n-k)!}. \quad \text{(9.5.3 and 9.4.3)}$$

(2) $1 \geq \dfrac{k}{n-k+1}$.   (Canceling in Step 1)

(3) $k \leq \dfrac{n+1}{2}$.   (Simplifying in Step 2)

Now let $\binom{n}{k} \geq \binom{n}{k+1}$. Then:

(4) $\dfrac{n!}{k!(n-k)!} \geq \dfrac{n!}{(k+1)!(n-k-1)!}$,

$$= \dfrac{n!(n-k)}{(k+1)k!(n-k)!}. \quad \text{(As in Step 1)}$$

(5) $k \geq \dfrac{n-1}{2}$.

(6) $\dfrac{n-1}{2} \leq k \leq \dfrac{n+1}{2}$.   (Steps 3 and 5)

When the proof is understood, we should ask how many numbers will satisfy this inequality. The answer apparently is that there are two: $k = \dfrac{n-1}{2}$ and $k = \dfrac{n+1}{2}$. But k can take on either of these values only if n is an odd number. (Why?) If n is even, then only the single number $k = \dfrac{n}{2}$ satisfies 9.5.9. (Again, why?) With all this, the reader should re-examine Table 9.1 and see that every other row, corresponding to odd values of n, has two maximum values. This is to say that:

(9.5.10) If n is odd, then,

$$\binom{n}{\dfrac{n-1}{2}} = \binom{n}{\dfrac{n+1}{2}}.$$

The proof is left as an exercise.

Exercises

9.23. List all ordered pairs in the set $\{1, 2, 3, 4\}$. Partition this set into equivalence classes by the relation "contains the same elements as."

(a) There are 12 ordered pairs. Why?

(b) There are six equivalence classes. Why?

(c) In each equivalence class there are two elements (ordered pairs). Why?

9.24. Repeat Exercise 9.23, locating and listing all ordered *triples* instead of pairs.

(a) There are 24 ordered triples. Why?

(b) There are only four equivalence classes. Explain why there are fewer than in Exercise 9.23.

(c) There are six elements in each equivalence class. Explain why there are more than in Exercise 9.24.

9.25. Repeat Exercise 9.24, locating and listing all ordered quadruples.

(a) Why cannot more ordered quadruples than triples be located?

(b) Is the result generally true? That is, determine whether or not:

$$\mathbf{P}\left(\begin{array}{c} n \\ n-1 \end{array}\right) = \mathbf{P}\left(\begin{array}{c} n \\ n \end{array}\right).$$

(c) Why is there just one equivalence class in this case?

9.26. Prove 9.5.3. $\left(\text{HINT: the trick consists of establishing that } k!\begin{pmatrix} n \\ k \end{pmatrix} = \mathbf{P}\begin{pmatrix} n \\ k \end{pmatrix}.\right)$

9.27. Madison, Wisconsin, has a population in excess of 100,000. Noahs, Arkansas, has a population of just 10,000. Prove that two people in Madison have the same three initials in their names, but that no two people in Noahs *necessarily* have the same initials. Assume that all residents have just three initials.

9.28. There are nine outside doors to one of the larger dormitories on an unidentified Ivy League campus. In how many ways can a person enter by one door and leave by another? In how many ways could two persons enter by one door and then sneak out by two separate doors?

9.29. From a set of 15 books, in how many ways can five be selected if:

(a) One specified book is always to be included?

(b) One specified book is always to be excluded?

(c) Both (a) and (b) are required?

9.30. In how many ways can words be formed from the word SOCIETY so that vowels occupy even places?

9.31. Suppose that we have two containers, the first containing six orange and five blue cubes, and the second containing five orange and six blue cubes. In how many ways can one select two orange and five blue cubes, all from one container?

9.32. In how many different ways can 12 sociologists check into three hotel suites at their annual convention if there are to be three men in the first suite, four in the second and five in the third?

9.33. Prove Theorem 9.5.5, using a direct proof.

9.34. Prove 9.5.8, using a direct proof form.

9.35. Prove 9.5.10, using Theorem 9.5.3.

9.6 The Binomial Theorem

There are many instances in social analysis in which an algebraic term of the form $(a + b)^n$ plays an important part. In general, the numbers a, b, and n can take on any value. For the present, let us consider the two terms, a and b, to be fixed numbers, or parameters, and n to be any positive integer. Thus, this term generates a function on the positive integers, n, to some subset of the real numbers and can be represented by $f(n) = (a + b)^n$. In order to explore the properties of this function, let us first examine one or two special cases. Consider first $f(2)$.

   (9.6.1)

(1) $(a + b)^2 = (a + b)(a + b)$,

(2) $\qquad = a(a + b) + b(a + b)$,   (M6)

(3) $\qquad = a^2 + ab + ba + b^2$,   (M6)

(4) $\qquad = a^2 + 2ab + b^2$.   (M4)

By the same reasoning it could be shown that:

   (9.6.2)

$$(a + b)^4 = a^4 + 4a^3b + 6a^2b^2 + 4ab^3 + b^4.$$

This form of expansion could, in fact, be repeated for any positive integer n. Rather than continue along this path, however, it will be more profitable for us to seek a general term to describe the *binomial in n*, $(a + b)^n$. To do this, notice first in 9.6.1 and 9.6.2 the neat progression taken by the exponents of a and b as the sequences progress. In each term the exponent of a decreases one and the exponent of b increases one, and in every case the sum of the two equals n. Moreover, a careful look at the integer by which each term is multiplied, called the *coefficient* of the term, shows that these numbers take on a familiar progression. For instance, the coefficients of 9.6.2, that is, the sequence $\langle 1, 4, 6, 4, 1 \rangle$, is just the combinatorial $\binom{4}{k}$ over $0 \leq k \leq 4$. Finally, notice that the expansion (the term on the right of 9.6.2) contains $5 = n + 1$ terms. These observations, when assembled shrewdly enough, suggest the following powerful theorem:

$$(9.6.3) \qquad (a + b)^n = \sum_{k=0}^{n} \binom{n}{k} a^k b^{n-k}, \; n \; \epsilon \; T+.$$

The proof is left as an exercise that requires mathematical induction. This theorem reverses the order of terms on the right. That is, this theorem has the exponents of a increasing from 0 to n instead of decreasing from n to 0. The axiom on commutativity of addition, however, assures that this is a trivial change. In order to put the binomial theorem to work, let us consider a few special cases. In particular, how does a binomial of the form $(a - b)^n$ expand?

(9.6.4) Expand $(1 - \frac{1}{3})^3$.   **Problem**

(1) $(1 + [-\frac{1}{3}])^3 = \binom{3}{0} 1^0 (-\frac{1}{3})^3 + \binom{3}{1} 1^1 (-\frac{1}{3})^2$

$\qquad\qquad\qquad + \binom{3}{2} 1^2 (-\frac{1}{3})^1 + \binom{3}{3} 1^3 (-\frac{1}{3})^0,$

(2) $\qquad = (1)(1)(-\frac{1}{27}) + (3)(1)(\frac{1}{9})$

$\qquad\qquad\qquad + (3)(1)(-\frac{1}{3}) + (1)(1)(1),$

(3) $\qquad = -(\frac{1}{27}) + \frac{1}{3} - 1 + 1,$

(4) $\qquad = \frac{8}{27}.$

Notice the way in which the negative term is treated. The expansion makes use of the fact that odd-numbered powers of negative numbers are themselves negative. One more completed example should permit the reader to work through exercises that use the binomial theorem without undue strain.

(9.6.5) Evaluate $(1.25)^4$:   **Problem**

(1) $(1.25)^4 = (1 + .25)^4,$

(2) $\qquad = 1^4 + 4(1)^3(.25) + 6(1)^2(.25)^2$

$\qquad\qquad\qquad + 4(1)(.25)^3 + (.25)^4,$

(3) $= 1 + 1 + (6)(.0625) + 4(.0156) + (.0039),$
(4) $= 2.4413.$

Notice that 9.6.5 could be solved as an expansion of $(1 + \frac{1}{4})^4$ as well as in the decimal form suggested.

Before we leave the binomial theorem, it will be worth-while to look at it from a somewhat different perspective. What this theorem represents can be expressed in terms of partitions. Consider the general term of the expansion:

$$(9.6.6) \qquad \binom{n}{k} a^k b^{n-k}.$$

For the moment, forget about the coefficient and the part involving b. The term a^k is just a (serially multiplied) string of a's, k of them in all. Think of this as a set of k elements, each of which is labeled a. Together with a parent set of n elements, this generates a second set consisting of $(n - k)$ elements, each labeled b. This second set is represented by the term b^{n-k}. We know from the previous section that a set of k elements can be chosen from n elements in $\binom{n}{k}$ different ways. Then the term $\binom{n}{k} a^k b^{n-k}$ represents all possible two-set partitions of n elements such that k elements are contained in the first and $(n - k)$ in the second. The binomial expansion thus represents a multiplicative operation on the set of all possible two-set partitions of n elements, with k elements in the first and $(n - k)$ in the second $(k = 0, 1, \cdots, n)$.

By the same reasoning, we can interpret $\binom{n}{k}$ as the number of possible two-set partitions of a set of n elements that contain k elements in one subset and $(n - k)$ in the second. This interpretation is mentioned both in its own right and because it suggests a possible generalization both of the combinatorial $\binom{n}{k}$ and of the binomial theorem.

Several special cases of the binomial are worth considering because they occur so regularly in algebraic analysis. Among the more common of these are the following:

(9.6.7) (*On Special Products and Factors*).   **THEOREM**

(1) $(a - b)^n = \sum_{k=0}^{n} (-1)^{(n-k)} \binom{n}{k} a^k b^{n-k}$.

(2) $a^2 - b^2 = (a - b)(a + b)$.

(3) $a^n - b^n = (a - b) \sum_{k=0}^{n-1} a^k b^{n-k-1}$.

In part 1, the coefficient $(-1)^{(n-k)}$ determines the sign of each term of the binomial, making each term with an odd-numbered value of k negative and each term with an even-numbered value of k positive. Part 2 is just a special case of part 3 and is noted separately only because it is so frequently encountered in algebraic work.

Exercises

9.36. Evaluate:

(a) The fourth term of $(a - b)^6$. (HINT: This is not the same as the term for which $k = 4$.)

(b) The middle term of $(a + b)^{10}$.

(c) The terms of $(a - b)^n$ for $k = 0$ and $k = n$.

(d) $(a^2 - b^3)^3$

(e) $\left(a + \dfrac{1}{a}\right)^3$

(f) $\left(a + \dfrac{1}{a}\right)^n$

9.37. Restate the binomial theorem for the special case $a = 1$ and $b = 1$.

9.38. Reconsider theorem 9.5.6. Does the preceding exercise constitute a proof? Explain.

9.39. Re-express $\sum_{k=0}^{1} \binom{n}{k} a^k b^{n-k}$.

9.40. Show that $(a + b) \sum_{k=0}^{n} \binom{n-1}{k} a^k b^{n-k-1}$ contains a^n and b^n.

9.41. Prove that $a \binom{n-1}{k-1} a^{k-1} b^{n-k} + b \binom{n-1}{k} a^k b^{n-k-1} = \binom{n}{k} a^k b^{n-k}$.

9.42. Prove 9.6.3 using induction and exercises 9.39–9.41. (HINTS: The inductive assumption is that $(a + b)^{n-1} = \sum_{k=0}^{n-1} a^k b^{n-k-1}$. By virtue of Exercise 9.40, it is sufficient to show that $\binom{n}{k} a^k b^{n-k}$ is in $(a + b)(a + b)^{n-1}$.)

9.43. Prove 9.6.7.1.

9.44. Prove 9.6.7.3.

9.7 The Multinomial Theorem

We have a good deal of information now about two-set partitions of a set of elements. But suppose that one wished to partition a set of n elements into three subsets, say with k_1, k_2, and k_3 elements, respectively, subject to $k_1 + k_2 + k_3 = n$. (Why?) Then, of course, the question arises as to just how many different partitions of this form are possible. By appealing to the Principle of Counting (9.4.2), and to the definition of combinatorial, we can obtain the answer with reasonable ease. First, in how many ways can one construct the first set, which must contain k_1 elements? This, of course, is given by $\binom{n}{k_1}$. With the first set cut out, there remain $(n - k_1)$ elements with which to operate. Of these, k_2 are to be poured into the second set. This is just the combination of $(n - k_1)$ things taken k_2 at a time, which can be achieved in $\binom{n - k_1}{k_2}$ different ways. With the second set chosen we have left just $(n - k_1 - k_2)$ elements, which is k_3 (Why?), all of which must be allocated to the third set, and this can be done in one way only. Now, the Principle of Counting tells us that the proper way in which to combine these results consists of multiplying them together:

(9.7.1)

$$\binom{n}{k_1}\binom{n - k_1}{k_2}(1) = \frac{n!}{k_1!(n - k_1)!} \cdot \frac{(n - k_1)!}{k_2!(n - k_1 - k_2)!},$$

$$= \frac{n!}{k_1!k_2!(n - k_1 - k_2)!},$$

$$= \frac{n!}{k_1!k_2!k_3!}.$$

which is certainly a pleasing enough result. Of course, there is no reason to restrict our interest to the case of 3 subsets. Suppose that one wished to partition a set of n elements into

m subsets with k_1 in the first, k_2 in the second, and so on. It must be the case that $m \leq n$. (Again the usual question, why?) A bit of added notation would be useful at about this point:

(9.7.2) Let the number of ways in which a set containing n elements can be partitioned into m subsets, $A_1, A_2, \cdots, A_m$, with elements $k_1, k_2, \cdots, k_m$, respectively, be noted by:

$$\binom{n}{k_1, k_2, \cdots, k_m} \quad \text{or} \quad \binom{n}{k_j}, \quad j = 1, 2, \cdots, m,$$

which is called the *multinomial combinatorial*.

Then, following out the reasoning used to derive 9.7.2, it can be seen that:

(9.7.3)

$$\binom{n}{k_1, k_2, \cdots, k_m} = \frac{n!}{k_1! k_2! \cdots k_m!} = \frac{n!}{\prod\limits_{i=1}^{m} k_i!}.$$

For instance, suppose that a group of 12 subjects is to be divided into two experimental and two control groups with 4 in each experimental and two in each control group. To discover in how many ways this can be done, we simply compute:

$$\binom{12}{4, 4, 2, 2} = \frac{12!}{4! 4! 2! 2!} = 207{,}900.$$

All this has a particularly useful application in an algebraic problem that is simply a generalization of the binomial theorem. Suppose that, rather than raising some added pair of numbers, $(a + b)$, to a power, one wished to compute the nth power of an entire string of summed numbers $(a + b + c + \cdots + k)$. To get at a general solution, let us begin with a simple case such as $(a + b + c)^4$.

(9.7.4)

$(a + b + c)^4$,

$\qquad = (a + b + c)(a + b + c)(a + b + c)(a + b + c).$
$\qquad\quad$ (1) $\qquad\qquad$ (2) $\qquad\qquad$ (3) $\qquad\qquad$ (4)

A number has been assigned to each of the four terms to help keep things straight. From the axioms on multiplication, we know that the product is obtained by selecting one number from each of the four terms, multiplying the four together, and repeating the process until all possible combinations of four have been exhausted, at which time the entire string is added together. This can be viewed as the problem of partitioning a four element set into three subsets in which the three subsets are associated with the numbers a, b, and c, respectively. Some of the possibilities are as follows:

(9.7.5)

(1) $\{\{1, 2, 3, 4\}, \{\phi\}, \{\phi\}\}$ $(a^4 b^0 c^0)$
       a b c

(2) $\{\{1, 2\}, \{3\}, \{4\}\}$ $(a^2 b^1 c^1)$
       a b c

(3) $\{\{3, 4\}, \{2\}, \{1\}\}$ $(a^2 b^1 c^1)$
       a b c

(4) $\{\{\phi\}, \{1, 3\}, \{2, 4\}\}$ $(a^0 b^2 c^2)$
       a b c

The partition of 9.7.5.1 represents the placing of each of the four elements in the set associated with the number a, which leaves none to be placed in either of the remaining sets. The multiplication operation associated with this partition is seen to be $a \cdot a \cdot a \cdot a = a^4 b^0 c^0$. Of course, some of these partitions can be constructed in several different ways. For instance, the partition associated with the product $a^2 b^1 c^1$ could be constructed in $\binom{3}{2, 1, 1}$ different ways. By this reasoning, one can conclude that:

MULTI-NOMIAL THEOREM

(9.7.6) In the expansion of $(x_1 + x_2 + \cdots + x_m)^n$, the general term is given by

$$\binom{n}{k_1, k_2, \cdots, k_m} x_1^{k_1} x_2^{k_2} \cdots x_m^{k_m} \left(= \binom{n}{k_j} \prod_{j=1}^{m} x_j^{k_j} \right),$$

subject to

$$\sum_{i=1}^{m} k_i = n,$$

and the expansion is given by adding all possible terms of this form.

From this it is seen that the binomial is just that special case of the multinomial theorem in which $m = 2$.

Exercises

9.45. Prove that $(a + b + c + d)^4 = \sum_{k_i} \binom{n}{k_j} \prod_{j=1}^{m} x_j^{k_i}$ by direct expansion. Note that $\sum_{k_i}$ indicates that all possible values of the four integers k_j are to be exhausted, subject to $\sum_{j} k_j = 4$.

9.46. Re-express $(a - b + c)^n$ in terms of the multinomial theorem.

9.47. Re-express $(a + b)^m(c + d)^n$.

Selected References

1. Feller, William. *An Introduction to Probability Theory and Its Applications*, Volume I (Second Edition), New York: John Wiley and Sons, Inc., 1957. Chapter 2.
2. Kemeny, John G., Snell, J. Laurie, and Thompson, Gerald L. *Introduction to Finite Mathematics.* Englewood Cliffs, New Jersey: Prentice-Hall, Inc., 1957. Chapter 3.
3. Mosteller, Frederick, Rourke, Robert E. K., and Thomas, George B., Jr. *Introduction to Probability.* Reading, Pennsylvania: Addison-Wesley Publishing Company, Inc., 1960. Chapter 2.
4. Walker, Helen M. *Mathematics Essential for Elementary Statistics* (Revised Edition), New York: Holt, Rinehart and Winston, Inc., 1951. Chapters 18–19.

Real Functions

In Chapter 4 a function was seen to be a relation between any two sets, one of which was called the domain and the other of which was called the range. In Chapter 9 an elegant class of functions was constructed by taking as the domain the ordered set of positive integers $\langle 1, 2, 3, \cdots \rangle$. The work of this chapter will be concerned with what happens when we consider functions whose domains contain not merely integers but whole *intervals* of real numbers. The increase in analytic power that this step permits is immense.

The mathematics of sequences and of series facilitate the analysis of broad classes of events. But the events must occur in discrete steps. For example, the size of one's vocabulary might be plotted as a sequential function of his age, say in years. For purposes of economical description or of precise comparison of different individuals, such a device can be invaluable. But consider the image of language development that this procedure imposes. The sequence provides information about the individual's vocabulary at annual instants in time, but nothing more. It almost suggests that, in between these annual time points, the individual in question is a wordless idiot. The sequence is unrealistic in this case because it chops up a *continuous* domain variable, age, into discrete units. Consider the number of domain variables in the social sciences that occur in continuous waves rather than in discrete units. Age, income, and intelligence of individuals, interaction rates, collective power, and solidarity within groups are only a few of the important variables in social science that can be thought of as comprising continuous sets. When the critically important concepts of distance, time, and force are added to these, the necessity for developing a mathematics of functions with continuous domains should be obvious.

In this chapter we shall proceed, as we did in Chapter 9, first by constructing several important classes of functions and then by examining some of the properties of such classes. First, however, some elementary ideas need to be reviewed and a few notational conventions should be established.

10

10.1 Basic Notions

Recall once again that a function is any relation, say R, such that, if aRb and aRc, then $b = c$. That is, to each element in the domain of a function, there must correspond just one element in the range. If, beyond this, the function is such that, if aRc and bRc, then $a = b$, the function is called a one-to-one correspondence, or simply a correspondence. In other words, a correspondence is a function, with the added constraint that no range element may be associated with more than one domain element. In many cases the distinction between function and correspondence will be unimportant but, in some instances that we shall encounter, a function can be analyzed in considerably greater depth if it is known that it is also a correspondence.

The topic of the present chapter is "real functions," by which is meant functions whose domains consist of subsets of the real number system. The adjective "real" will be dropped after this point, but it will be implied unless a statement to the contrary appears. In general, the domain of a function is an *interval* of real numbers, or a union of such intervals. An interval is defined by any two limiting numbers, say a and b, such that $a < b$. An open interval, designated $I_{(a, b)}$, is an interval that does not contain the limiting numbers so that, in the language of sets $I_{(a, b)} = \{x: x \in R$ and $a < x < b\}$ where R is the set of real numbers. A *closed* interval, designated by square brackets as $I_{[a, b]}$, on the other hand, is one that does contain its limiting numbers. Thus, $I_{[a, b]} = \{x: x \in R$ and $a \leq x \leq b\}$.

The inverse of a function, labeled f^{-1}, was discussed in Section 4.3. There it was seen that inverses are functions made by inverting the domain and range of a one-to-one correspondence, f. The notion of a functional inverse will prove useful in some of the analyses of this chapter and of subsequent ones.

By now the reader has probably often felt himself put upon outrageously in the matter of notation. The meanings that symbols take on appear to shift haphazardly at different times. Because of the large number of mathematical notions that must be represented symbolically, it is inevitable that some of our limited stock of symbols must do multiple duty. It should be recognized, however, that certain informal conventions have been adopted already. For example, variables that can take on different *integral* values usually are noted by one of the letters i, j, k, l, m, or n. Variables that are thought of as being assigned a single fixed value, called *parameters*, usually are denoted by one of the letters a, b, c, d, or their Greek counterparts. In dealing with functions from now on, the letters f, g, and h will be set aside to represent functions themselves. The letters U, V, W, X, Y, and Z will represent domain or range sets, while their lower-case correspondents will represent elements in the domain or range. In particular, X will represent a domain set, and Y will represent a range set. In any case, the context of the discussion should make clear just what a particular symbol represents.

Exercise

10.1. Describe what each letter indicates in the following:

(a) $f(x) = a_1 x + a_2 x^2$.

(b) $g(n) = \dfrac{1}{n}$.

(c) $h(x) = k$.

(d) $f(x) = g^{-1}(y)$.

10.2 Absolute Value Function

On many occasions the signed values ("plus" or "minus") of numbers do no more than get in the way. The measurement of differences provides a good example. Suppose that two objects are assigned a value such as the distance from Mecca in miles, the height of each in inches, or the number of school years completed by each. To measure the difference in each value between a given pair, it seems reasonable enough to subtract the value of one from the value of the other. But if the first value is subtracted from the second and the remainder is positive, it follows that, had the second been subtracted from the first instead, the remainder would have been negative. In many cases, which member of a pair is chosen to be subtracted from the other is quite an arbitrary matter. In other words, the signed value of a difference really has no interpretive meaning in some cases. The absolute value function is useful to eliminate bothersome and uninterpretable signs in cases such as this.

(10.2.1) The *absolute value* of any number, a, is written $|a|$, and is given by: **Definition**

$$|a| = \begin{cases} a \text{ if } a \geq 0 \\ -a \text{ if } a < 0 \end{cases}.$$

The absolute-value function turns out to have some interesting properties, as is shown by the following:

(10.2.2) (*Properties of Absolute-Value Function*).   **THEOREM**

(1) $|a + b| \leq |a| + |b|$.
(2) $|a \cdot b| = |a| \cdot |b|$.
(3) $|a - b| \geq ||a| - |b|| \geq |a| - |b|$.
(4) $|a - b| = |b - a|$.
(5) $|a - b| \leq \frac{1}{2}|b| \rightarrow |a| \geq \frac{1}{2}|b|$.

If a and b are greater than zero, $|a + b| = a + b = |a| + |b|$. If a and b are less than zero, $|a + b| = -a + (-b) = |a| + |b|$. Let $a < 0 \leq b$ (note that the same results would obtain if the inequalities were reversed). Then either $(a + b) < 0$ or $(a + b) \geq 0$. Let $(a + b) < 0$.   *Proof* (1)

(1) $|a| + |b| = -a + b$.   (Hypothesis)
(2) $|a + b| = -(a + b) = -a - b$.   (Hypothesis)
(3) $|a + b| \leq |a| + |b|$.   (Steps 1 and 2, and
                                                       because $-b \leq b$
                                                       for $b \geq 0$)

Now let $(a + b) \geq 0$.

(4) $|a + b| = a + b$.
(5) $|a + b| < |a| + |b|$.   (Steps 1 and 4, and
                                                       because $-a > a$
                                                       for $a < 0$)

The remaining proofs proceed along the same route of exhausting the possible permutations of a, b, and 0.

Exercises

10.2. Prove 10.2.2.2.

10.3. Prove 10.2.2.3.

10.4. Prove 10.2.2.4.

10.5. Prove 10.2.2.5, but first prove that $|a - b| \leq \frac{1}{2}|b| \rightarrow a \cdot b > 0$.

10.6. Prove $|a + b + c| \leq |a| + |b| + |c|$.

10.7. Evaluate each of the following:

(a) $-|-2 + 3|$
(b) $|-3| + |2| - |-4|$
(c) $|-2| \cdot |-3|$
(d) $|-2| \cdot |3|$
(e) $|4 - 2| - |2 - 4|$
(f) $|(-2)(3) - (-2)(2)|$

10.3 Power Functions

The class of real functions to be discussed in this section is already familiar in many respects as a result of the exploration of exponents in Section 7.2. In that section a number, x^n, was considered to be a binary operation on ordered pairs, $\langle x, n \rangle$ to the real numbers. The shift from binary operations is accomplished by the simple expedient of giving the exponent the status of a parameter. In this sense a power function is one in which a functional correspondent of x is obtained by raising x to a given power, say α. That is,

(10.3.1) f is a power function if there is a real number, α, **Definition**
such that:
$$f(x) = ax^\alpha, \quad a \neq 0.$$

In the present discussion a will be set equal to one, which is tantamount to ignoring it.

A good way in which to get an idea about the properties of this function is to examine its graphs for selected values of α. Figure 10.1 contains sketches of a few such graphs. Incidentally, figures such as this cannot properly be called graphs because they do not represent the entire domain on which the function is defined. Since "sketch of the graph" is an awkward phrase, this technicality will be dismissed with a brush of literary license.

Figure 10.1 reflects several properties of power functions. As an exercise, the reader should attempt to list these properties and then to construct a second graph with other values of α in order to see whether these apparent characteristics are true generally. In order to discuss these evident properties, it will be convenient to adopt a convention of mathematicians. Let us number each of the four major sections of a graph (called *quadrants*) from I through IV in a *counter*-clockwise manner, beginning in the upper right-hand corner (see Figure 10.1). Thus, quadrant I contains only those points, $\langle x, f(x) \rangle$, such that $x > 0$, $f(x) > 0$; quadrant II contains points for which $x < 0$, $f(x) > 0$; and so on.

Now let us consider some of these evident properties in order to determine whether they are true in general or whether they result merely from the choice of values of α. First, it is clear that quadrant IV is entirely empty. No points are to be observed for which $x > 0$ and $f(x) < 0$. It appears also that all graphed functions have points in quadrant I and that some of these are contained entirely in that quadrant, whereas none is contained entirely in another quadrant. Moreover, the points in quadrants II and III belong to functions that seem to be systematically different from the functions that are entirely in quadrant I. Can the reader discover what these differences are? Again, reference to Section 7.2 will be helpful.

(10.3.2) Let f be a power function given by $f(x) = x^\alpha$. **THEOREM** Further, let $\alpha = \dfrac{m}{n}$, m and n integers, $n \neq 0$ and m, n or both odd. Then:

(1) f is *undefined* $\leftrightarrow$ either $x = 0$ and $\alpha \leq 0$, or $x < 0$ and n is an even integer, with $m \neq 0$.

(2) $\alpha = 0 \leftrightarrow f(x) = 1$, all $x \neq 0$.

Figure 10.1 SKETCHES OF SELECTED POWER FUNCTIONS

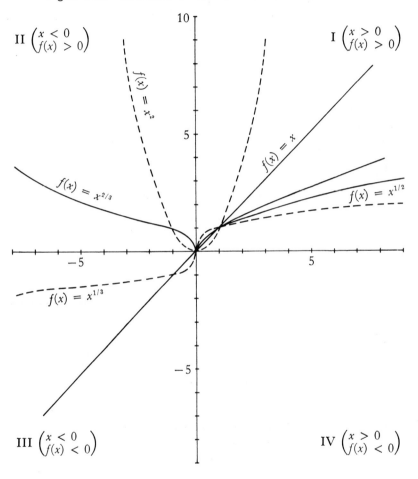

(3) $x = 0 \leftrightarrow f(x) = 0$, all $\alpha > 0$.

(4) $x = 1 \leftrightarrow f(x) = 1$, all α.

(5) $x = -1 \to f(x) = \begin{cases} 1 & \text{if } m \text{ is even and } n \text{ is odd} \\ -1 & \text{if } m \text{ is odd and } n \text{ is odd} \end{cases}$.

If $f(x)$ is defined, then:

(6) $f(x) < 0 \leftrightarrow x < 0$ and m and n are both odd.

(7) $|f(x)| > 1 \leftrightarrow \begin{cases} \alpha > 0 \text{ if } |x| > 1 \\ \alpha < 0 \text{ if } 0 < |x| < 1 \end{cases}$.

(8) $0 < |f(x)| < 1 \leftrightarrow \begin{cases} \alpha < 0 \text{ if } |x| > 1 \\ \alpha > 0 \text{ if } 0 < |x| < 1 \end{cases}$.

For the greater part, the proofs are straightforward consequences of Theorems 7.3.4 and 7.2.5. Figure 10.1 should be scrutinized carefully in light of the several parts of this theorem. For instance, parts 3 and 4 give the reason for the graphs of the several functions intersecting at two particular points.

One property reflected by these graphs is that of *monotonicity*, which has not been considered to this point.

(10.3.3) A function, f, is said to be monotone increasing **Definition** (or, sometimes, strict monotone increasing) on an interval $I_{(a,b)}$ if for all $a \leq x < y \leq b$,

$$f(x) < f(y),$$

and f is said to be monotone (or strict monotone) decreasing if, under the same conditions

$$f(y) < f(x).$$

In other words, if given an increase in the domain value, the range value always increases, the function is said to increase monotonically. If an increase in the domain value is always accompanied by a decrease in the corresponding range value, then the function is said to decrease monotonically. The term *strict* is sometimes used to contrast functions from those that are called weakly monotonic. The distinction, of course, hinges on whether strict or weak inequalities are located between the terms $f(x)$ and $f(y)$ in the definition. This definition provides us with an immediate theorem about power functions:

(10.3.4) If a function, f, on R^+, the positive real numbers, is defined by $f(x) = x^\alpha$, then f is monotone increasing $\leftrightarrow$ $\alpha > 0$ and f is monotone decreasing $\leftrightarrow \alpha < 0$.

Let α and $\delta > 0$ so that $(x + \delta) > 0$ if $x > 0$.

(1) *Assume* $(x + \delta)^\alpha < x^\alpha$, $x > 0$.

(2) $(x + \delta) < x$.   (7.3.4.5)

(3) $\delta < 0$.   (Subtracting x from both sides)

      (which contradicts assumption)

Now let $\alpha < 0$, say $\alpha = -\beta$, $\beta > 0$. Then:

(4) $(x + \delta)^\alpha = \dfrac{1}{(x + \delta)^\beta}$, $x^\alpha = \dfrac{1}{x^\beta}$.

(5) Assume $\dfrac{1}{(x + \delta)^\beta} > \dfrac{1}{x^\beta}$.

(6) $x^\beta > (x + \delta)^\beta$, which contradicts the first part of the theorem.

Proofs of the two converses are left as exercises.

As examples of monotone functions (but, as we shall see, not their *only* examples), power functions have many physical analogues in human behavior. For example, monotone increasing functions, including power functions with $\alpha > 0$, have been hypothesized to describe pressures to communicate messages in a group as functions of perceived discrepancy in opinion regarding the content of the messages. Population growth rates have been described as monotone increasing functions of time. If the growth rate were characterized by a power function, then the constant α could be called the *growth* parameter. Much of psychological learning theory can be described in terms of monotone functions. Classical stimulus-response theory, for instance, postulates that response strength is a monotone increasing function of stimulus strength. Suppose that this S-R relation could be described efficiently by a power function. Does the reader then agree that a good label for α would be "stimulus efficiency parameter"?

Power functions with $\alpha < 0$ were seen (in 10.3.4) to be members of the class of monotone decreasing functions.

This class plays a particularly important role in the construction of social science theory. In cases where the domain set represents points in time, decreasing functions are frequently referred to as *decay* functions. For instance, strength of response might be expected to diminish monotonically in time since last stimulus. Nor is time the only sensible domain variable of decay functions. The economist's analytic right arm, the consumer demand curve, is nothing but a function that depicts the demand for a commodity (the range variable) as decreasing monotonically with an increase in the price (the domain variable). The reader should be able to supply several additional examples of monotone increasing or decreasing functions in his own field of interest.

Exercises

10.8.   Construct two functions whose graphs are contained entirely in quadrant IV.

10.9.   Translate each of the eight parts of 10.3.2 into an English sentence.

10.10. Prove 10.3.2.3.

10.11. Prove 10.3.2.5.

10.12. Prove both the implication and the converse of 10.3.2.8.

10.13. Let amount of return, $f(x)$, on an investment of x dollars after a period of time be given by $f(x) = x^\alpha$.

(a) Interpret the investment if $0 < \alpha < 1$.
(b) Interpret the investment if $\alpha < 0$.
(c) If $\alpha = 1.5$, how great an investment would be required to earn a return of $100? of $1000? (HINT: Use logs.)

10.14. Translate the definition of monotonicity into an English sentence.

10.15. Construct two functions that are not explicit power functions but that are monotone increasing.

10.16. Describe two variables in your field of specialization that ought to bear a monotone relation to one another.

10.4 Exponential and Logarithmic Functions

Monotone functions are indeed critically important in the analysis of social behavior. Power functions are but one subset of the family of monotone functions. Another subset is made up of exponential functions.

(10.4.1) A function, f, is said to be an exponential function if, for real numbers a and α, f is defined by:

$$f(x) = a\alpha^x, \quad 1 \neq \alpha > 0, \quad a \neq 0.$$

Note carefully the way in which this class of functions differs from power functions. In this case the function has a variable exponent and a constant (parametric) base, whereas a power function consists of a parametric exponent and a variable base. Despite this difference, an exponential function behaves quite like a power function in many regards. A major similarity is that exponential functions also are monotonic.

(10.4.2) An exponential function (with $a = 1$) is mono-
tone increasing $\leftrightarrow \alpha > 1$ and is monotone decreasing $\leftrightarrow$
$\alpha < 1$.

Let $f(x) = \alpha^x$ and $\alpha > 1$. For each $\delta > 0$,

(1) $f(x + \delta) = \alpha^{(x+\delta)} = \alpha^x \alpha^\delta$.   (7.2.3.2)

(2) $\alpha^\delta > 1$.   (Since $\delta > 0$, $\alpha > 1$ and
        10.3.2.7)

(3) $\alpha^x \alpha^\delta > \alpha^x$.   (By step 2)

(4) $f(x + \delta) > f(x)$.   (By step 3 and hypothesis
        about f)

Conversely, let $f(x + \delta) > f(x)$ (that is, let f be monotone increasing).

(5) $\alpha^x \alpha^\delta > \alpha^x \rightarrow \alpha > 1$.   (Since $\delta > 0$)

Proof of the second part follows by recognizing that $\alpha^\delta < 1 \leftrightarrow \alpha < 1$ from (10.3.2.8). The restriction that $a = 1$ in this theorem requires no loss of generality because a is a constant in the function. It should be intuitively clear that the magnitude of the coefficient a should not alter the truth of the theorem. If $a < 0$ however, the monotone direction of f is just reversed.

In the monotonic property, then, power and exponential functions are quite similar. If these two classes of functions turn out to be so similar in a number of regards, one ought to question the necessity of distinguishing between them at all. That they are really quite different however, becomes apparent upon comparing their two definitions. Notice that some power functions are defined only on some subset of the positive integers, whereas an exponential function can be defined on any subset of the real numbers. Perhaps a more important difference is that the two behave quite differently as monotone functions. As increasing functions, one accelerates much more rapidly beyond a certain point than does the other. As decreasing functions, one decelerates more rapidly beyond a certain point than the other. Before going on, the reader ought to try to guess which might be expected to move more rapidly in each case. After doing so, guesses can be compared with the following, or with Figure 10.2, which contrasts the graphs of two power and exponential functions.

(10.4.3) If a function, f, is exponential, so that $f(x) = a\alpha^x$,   **THEOREM**
and if a second function, g, is a power function, so that $g(x) = bx^\beta$, then if α, $\beta > 1$, there exists a point x_0 such that, for all $x > x_0$, $f(x) > g(x)$. If α, $\beta < 1$, there exists a second point, x_1, such that for all $x > x_1$, $f(x) < g(x)$.
This theorem will not be proved here.

In the last chapter, the gloomy words of Malthus were recalled to illustrate the difference between arithmetic and geometric progressions. This theorem should make clear that the sense of Malthus' characterization of man's plight would be unchanged if it said that means of subsistence increase as a power function but population increases as an exponential function.

The logarithmic function, some elementary properties of which were considered in Section 7.3, is a close cousin of the exponential function. A review of that section should make clear that the following alters Definition 7.3.3 only by stating it explicitly as a function.

Figure 10.2   SKETCHES OF CONTRASTING POWER
AND EXPONENTIAL FUNCTIONS

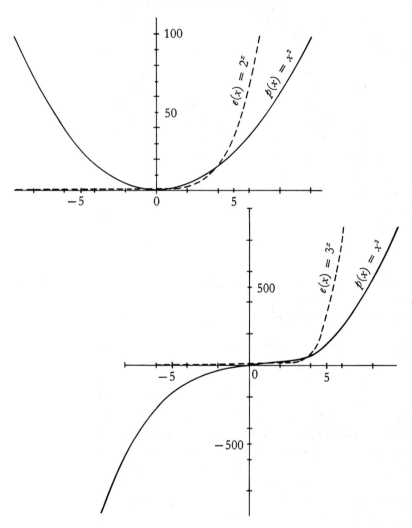

(10.4.4) For all real numbers, k, α, and x such that $k \neq 0$ and α, $x > 0$, if a function, f, is defined by $\alpha^{f(x)} = x^k$, we say that f is a logarithmic function (to the base α) and write:

$$f(x) = k \log_\alpha x.$$

At this point, the notion of inverse functions becomes useful as a device for making clear the exact relation between logarithmic and exponential functions. It was seen in Section 4.3 that the inverse of a function (if it exists!) is just the original function with domain and range variables inverted. Thus, if $f(x) = y$, then $f^{-1}(y) = x$, where f^{-1} is read "f inverse." Now consider in particular an exponential function, $f(x) = \alpha^x$. Can the reader satisfy himself that f^{-1} is defined so long as α, $x > 0$? In fact, does this appear to be the case for any (strict) monotone function? In the exponential case, the result of inverting the domain and range variables, x and $f(x)$, respectively, is just a new function, f^{-1}, which is given by $x = \alpha^{f^{-1}(x)}$. This, by comparison with 10.4.4, is seen immediately to be a logarithmic function (with $k = 1$). All this leads to an alternative to the preceding definition:

(10.4.5) (*Alternative*). If f is an exponential function defined by $f(x) = \alpha^x$, then a function $g = f^{-1}$ is called a *logarithmic* function to the base α.

Figure 10.3 contrasts several exponential functions with their logarithmic inverses.

It should become clear later in this book that much of the value of log functions is realized in purely mathematical analysis. Nonetheless, such functions have immediate and powerful applications in research. For example, suppose that population size is given by the following exponential function of time, t: $f(t) = \alpha^t$, $\alpha > 1$, so that population is seen to rise monotonically in time. Factors such as usable land and minimum levels of living may indicate that after the population reaches a critical number, say y, chaos will result. It is crucially important, then, to determine *when* this will occur. If we take f^{-1} and use logs, the answer is obtained quickly, for t_0 ($= f^{-1}(y)$) $= \log_\alpha y$. In other words, given the original population function and the critical

Figure 10.3 SKETCHES OF CONTRASTING EXPONENTIAL
AND LOGARITHMIC FUNCTIONS

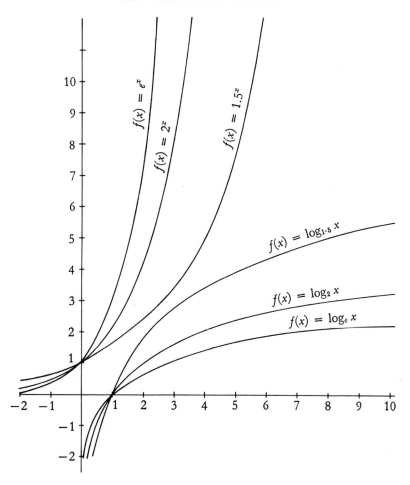

point, y, it is necessary only to obtain $\log_\alpha y$ in order to locate the cataclysmic point in time, t_0.

Occasionally, it is necessary to look at numbers in a different light. This necessity provides a second important application of log functions. The situation is illustrated by a violent disagreement that occurred recently between the mayors of two thriving cities. The debate concerned which of the two cities represented was growing at a faster pace. Each mayor argued long and heatedly that the claim must go to his community. The facts that were presented to bolster the arguments are contained in Table 10.1.

Table 10.1 HYPOTHETICAL POPULATIONS OF TWO HYPOTHETICAL COMMUNITIES, 1950 AND 1960

	Population	
Community	1950	1960
Oneville	450	750
Twoville	25,000	30,000

The mayor of Twoville argued correctly that his city had increased in much greater number than had the population of Oneville. The mayor of Oneville readily agreed to this fact but maintained that, nonetheless, his community was the more rapidly growing of the two because Oneville had increased during the 1950 decade by a rate of 1.67 ($= 750/450$), while Twoville had increased by the smaller rate of 1.2 ($= 30,000/25,000$). Needless to say, the argument was never resolved for the simple reason that the two debaters were looking at the same data in terms of radically different number systems. The mayor of Twoville employed the familiar arithmetic scale in which units of *absolute* magnitude are established. The other relied on a scale in which units of measurement are established with respect to *ratios* of numbers rather than numbers themselves. If he agrees that a measure of growth should reflect mass at the initial point, the reader must recognize that the view taken by the mayor of Oneville provides a more sharply realistic picture of the situation.

In general, let x_i ($i = 1, 2, 3, \cdots$) be a measure of a property at time t_i. Then a measure of *absolute* growth of this property between times t_{i-1} and t_i is given by $(x_i - x_{i-1})$. A measure of *relative* growth during the same period is given by x_i/x_{i-1}, which is equivalent to substituting a logarithmic for an absolute scale. Two properties, say x and y, have equal *absolute* growth between times i and j only if $(x_j - x_i) = (y_j - y_i)$. They have equal *relative* growth only if $x_j/x_i = y_j/y_i$. But this latter identity implies that $\log (x_j/x_i) = \log (y_j/y_i)$, which, in turn, implies that $(\log (x_j) - \log (x_i)) = (\log (y_j) - \log (y_i))$. Pictures of relative changes frequently are constructed on logarithmic graph paper in which logarithmic values (usually to the base 10) are substituted for arithmetic values on one scale or on both.

Exercises

10.17. If $f(x) = 4^x$ and $g(x) = x^4$, locate a point x such that $f(x) = g(x)$. Investigate the two functions for values first greater than, then less than this number.

10.18. Sketch the graphs of the following functions in the interval $[-10, 10]$:

(a) $f(x) = x^{3/2}$.
(b) $f(x) = (\frac{3}{2})^x$.
(c) $f(x) = x^{-2}$.
(d) $f(x) = x^2/2^x$.
(e) $\log_{1.5} x$
(f) $\log_{10} x$
(g) $\log_e x$
(h) $\log_e (x^2)$

10.19. Prove that a strict-monotone function is a one-to-one correspondence. Use an indirect proof.

10.20. Suppose that the population growth function in millions of people in a region is given by $f(t) = 2(1.5)^t$. Thus, at time $t = 0$ the region contains two million people.

(a) If it is determined that the region can support no more than 30 million people, when will the critical time occur?
(b) Suppose that it is predicted that at $t = 4.5$ (say, at 4.5 years after the initial time) the growth function will change to $g(x) = a(1.1)^T$. Determine the value of a. (HINT: The constant a must be such that at $T = 0$, and $t = 4.5$, $f(x) = g(x)$.)
(c) Determine the new critical time point of part a under the prediction of part b.

10.21. The population and urban population of the State of Wisconsin during the period 1840–1950, as reported by the Bureau of the Census, is:

Census year	State population	Urban population
1950	3,434,575	1,906,363
1940	3,137,587	1,679,144
1930	2,939,006	1,553,843
1920	2,632,067	1,244,858
1910	2,333,860	1,004,320
1900	2,069,042	790,213
1890	1,693,330	562,286
1880	1,315,497	317,204
1870	1,054,670	207,099
1860	775,881	111,874
1850	305,391	28,623
1840	30,945	. . .

Source: U. S. Bureau of the Census: *1950 Census of Population*, Volume II: Characteristics of the Population, Part 49: Wisconsin, Table 1.

(a) Plot the absolute growth of the total and urban population on graph paper.
(b) Convert the values to logs and plot.

10.5 Polynomial Functions

We are now ready to construct new functions by putting together two or more familiar functions. A polynomial function is nothing more than a sum of power functions whose exponents are integers:

(10.5.1) A function, f, is said to be a polynomial function **Definition** of degree n if f is defined by:

$$f(x) = \sum_{i=0}^{n} \alpha_i x^i, \quad \alpha_n \neq 0, \ \alpha_i \text{ a real number,}$$

in which α_i is called the coefficient of the ith term. In particular, if

$n =$	the function f is called
0	constant
1	linear
2	quadratic
3	cubic
4	quartic

When it is written out in detail, a polynomial function has this form: $f(x) = \alpha_0 + \alpha_1 x + \alpha_2 x^2 + \cdots + \alpha_n x^n$. Note that any of the coefficients, α_i, may be zero, except for α_n, so that a polynomial can contain far fewer than $n + 1$ terms. For example, $f(x) = x^n$ is itself a full-fledged polynomial function of degree n with $\alpha_n = 1$ and $\alpha_i = 0$, all $i < n$.

In order to get an initial idea of the way in which polynomials work, consider Figure 10.4, in which the graphs of four different polynomials are sketched. Notice that the functions were constructed in a lazy fashion, simply by adding one new term to each preceding function. It might appear that such a procedure should yield a set of very similar functions, but Figure 10.4 shows that this is far from true. Notice that the functions have just one common point, $(0, -6)$, the point at which each graph intersects the $f(x)$ axis of the graph. The number $f(0)$ is important enough to merit a special name of its own.

(10.5.2) For any function, f, the number $f(0)$ is called the *intercept* of the graph of f. **Definition**

Thus, the intercept of a power function is always zero, and the intercept of an exponential function is always 1. The intercept of a polynomial function is α_0. (Why?)

Although each of the functions graphed in Figure 10.4 crosses the $f(x)$ axis just once—otherwise they would not be functions (Why?)—some of them cross the x axis several times. These points represent values of x such that $f(x) = 0$.

(10.5.3) For any function, f, a number x for which $f(x) = 0$ is called a *root* or, synonymously, a *zero*, or a *solution* of f. **Definition**

It often happens that the entire key to a proof of some proposition about a function consists of locating a solution to the function. For example, suppose that two corporations compete with one another in the production of a certain commodity and that the production of each can be represented by a polynomial function of time. Then the productive superiority of one over the other can be measured

Figure 10.4 SKETCHES OF POLYNOMIAL FUNCTIONS

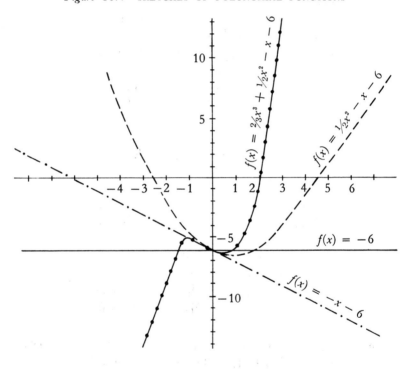

simply by subtracting one polynomial from another (which, as will be seen later, yields another polynomial). Then, a zero of this new function represents a point at which the underdog has overtaken his competitor in production. Figure 10.4 suggests that some functions have several roots and that the number might go up as a function of the degree, n. That this is exactly the case is shown by the following:

(10.5.4) A polynomial of degree n has at most n real roots.   **THEOREM**

The proof of this theorem is not particularly elaborate, but it requires a greater number of tools than have been developed here (see Allendoerfer and Oakley, *Principles of Mathematics* [1], pages 170–171.)

Since the theorem does not assert that the n roots of an nth-degree equation are unique, it may be that, in a particular case, two or more of the solutions turn out to be the same number.

The preceding theorem tells us how many numbers x there are such that for a polynomial function f, $f(x) = 0$. However, it does not tell us anything at all about procedures for locating the values of x. A general algebraic solution turns out to be impossible in the case $n \geq 5$. Most of our work will require the solution of nothing higher than second degree polynomials; therefore, only these special and relatively simple cases will be considered here. (For a discussion of solutions of cubic, $n = 3$, polynomials, see Birkhoff and MacLane, *A Survey of Modern Algebra* [2], page 96.)

By Theorem 10.5.4, a first degree polynomial, $f(x) = \alpha_0 + \alpha_1 x$, must contain exactly one domain value, x, such that $f(x) = 0$. To locate this value, we have:

(10.5.5) If f is a first-degree polynomial, then $f(x) = 0 \leftrightarrow$ **THEOREM**

$$x = -\frac{\alpha_0}{\alpha_1}.$$

The simple proof of this theorem is left as an exercise. In 10.4.1 a first degree polynomial was called a linear function. A glance at the graph of such a function in Figure 10.4 should make it clear why this label makes sense. Because of its linearity, one could plot the graph of the function simply by locating the intercept and the root of the function and by drawing the straight line that connects these points. It will be seen later that statisticians rely heavily on linear functions in their analysis of data.

A quadratic function of the form $f(x) = \alpha_0 + \alpha_1 x + \alpha_2 x^2$ must have at most two solutions, which may or may not be distinct. A function defined by $f(x) = x^2$ is clearly a quadratic, the solutions of which should be almost immediately apparent. We learned earlier that if any real number is unequal to zero, its square must be strictly greater than zero. Hence, the only number whose square is zero must be zero itself, so that the two solutions of this particular quadratic are both equal to zero. A second example of polynomial functions of second degree is $g(x) = x^2 - x - 6$. The solutions of this particular quadratic are anything but apparent, at least until it dawns upon one that $x^2 - x - 6 = (x - 3)(x + 2)$. Recognition of this identity helps us to see that $g(3) = g(-2) = 0$ and the two solutions are located. This solution required that the initial quadratic be *factored* into a product of two linear functions. Whenever one works with polynomials, it is a good idea to attempt to reduce them to products of polynomials of lower degree. A successful factorization sometimes makes the problem radically simpler.

More often than not a quadratic cannot be factored into a product of linear functions in any convenient form. The location of roots then requires a more general procedure, which is provided below.

(10.5.6) If f is a quadratic polynomial, so that $f(x) = \alpha_0 + \alpha_1 x + \alpha_2 x^2$, then real solutions of $f(x) = 0$ are given by: **THEOREM**

$$x = \frac{-\alpha_1 \pm [\alpha_1^2 - 4\alpha_0\alpha_2]^{1/2}}{2\alpha_2} \quad \text{if } \alpha_1^2 \geq 4\alpha_0\alpha_2.$$

Let $\alpha_0 + \alpha_1 x + \alpha_2 x^2 = 0$.   *Proof*

(1) $\dfrac{\alpha_0}{\alpha_2} + \dfrac{\alpha_1}{\alpha_2} x + x^2 = 0$.   (Divide both sides by α_2 since $\alpha_2 \neq 0$ by 10.5.1)

(2) $\dfrac{\alpha_1}{\alpha_2} x + x^2 + \dfrac{\alpha_1^2}{4\alpha_2^2} = \dfrac{\alpha_1^2}{4\alpha_2^2} - \dfrac{\alpha_0}{\alpha_2}.$ $\left(\text{Subtract } \dfrac{\alpha_0}{\alpha_2} \text{ and add}\right.$

$$\left.\dfrac{\alpha_1^2}{4\alpha_2^2}\right)$$

(3) but $\dfrac{\alpha_1}{\alpha_2} x + x^2 + \dfrac{\alpha_1^2}{4\alpha_2^2}$

$$= \left(x + \dfrac{\alpha_1}{2\alpha_2}\right)^2.$$

(4) $\left(x + \dfrac{\alpha_1}{2\alpha_2}\right)^2 = \dfrac{\alpha_1^2 - 4\alpha_0\alpha_2}{4\alpha_2^2}.$ (Expressions 2 and 3, transitivity, and locating a common denominator on the right side of expression 2)

(5) $x = \dfrac{-\alpha_1 \pm [\alpha_1^2 - 4\alpha_0\alpha_2]^{1/2}}{2\alpha_2}.$ (By taking square roots in expression 4, and solving for x)

The expression $\pm$ that popped up is to be read "plus or minus," so that the expression for x really consists of two separate (but not necessarily unequal) solutions. If we let $(\alpha_1^2 - 4\alpha_0\alpha_2) = d$, then one value of x such that $f(x) = 0$ is given by $x = (-\alpha_1 + d^{1/2})/2\alpha_2$, and the other by $x = (-\alpha_1 - d^{1/2})/2\alpha_2$. The term d has a name of its own:

(10.5.7) If f is any quadratic polynomial function, then   **Definition**
$d = (\alpha_1^2 - 4\alpha_0\alpha_2)$ is called the discriminant of the root of f.

The two solutions of $f(x) = 0$ involve $d^{1/2}$ and $-(d^{1/2})$, because square roots were taken in step 4 of the proof and because $x^2 = (-x)^2$.

The discriminant of a root can be an unhappy affair, because there is nothing to prevent its being less than zero. This would require that $\sqrt{d} < 0$ in 10.5.6, which is impossible for any real number. If $d < 0$, that is, if $\alpha_1^2 < 4\alpha_0\alpha_2$, the roots of the quadratic function are said to be complex, which means that they do not lie in the real number domain. It should be clear that $d = 0$ implies that both solutions are $x = -\alpha_1/2\alpha_2$.

Solutions of cubic and quartic functions, although they

can be obtained, are often extremely difficult to locate. Only if these functions can be factored into polynomials of lower degree are solutions readily available.

A simple modification of polynomial functions yields a new class, with which this brief survey of the basic real functions will be concluded. Notice that, in the classes of functions considered to this point, the operation of division has been ignored completely. The other algebraic operations—addition, multiplication, and exponentiation—have been thoroughly exploited to construct real functions, but division has not. This neglect of a deserving algebraic operation is remedied by the following:

(10.5.8) If f and g are polynomial functions, then a function, h, defined by:

$$h(x) = \frac{f(x)}{g(x)} \left(= \frac{\sum\limits_{i=0}^{n} \alpha_i x^i}{\sum\limits_{j=0}^{m} \beta_j x^j} \right), \quad g(x) \neq 0,$$

Definition

is called a *rational polynomial* function.

The term rational was selected for the same reason for which it was used to represent an ordered pair of integers. This definition should make clear the fact that polynomial functions are merely special cases of rational polynomials, with $g(x) = 1$, just as integers are special cases of rational numbers. The reader should convince himself that each of the following is a perfectly well-defined rational polynomial function.

(10.5.9)

ILLUSTRATIVE RATIONAL POLYNOMIAL FUNCTIONS

(1) $\dfrac{\alpha_0 + \alpha_1 x + \alpha_2 x^2 + \cdots + \alpha_n x^n}{\beta_0 + \beta_1 x + \beta_2 x^2 + \cdots + \beta_m x^m}, \quad \sum\limits_{j=0}^{m} \beta_i x^i \neq 0,$

(2) α_0

(3) $\dfrac{(x + 3x^2)(1 + x)}{(4 - x^2)(x^3 + 4x)}, \quad x \neq 2,$

(4) $\dfrac{x}{x}, \quad x \neq 0.$

There is very little to be said about rational polynomials that has not been said already in the discussion of polynomials. As is so frequently the case, however, this evidently straightforward addition to the class of polynomials carries with it a trap in which the unwary are often caught. Much of the game of mathematics consists of good housekeeping, of leaving things in a more orderly state than that in which they appeared initially. This sense of orderliness frequently calls for the reduction of needlessly complicated terms to a simpler and more obvious form. The only restriction on this process is that the new form must remain equal to (or congruent with) the old. It is here that the student so often trips. In the case of functions, it must be perfectly clear what is meant by the term equality.

(10.5.10) Two functions, f and g, are said to be equal $\leftrightarrow$ **Definition**
Domain of f = Domain of g = X and $f(x) = g(x)$, all $x \in X$.

The pitfall usually takes the form of failure to remember that the inverse of zero is an undefined term. For example, the fourth illustrative rational function, $f(x) = x/x$, tempts one to reduce it to the simpler and seemingly identical function, $g(x) = 1$, since it was learned earlier that x/x is congruent to the integer 1 for *nearly* all values of x. The exception, of course, occurs at $x = 0$.

Exercises

10.22. What kind of function is each of the following?

(a) $f(x) = x^5$.
(b) $f(x) = x^{5.5}$.
(c) $f(x) = k$.
(d) $f(x) = (2x + 1)(3 + x)^2$.

(e) $f(x) = \dfrac{2x + 1}{(3 + x)^2}$, $x \neq -3$.

(f) $f(x) = \sqrt{x}$.

10.23. Prove the implication and the converse of 10.5.5.

10.24. If f is a linear function, what is the minimum number of values of $f(x)$ required to graph the function? Explain.

10.25. Factor each of the following polynomials into products of polynomials of lesser degree:

(a) $f(x) = 2 + 3x + x^2$.
(b) $f(x) = 10 + 15x + 5x^2$.
(c) $f(x) = 1 - x^2$.
(d) $1 - 2x + x^2$
(e) $4 + x + 4x^2 + x^3$
(f) $4 - x - 4x^2 + x^3$

10.26. Locate solutions of each function in Exercise 10.25.

10.27. Locate solutions of the following (if they exist), using 10.5.6:

(a) $f(x) = 1 - x^2$.
(b) $f(x) = 3 + 2x - 5x^2$.
(c) $f(x) = -3 - 2x + 5x^2$.
(d) $f(x) = 3 - 2x + 5x^2$.
(e) $f(x) = 4 + 4x + 5x^2$.
(f) $f(x) = 4 + 4x - 5x^2$.

10.28. In Exercise 10.27, carefully contrast the outcome of parts b, c, and d; of parts e and f.

10.6 Multivariate Functions

Functions are highly important to the social scientist because they provide for him an efficient, parsimonious model of the sorts of relations in which he is interested. Thus, for example, the economist who wishes to express a relation between the cost of a commodity and the corresponding demand for it can use the notion of a (monotone decreasing) function rather than treating each different value of price as a separate situation. Even so, the functions that have been explored to this point, complicated and rich in properties though they are, are too simple to reflect accurately the vast complexity of much social behavior. Thus far, functions have expressed the range of values, $f(x)$, in terms of a *single* domain variable, x. This provides a model of the naive single-factor theory, in which a dependent variable is pictured as depending upon one independent variable only.

It is generally recognized today that no social phenomenon of any consequence can be said to depend entirely upon just one other variable. Economists agree, for instance, that demand for a commodity does not depend solely upon price, but that such factors as utility and available substitute commodities at a competitive price have a bearing on the demand. Nor would any reasonable sociologist assert that a particular behavior pattern, such as vertical social mobility, results from the operation of a single second variable, such as achievement motivation, access to the market place, socio economic status of the father, or type and level of education. Instead, he would recognize that these factors, together with many others, operate *jointly*—each with more or less force—in the determination of the dependent variable. Such a recognition demands of the mathematician more realistic functions with which to represent the interplay of several variables simultaneously. The answer to this demand is called a multivariate function.

Definition

(10.6.1) Any set of ordered $(n + 1)$-tuples of the form $\langle x_1, x_2, \cdots, x_n, f(x_1, x_2, \cdots, x_n)\rangle$ is called a multivariate function of n independent variables if, to each $n$tuple, $\langle x_1, x_2, \cdots, x_n\rangle$, there corresponds one and only one value, $f(x_1, x_2, \cdots, x_n)$.

Thus, a multivariate function expresses the dependent variable as the result of the joint values of a set of independent variables. The relative importance of each independent variable depends, of course, upon the way in which each is fitted into the function.

Multivariate functions can be put together in any of the ways in which functions of a single independent variable were constructed. The following illustrates a few of the endless forms that multivariate functions can take.

ILLUSTRATION OF MULTIVARIATE FUNCTIONS

(10.6.2)

$$f(x_1, x_2) = x_1/x_2, \quad (x_2 \neq 0).$$
$$g(x_1, x_2, x_3) = x_1(x_2 + x_3).$$
$$h(x_1, x_2, \cdots, x_n) = \left(\sum_{i=1}^{n} \alpha_i x_i\right)^k, \quad (k \neq 0).$$
$$p(x_1, x_2, \cdots, x_n) = \sum_{i=1}^{n-1} x_i^{x_{i+1}}.$$

Whenever it is convenient and reasonably clear, a function of n variables will be noted $f(x_i)$, with the range of i being indicated as needed. Whatever the vagaries of notation, the underlying idea of what a multivariate function is should be clear: A multivariate function is a representation of the way in which a *set* of events (values of each independent variable) operates to produce a particular event (a value of the dependent variable).

Exercises

10.29. For the function $f(x_1, x_2) = (x_1 + x_2)^2$:

(a) Sketch the graph of f at the point $x_2 = 0$, for $-5 \leq x_1 \leq 5$.
(b) Sketch the graph of f at the point $x_1 = 0$, for $-5 \leq x_2 \leq 5$.
(c) Describe the way in which the graph of f would appear in three-dimensional space.

10.30. The correlation coefficient, ρ, is given by:

$$\rho = \sum_i \frac{(x_{1i} - \mu_1)(x_{2i} - \mu_2)}{n\sigma_1\sigma_2},$$

where $i = 1, 2, \cdots n$,

$$\mu_1 = \frac{1}{n} \sum_{i=1}^{n} x_{1i}, \quad \sigma_1 = \left[\frac{1}{n} \sum_{i=1}^{n} (x_{1i} - \mu_1)^2\right]^{1/2},$$

and μ_2 and σ_2 are similar measures for X_2. Simplify this expression.

10.31. If they exist, locate solutions, as values of x_1, of each of the following functions:

(a) $f(x_1, x_2) = 2x_1 + 3x_2$.

(b) $f(x_1, x_2) = \dfrac{x_1}{2 + x_2}, \quad x_2 \neq -2$.

(c) $f(x_1, x_2) = (x_1 + 3x_2)^2$.

10.7 Operations on Functions

A phrase such as the sum of two real numbers certainly should make good sense to the reader by now. Since real functions produce sets of real numbers, a phrase such as the sum (or difference or product or quotient) of two *functions* ought to make equally good sense. Such algebraic combinations of functions often make substantive as well as mathematical sense. As an example, suppose that f is a function that gives the wages a man earns, $f(x)$, for x hours of work (ordinarily, but not necessarily, f would be a linear function with $\alpha_0 = 0$). Suppose also that g is a similar income function for his wife. Then the sum of the two functions, $(f + g)$, gives the total wages of the couple for a unit period of work. The ratio of the two functions, f/g, gives the ratio by which the man's wages exceed those of his wife. Both because algebraic operations on functions often do "make sense" and because they prove to be useful for further mathematical analysis, a few results of such operations will be considered here.

The set property called closure was discussed first in Chapter 5. To say that a set is closed under a particular operation means that when the operation is performed on two or more elements of the set, the result is itself an element in the set. The set of rational numbers, for instance, is closed under the operations of addition, multiplication, and division. The set of all functions of a particular class also can be examined for closure properties. First, however, we must understand clearly what is meant by algebraic operations on functions.

(10.7.1) If f and g are any two real functions, then,   **Definition**

(1) $(f \pm g)(x) = f(x) \pm g(x)$.
(2) $(f \cdot g)(x) = f(x) \cdot g(x)$.
(3) $(f/g)(x) = f(x)/g(x)$.

With this, closure properties under these basic operations can be examined. Here we shall consider only the sets of power, exponential, and polynomial functions.

(10.7.2) The set of power functions is closed under the   **THEOREM** operations of multiplication and division (barring division by zero).

Let f and g be power functions, say $f(x) = ax^\alpha$ and   *Proof* $g(x) = bx^\beta$. Then the product $(f \cdot g)(x)$ is given by:

(1) $(f \cdot g)(x) = ax^\alpha bx^\beta$,
(2) $= (ab)x^{(\alpha+\beta)}$, which is a power function.

The quotient, f/g, where $g(x) \neq 0$, is given by:

(3) $(f/g)(x) = \dfrac{ax^\alpha}{bx^\beta}$,

$$= \left(\dfrac{a}{b}\right) x^{(\alpha - \beta)}, \text{ which is a power function.}$$

Notice that the sum of power functions is not necessarily a power function. Can the reader locate two power functions whose sum *is* a power function? If it is recalled that exponential functions behave much like power functions, the following should come as something less than a jolt:

(10.7.3) The set of exponential functions is closed under the operations of multiplication and division. The proof is left as an exercise.

THEOREM

If the functions in the prior example, which gave wages of husband and wife for hours worked, were of power or exponential form, their ratio but not their sum would be of the same type. On the other hand, if the two functions were rational polynomials, then both their ratio (except for division by zero) and their sum would be of the same type, as is seen by the following:

(10.7.4) The set of polynomials is closed under addition and multiplication. The subset of rational polynomials, moreover, is closed under division (except by zero).

THEOREM

Let f be a polynomial function of degree m, with coefficients α_i, and let g be a polynomial function of degree n, with coefficients β_i. With no loss of generality, we can say that $m \leq n$ and $j = m + 1, m + 2, \cdots, n$. Then,

Proof

(1) $(f + g)(x)$

$$= \sum_{i=1}^{m} \alpha_i x^i + \sum_{i=1}^{m} \beta_i x^i + \sum_{j=m+1}^{n} \beta_i x^i, \quad \text{(by 10.7.1)}$$

(2) $$= \sum_{i=1}^{m} (\alpha_i + \beta_i) x^i + \sum_{j=m+1}^{n} \beta_j x^i, \quad \text{(by 7.1.2.1)}$$

(3) $$= (\alpha_0 + \beta_0) + (\alpha_1 + \beta_1)x + \cdots$$
$$+ (\alpha_m + \beta_m)x^m + \beta_{(m+1)}x^{m+1}$$
$$+ \cdots + \beta_n x^n,$$

which is a polynomial function. The remainder of the proof
is left as an exercise.

As a further exercise, the reader should determine the *degree*
of polynomial functions that are sums, products, or quotients of f and g.

Exercises

10.32. Prove Theorem 10.7.3.

10.33. Prove that the class of rational polynomials is closed under division (except by
zero.

10.34. Suppose that f is strength of response to stimulus one, that g is strength of response
to stimulus two, and that both stimuli can be measured in terms of a common
unit. Interpret each of the following:

(a) $(f + g)(x)$

(b) $\left(\dfrac{f}{g}\right)(x)$

(c) $(f - g)(x) = 0$.

10.35. If f and g are polynomial functions of degree m and n, respectively, $m > n$,
what is the degree of each of the following?

(a) $(f + g)$
(b) $(f \cdot g)$
(c) $(f - g)$

10.36. Let f represent a measure of earning power in dollars as a function of length of
education on a set of humans, let g represent length of education as a function
of annual income of father, and let h represent annual income of father as a
function of length of education of father. Let X represent the set of incomes;
Y, the set of lengths. Characterize the cross-product sets on which f, g, and h are
defined.

10.37. Determine which of the following compositions of functions given in Exercise
10.36 are defined. For each defined composition, determine its cross-product set:

(a) $f(g(x))$
(b) $g(f(y))$
(c) $g(h(y))$
(d) $h(f(y))$
(e) $f(h(y))$
(f) $h(f(g(y)))$

10.38. In Exercise 10.37, state what each defined composition represents.

10.39. Let f be a power function, let g be an exponential function, and let h be a polynomial function of degree $n > 0$. Represent each of the following:

(a) $f(g(x))$
(b) $g(f(x))$
(c) $h(g(x))$
(d) $f(g(h(x)))$
(e) $h(f(g(x)))$
(f) $g(h(f(x)))$

Selected References

1. Allendoerfer, C. B., and Oakley, C. O. *Principles of Mathematics.* New York: McGraw-Hill Book Company, Inc., 1955. Chapters 6, 8, 9.
2. Birkhoff, Garrett, and MacLane, Saunders. *A Survey of Modern Algebra.* New York: The Macmillan Company, 1953. Chapter 3.
3. Moore, John T. *Fundamental Principles of Mathematics* (Revised Edition). New York: Rinehart and Co., 1960.
4. Richardson, Moses. *Fundamentals of Mathematics.* New York: The Macmillan Company, 1958. Chapter 10.
5. Walker, Helen M. *Mathematics Essential for Elementary Statistics* (Revised Edition). New York: Holt, Rinehart and Winston, Inc., 1951. Chapters 10, 11, 16, 17.

Functions and Classes of Numbers: Measurement

In preceding chapters we have considered a remarkable set of entities: numbers; their fundamental properties; and relations that can be constructed on them. Illustrations and exercises have shown how these entities can serve as tools of theory and research in the analysis of social behavior. In this chapter the connection between mathematics and social science—and, indeed, science generally—is made explicit. The world of mathematics, represented here as numerical systems, and the phenomenal world of empirical systems are linked by the concept of *measurement*.

11.1 Numerical and Empirical Systems

The social scientist is concerned with sets of phenomena such as roles, choices, costs, or experimental responses. Yet more important to him are relations that obtain among elements of such sets. It is the investigation of relations on sets that transforms description into analysis. This fact is reflected in the following definition.

Definition

11

(11.1.1) If E is a nonempty set of observed (or empirical) elements, and R_i, $i = 1, 2, \cdots, n$, is a relation on $E \times E$, then the ordered $n + 1$tuple,

$$\mathcal{E} = \langle E, R_1, \cdots, R_n \rangle,$$

is called an *empirical system* (or sometimes an empirical relational system).

Thus, $\mathcal{E}$ might consist of a set of bureaucratic statuses—R_1, the relation given by the relationship "can fire"; R_2, by "has greater prestige than"; R_3, by "has more tenure than"; and so on. It is by means of empirical systems such as this that such phenomena as bureaucratic structures are analyzed.

It should be clear that there could be great advantages to identifying such empirical systems with systems of numbers in some way. If the relations of an empirical system could be identified with axioms or theorems on numbers, then the panoply of consequent theorems explored in earlier chapters could be embedded in the system, possibly enriching it. The following is useful to this end:

(11.1.2) If A is any nonempty subset of the real numbers, and R_i, $i = 1, 2, \cdots, m$, is a relation on $A \times A$, then the ordered $m + 1$ tuple,

$$\mathfrak{N} = \langle A, R_1, \cdots, R_m \rangle,$$

is a *numerical system* (or sometimes a numerical relational system).

Definition

To use numbers as meaningful representations of physical objects, it is clearly necessary to connect a numerical system to an empirical system in some orderly fashion. A first step toward this connection is given by the following:

(11.1.3) If E is any nonempty set of (observable) elements, and A is a subset of the real numbers, then a *measurement* of E is any function, f on E to A, and f is called a *measurement function*.

Definition

Now this certainly establishes a tie between observable phenomena and numbers, but it fails utterly to assure us that numbers so assigned to objects meaningfully embed the number properties in the objects.

Suppose that we were to partition a set of voters, V, into three equivalence classes labeled Democrat, Independent, and Republican (call the classes D, I, and R, respectively). To establish a measurement on these elements of V, let f be given by the following:

(11.1.4)

$$f(x) = \begin{cases} 1 \text{ if } x \in D \\ 2 \text{ if } x \in I \\ 3 \text{ if } x \in R \end{cases}.$$

Definition

By this definition, the reader must surely agree, $f(D) + f(I) = f(R)$, since $1 + 2 = 3$. However, the sentence "Democrat + Independent equals Republican" is nonsensical. The meaninglessness here arises from the fact that there exists no relation in the empirical system on V that has the properties of the relation $+$ on the set of real numbers. However, this is not to say that V has no number properties.

By its very construction, the set V has an associated relation, that of equivalence. It should be recalled that the equivalence relation is reflexive, symmetric, and transitive, and that these are precisely the properties of the numerical relation of equality. Thus, the two systems $\langle V, R \rangle$ and $\langle \{1, 2, 3\}, = \rangle$, where R is the equivalence relation, have a close structural connection that is cemented by 11.1.4 and the following:

(11.1.5) If A and B are sets and f is a one-to-one corre-   **Definition**
spondence on $A \times B$, then the two systems,

$$\mathcal{Q} = \langle A, R_1, \cdots, R_n \rangle$$

and

$$\mathcal{B} = \langle B, S_1, \cdots, S_n \rangle$$

are said to be *isomorphic* if and only if, for each $x, y \in A$,

$$\langle x, y \rangle \in R_i \leftrightarrow \langle f(x), f(y) \rangle \in S_i, \quad i = 1, 2, \cdots, n.$$

In the event that A and B are both numerical sets, only the two relations, $+$ and $\cdot$, need be considered, and f must satisfy $f(x + y) = f(x) + f(y)$ and $f(x \cdot y) = f(x) \cdot f(y)$, for each $x, y \in A$. If f in 11.1.5 is a function but *not* a one-to-one correspondence, then it is sometimes called a *homomorphism* rather than an isomorphism.

Since R in the above illustration is an equivalence relation having exactly the properties of equality, it should be perfectly clear that the two systems $\langle V, R \rangle$ and $\langle \{1, 2, 3\}, = \rangle$ are isomorphic. That is, the numerical properties of equality are embedded in the empirical system of voters partitioned by similarity of party label. However, the two systems $\langle V, R_1, R_2 \rangle$ and $\langle \{1, 2, 3\}, =, < \rangle$ are not isomorphic, since nothing in the partitioning process *orders* the classes. Thus, there is no guarantee that $\langle x, y \rangle \in R_2 \leftrightarrow x < y$. A measurement function carries number properties into an empirical system only if equivalent properties can be shown to obtain on the empirical set. The demonstration of such an isomorphism is sometimes called the representation problem of measurement.

Representation is not the only fundamental measurement problem. Obviously, $\{1, 2, 3\}$ was not the only possible set of numbers that could have been used in 11.1.4. The sets

$\{12, 22, 0\}$, $\{-1, -2, -3\}$, or any of an endless number of distinct sets could have been substituted. However, a set such as $\{1, 2\}$ could not have been substituted. Why? Determining what classes of numbers can be substituted in the range of a measurement function without violating isomorphisms is sometimes called the uniqueness problem. This is attacked in the next section, by bringing into play the notion of invariance.

Exercises

11.1. Explain what sort of an empirical relation, R_2, in the preceding illustration would be needed to make the system $\langle V, R_1, R_2 \rangle$ isomorphic to $\langle \{1, 2, 3\}, =, < \rangle$. Use the necessary order axioms.

11.2. What would be necessary to make an empirical system of social stratification isomorphic to the numerical system $\langle A, =, + \rangle$?

11.2 The Notion of Invariance

Invariance has been called "changelessness in the midst of change." For our purposes, invariance refers to the property of changelessness in operations and relations of a measurement when the assigned numbers themselves are changed in some uniform fashion, that is, by a transformation function. As an example, let us return to the measurement defined by 11.1.4. Although the operation of addition in this case turned out to be meaningless, the relation of equality was seen to have meaning there. It is clear, for example, (by the reflexive property of equality) that $3 = 3$. Any two voters who are assigned the number 3 are equal in the sense that they have identical party affiliation. That is, they are equivalent on this measure. In fact, one could make any one-to-one substitution of other numbers for the numbers actually assigned without destroying the equality relation.

To understand better the notion of invariance, it will help to think of certain functions as mechanisms that operate on other functions rather than directly on sets of numbers. Such mechanisms are usually called *transformation functions* and are classified according to properties considered in the preceding chapter. For instance, a linear function, say $f(x) = \alpha_0 + \alpha_1 x$, can be thought of as generating a linear *transformation* of a second function, g, which would be noted $f(g(x)) = \alpha_0 + \alpha_1(g(x))$.

The question now can be asked, if g is a measurement function, what *properties* of $g(x)$ also are true of $f(g(x))$? For example, if $g(x) = g(y)$, does it necessarily follow that $f(g(x)) = f(g(y))$; that, if $g(x) < g(y)$, then $f(g(x)) < f(g(y))$; that, if $g(x) = 2(g(y))$, then $f(g(x)) = 2(f(g(y)))$? The reader should convince himself that the answers are yes, yes, and no, respectively, so long as α_1 is positive and unequal to one. It should be intuitively clear that some functions fail to preserve certain properties, such as inequality relations, whereas others do maintain them. Properties of functions that remain unchanged under a particular transformation are said to be *invariant* under that transformation. With this intuitive notion of invariance in mind, we can proceed to a fourfold classification of measurement functions.

11.3 Nominal Scales

The term scale unfortunately carries with it several rather different connotations. However, we shall think of a scale as a class of measurement functions that are equivalent with respect to the operations they permit. In this sense, the simplest possible scale is called *nominal*:

(11.3.1) If f is any measurement function on a set, A, to a subset of R, then f is a nominal scale if $f(x)$ is equivalent to $g(f(x))$, all $x \in A$, where g is any one-to-one correspondence on the range of f to a subset of R.   **Definition**

This definition sometimes is paraphrased in a statement that a nominal scale is unique up to any one-to-one transformation. The important thing is that, for any number assigned by f to an element x, any other number could be substituted, so long as the second number is used just once.

Thus, the numbers 1, 2, 3 that comprised the range of f in 11.1.4 could be replaced under a transformation g by, say, 18, -150, 0, 3, respectively, if f is a nominal scale. If two elements, a Democrat and an Independent, were assigned the numbers 1 and 2 by f, they would be given the values 18 and -150 by g. By either assignment, we recognize that the two are unequal because $1 \neq 2$ and $18 \neq -150$. By the first function, however, the Democrat would be said to be "less than" the Independent, since $1 < 2$; but by the second, he would be said to be "greater," since $18 > -150$. The sense of this definition, then, is that a nominal scale does not preserve inequality relations. By the same reasoning it should be clear that, under a nominal scale, no mathematical property necessarily remains invariant except for that of equality. The empirical system is made isomorphic to the numerical system $\langle B, = \rangle$, where B is a subset of the real numbers.

This definition gives the most primitive of all empirical research operations, classification according to some property. If two elements in the domain are identical in that property, then they are said to be equivalent. If they do not share the property, then nothing can be said about them other than that they are not equivalent. The construction of a nominal scale is nothing more than an arbitrary coding operation. Examples of nominal measurement scales are the numbering of prisoners, the assigning of squad numbers to an infantry platoon, the assigning of class numbers to individual students, and so on. A nominal scale, in other words, is any partitioning of a set into (mutually exclusive and exhaustive) subclasses according to any equivalence relation.

Once a nominal scale has been constructed on a set, it really makes little difference, from a mathematical point of view, what labels are assigned to the various subclasses. More often than not, words rather than numbers are assigned as distinguishing labels. The important point is that, whatever the label, the only thing that one can say about two elements in the partitioned set is either that they are equivalent or that they are not. Even though the nominal scale is primitive in nearly every sense of the word, it continues to be, probably, the most frequently used class of measurement function in social science research.

Exercises

11.3. By definition, the relation $=$ is reflexive, symmetric, and transitive. State in words what these three properties require of the measurement function of 11.1.4 if it is to be a nominal scale.

11.4. Can the measurement function of 11.1.4 be thought of as having higher algebraic properties than that of equality?

11.5. Let g be any one-to-one correspondence on the range of a measurement function. Prove that $g(f(x))$, where f is the original function, preserves the operation of equality. (HINT: Assume the existence of three elements, x_1, x_2, and x_3 such that $f(x_1) = f(x_2)$ and $f(x_2) \neq f(x_3)$.)

11.4 Ordinal Scales

By its very construction, the nominal scale tells us nothing about two inequivalent elements except that they are indeed "unequal." But there are, after all, many properties in nature that permit us to say things, sometimes a great deal, about unequal elements. To choose a rather morbid example, consider the assignment of letter grades to final examinations. Notice first that numbers, say 4, 3, 2, 1, 0, could be substituted quite readily for the usual sequence of letters, A, B, C, D, F. Suppose that two students compare their final examination grades and discover that one has received a 4, while the other, unhappily, has earned a 1. The two students certainly can agree that they are not equal with respect to this measurement, but they can also say more. The first, at the risk of sounding a braggart, can point out that he has a "higher" score than has the second. It would not be correct to say that the first has a score four times as high as the second has, but still something can be said about the *relative ordering* of the two. This is but one example of a large class of measurement functions in which not only equality but also *order* can be determined. This class of functions is called, collectively, the *ordinal scale class*.

(11.4.1) An ordinal scale is any measurement function   **Definition**
on a set A that is equivalent to any monotone-increasing
correspondence on A to a subset of R.

In other words, an ordinal scale is an assignment of numbers to elements of a set that preserves equality, like a nominal scale, and that, moreover, preserves order. In recent
years major efforts have been given over to the construction
of ordinal scales for such phenomena as attitudes, beliefs,
social class, and political orientation.

The fact that an ordinal scale carries more empirical
operations and relations with it than does the nominal scale
means that one has less freedom in effecting transformations
on the values of any ordinal measurement function. In the
values of a nominal scale, any one-to-one transformations
could be effected, and the relation of equality would remain
invariant. But this is not the case when the order relation is
added. In 11.1.4 the numbers 18, 12, 6, could have been
substituted for those from 1 through 3 without affecting the
relation of equality. But since integers are ordered, a substitution of this sort would wreck any empirical *order* relation. We can certainly make many transformations of ordinal scales; but, if the properties of equality and order are to
remain invariant, these transformations must be of a restricted class. If the notion of monotone function is recalled
from Definition 10.3.3, the reader should recognize that an
ordinal scale is invariant under any monotonic-increasing
transformation. In a numerical grading of examinations, for
example, the scores 0 through 4 could be converted into
the scores 0, 10, 100, 1,000, 1,000,000, or in any other
monotonic-increasing fashion, without destroying the notion
of order. That is, if $f(x) < f(y)$, then $g(f(x)) < g(f(y))$ for
g any monotone increasing transformation. The proof is left
as an exercise.

Exercises

11.6. Rephrase the statement "a monotone transformation preserves order" as a formal
proposition and prove it, using 10.3.3.

11.7. Suppose that a subject ordered a set of four comparable commodities by the relation "is preferred to." Assume that this preference relation is connected.

(a) What does the connectedness assumption require?

(b) What would have to be determined in order to learn whether the preference relation comprises an ordinal measurement scale? (HINT: See 5.4.6.7 and determine that the properties of $<$ are satisfied by the subject's preference ordering.)

11.8. A subject constructs a preference relation on a set of four sports cars, $X = \{$Ace Bristol, Jag, Alfa, Elva$\}$ by exhausting the ordered pairs. The ordered pair $\langle$Alfa, Jag$\rangle$ is read "Alfa is preferred to Jag." The subject's preference relation is: $\{\langle$Alfa, Ace$\rangle, \langle$Elva, Jag$\rangle, \langle$Ace, Elva$\rangle, \langle$Elva, Alfa$\rangle, \langle$Jag, Ace$\rangle, \langle$Alfa, Jag$\rangle\}$. Is this preference relation an ordinal scale? Why?

11.9. On the domain set of Exercise 11.8, construct an ordinal measurement function, f. Let $g(x) = 2 + x^2$. Does $g(f(x))$ preserve the order relation of $f(x)$? Prove your answer.

11.5 Interval Scales

When a student seeks admission to a university, among the most important of his credentials is his "standing" or rank order in his high-school graduation class. Although this is indeed a useful predicter of academic performance in college, there remain a great many things that it does not tell. Suppose that two pairs of students from the same high school apply for admission. Suppose that the class standings of the first pair are first and tenth and that the standings of the second pair are ninety-first and one-hundredth. What can we say about the relative "distance" of the two pairs? Certainly, both are separated by the same number of units; but this does not mean at all that the two distances are equal. It could easily be that the upper half of the graduating class evinced a considerable spread in academic performance, while the students in the lower half were all quite uniformly mutton-headed. In this case, the distance between first and tenth could represent vastly more inequality in achievement than would be represented by the distance between ninety-first and one-hundredth.

The notion of distance, then, is meaningless in respect to an ordinal scale, but in many others it carries a directly interpretable, physical meaning. This class is given the label *interval scale*.

(11.5.1) If f is any measurement function on a set A, then f is an interval scale if $f(x)$ is equivalent to $g(f(x))$, each $x \in A$, for any linear transformation, g, given by $g(f(x)) = \alpha_0 + \alpha_1 f(x)$, $\alpha_1 > 0$.

Definition

Since a linear function is both a one-to-one correspondence and a monotone function, it is clear that an interval scale preserves those properties that are maintained by nominal and ordinal scales—equality and order, respectively. As the reader ought to suspect, the interval scale accomplishes much more than this. The distinguishing characteristic of this scale, as its name should suggest, is that it preserves equalities of intervals, where an interval may be thought of as a distance between two points measured by the difference or sum of the value of the points. This property is summarized by the following:

(11.5.2) If $x \pm y = u \pm v$ and if g is a linear transformation function, then $g(x) \pm g(y) = g(u) \pm g(v)$.

THEOREM

Let $x \pm y = u \pm v$ and $g(x) = \alpha_0 + \alpha_1 x$.

Proof

(1) $g(x) \pm g(y)$
$\quad = \alpha_0 + \alpha_1 x \pm (\alpha_0 + \alpha_1 y)$,
(2) $\quad = \alpha_0 \pm \alpha_0 + \alpha_1(x \pm y)$.
(3) $g(u) \pm g(v) = \alpha_0 + \alpha_1 u \pm (\alpha_0 + \alpha_1 v)$,
$\quad = \alpha_0 \pm \alpha_0 + \alpha_1(u \pm v)$,
(4) $\quad = g(x) \pm g(y)$.   (By step 2 and hypothesis
$\qquad\qquad\qquad\qquad$ that $x \pm y = u \pm v$)

Some of the major break-throughs in physical research have been the construction of interval measurement scales on such properties as temperature and energy. In the social sciences today, a great deal of effort is being given to the construction of interval measurements of psychophysical phenomena, such as pitch discrimination, and of certain social psychological variables, such as subjective probability and attitudes.

If the equal interval property is to be maintained under transformations of measurement values, it is clear that some monotone transformations simply do not work. In fact, if the equality and order properties of *differences* between measures are to be maintained, as well as those properties of the measures themselves, then the only admissible class of transformations is the set of linear functions such that $\alpha_1 > 0$ (see 10.5.1). For example, a measurement of the position of points on a line carries with it the relations of equality and order of measurement values as well as equality and order of differences between pairs of values. To see this, draw a straight line and designate any arbitrary point 0. Then select any arbitrary unit of length, such as an inch, a foot, or a centimeter. Strike off unit lengths about 0 along the line. Next, select any two pairs of points such that the distance associated with each pair is equal. The pairs $\langle 20, 5 \rangle$ and $\langle 50, 35 \rangle$ are examples. Next, transform these values by any positive linear function, for instance, let $\alpha_0 = 5$ and $\alpha_1 = 2$, so that:

$$(11.5.3) \qquad\qquad f(x) = 5 + 2x.$$

Under this transformation, the values are all shifted uniformly, as are the values of differences between points; the relations among differences, however, remain constant. For instance, the ordered pairs $\langle 20, 5 \rangle$ and $\langle 50, 35 \rangle$ are transformed to the ordered pairs $\langle 45, 15 \rangle$ and $\langle 105, 75 \rangle$. The original difference in each of the two pairs was 15. In each pair the difference is now 30, but equality and order of differences remain unchanged. Thus, we see that the operations associated with an interval scale are invariant under any positive linear transformation.

Exercises

11.10. Let x, y, u, v all be greater than zero. Then $g(x) = 1 + x^2$ is a monotone transformation. Is 11.5.2 true with respect to this transformation? Prove your answer.

11.11. Sociologists have constructed ordinal scales of "favorability of attitude toward X" by ordering response patterns to batteries of questions about X.

(a) What properties of the respondents must three numbers represent—say, $f(x_1)$, $f(x_2)$, and $f(x_3)$—where x_1, x_2, and x_3 are response patterns, if f is to be an ordinal measurement scale?

(b) Suppose that a sociologist were so naive as to add or subtract the numbers $f(x_i)$ and assume that they equalled $f(x_1 + x_2 + \cdots + x_n)$. Convince him that he is taking f to be an interval scale and show him that this assumption is too strong.

11.12. Construct two scales on sets in your field of specialization. How would you test to determine whether these are interval scales?

11.6 Ratio Scales

An interval scale is certainly powerful in that it gives a great deal of information not contained in either nominal or ordinal scales. Statistics texts show that it also permits considerably more complex statistical manipulations than do either of the others by permitting the use of addition and subtraction. However, the interval scale is by no means the ultimate in scales. One point is particularly important to notice here. The location of the point called 0 is really quite an arbitrary matter with respect to some sets. For instance, the 0° ("zero degrees") point on a centigrade scale of temperature is the 32° point on the Fahrenheit scale. This means that, so far as these two scales are concerned, the label 0 carries no firm, "absolute" meaning. However, it is possible to locate, theoretically at least, an absolute 0 point of temperature—that is, a temperature so cold that it cannot be reduced further. We can then consider a fourth class of scales that carry with them certain extremely useful added properties. These we shall call the class of *ratio scales*.

(11.6.1) If f is any measurement function on a set A, **Definition** then f is a ratio scale if $f(x)$ is equivalent to $g(x)$, all $x \in A$, for any proportionality transformation g given by $g(f(x)) = \alpha f(x)$, $\alpha > 0$.

The crucial difference between an interval scale and a ratio scale is made immediately apparent if one considers $x \in A$ such that $f(x) = 0$. If f is a ratio scale, then $f(x)$ is equivalent to $g(f(x))$ only if g is a similarity transformation. In particular, if $f(x) = 0$, then $g(f(x)) = \alpha(0) = 0$, so that the zero point remains invariant. (What happens to the zero point in a linear transformation?)

This difference may seem rather minor, but it has an extremely important consequence. Any discussion of the relation "times as great as" requires an invariant zero-point. It makes good sense, for example, to say that a city with a population of 10,000 is five times as great as a city with a population of 2,000. This says, in effect, that the ratio $\frac{10,000}{2,000} = 5$. On the other hand, it makes no sense at all to say that a Centigrade temperature of 80°F is twice as great as a temperature of 40°, even though $\frac{80}{40} = 2$.

The more properties a scale possesses, the fewer the transformations that can be effected. A nominal scale remains invariant under any one-to-one substitution. An ordinal scale permits any monotone-increasing transformation. Linear transformations only can be made on an interval scale. The ratio scale carries with it all mathematical properties of the other three scales. Equality, order, and distance (or the operation of addition, if the reader prefers) are all defined on a ratio scale. In addition, the notion of proportionality (the mathematical operation of multiplication by a constant) is defined both for values and for intervals for the ratio scale, but for none of the others. That is,

(11.6.2) If $\dfrac{f(x) \pm f(v)}{f(u) \pm f(v)} = k$, and if g is any proportion-   **THEOREM**

ality transformation given by $g(x) = \alpha f(x)$, then:

$$\frac{g(f(x)) \pm g(f(v))}{g(f(u)) \pm g(f(v))} = k,$$

the simple proof of which is left as an exercise. The reader should, in addition, convince himself that this property is true only of proportionality transformations. Thus, only the ratio scale preserves ratios of intervals.

Exercises

11.13. Prove 11.6.2.

11.14. Let h be a linear transformation function, $h(x) = \alpha_0 + \alpha_1 x$, such that $\alpha_0 \neq 0$. Prove that $h(f(x))$ does not satisfy theorem 11.6.2.

11.15. A common measurement in social science is the relative frequency or proportion, $p(x) = x/n$, where x is the number of elements having an attribute and n is the total number of elements in the set. Thus, $p(x)$ might represent the proportion of residents of a city of size n who are classed as skilled workers. Let p_1 and p_2 be two proportions.

(a) Assume $n_1 \neq n_2$ (that is, that p_1 and p_2 are proportions from two distinct sets with different sizes). Interpret $p_1 = kp_2$.
(b) Explain why the identity of (a) "makes sense" even though $n_1 \neq n_2$.
(c) Under what condition would $p_1 + p_2$ be interpretable?
(d) Under what condition would $n_1 p_1 + n_2 p_2$ be interpretable?

11.7 Scale Classes in the Social Sciences

This chapter has suggested, among other things, that measurement is, decidedly, a cumulative proposition. The analogy with a ladder is a rather useful one, especially if we think of a ladder that becomes narrower toward the top. As the measurement ladder is scaled, one has less lateral freedom in that the class of transformations which can be effected on a set of data becomes more restricted. At the same time, ascension of the ladder increases the scope of one's view by permitting more and more operations that are meaningful mathematically. The English statistician Karl Pearson once asserted that science is measurement. Although his view of measurement was perhaps broader than that represented by this chapter, since it included reference to instruments as well as to theories of measurement, the assertion does require our careful consideration. Specifically, we might raise three questions for consideration at this point: Is measurement truly a prerequisite of science? What is the status of measurement in the social sciences? What courses of action are suggested?

Another eminent scientist, Robert Oppenheimer, has suggested that science is analogy. This means that dynamic systems are selected by scientists as *models* for phenomena under investigation. Each aspect of the investigated situation is represented by some relevant part of the system chosen as a model. The system chosen for the analogy might be a biological, mechanical, physical one, or any other of a variety of thoroughly studied entities. Among all these, one analogy system gives every indication of being more powerful, more efficient, and less likely to provide blind alleys than any of the others. This, of course, is the mathematical model.

It seems clear that, if mathematical models are to be used as scientific analogies, a fairly sophisticated level of measurement is required. Much of mathematics assumes measurement in terms of the real numbers, requiring ratio scales. Thus, although science obviously is far more than sheer measurement, this process is an undeniably important early step in the scientific process.

Where do we stand in the social sciences so far as measurement is concerned? Any attempt to assess the level of measurement sophistication in most fields of social science would suggest fairly dreary conclusions. Sociologists, for instance, are rich to the point of satiation in concepts. Norms, social class, attitudes, social distance, needs, adjustment, and other such notions make up the skeleton of most of sociological theory; but how many of these can be measured in any invariant fashion? What thermometers, what yardsticks does the social scientist have? In sociology, the height of sophistication in recent years has been evidenced by the construction of ordinal scales. It would seem clear that, if the mathematical model is to be employed to any considerable effect in the social sciences, measurement functions with considerably more powerful properties than those of ordinality are needed.

To the extent to which these conclusions are accepted, an answer to the third question above is suggested at once. Perhaps social scientists would do well to devote at least some of their energies to the construction of interval and ratio measurement functions on their already well-established theoretical concepts. The way in which this can be done is a subject we can dispose of here only by avoiding it altogether. A variety of leads is suggested, however, in the list of readings.

Selected References

1. Churchman, Charles West. *Measurements, Definitions and Theories*. New York: John Wiley and Sons, 1959.
2. Coombs, C. H. "Theory and Methods of Social Measurement," in L. Festinger and D. Katz, *Research Methods in the Behavioral Sciences*. New York: The Dryden Press, 1953.
3. ———. "Psychological Scaling Without a Unit of Measurement," *Psychological Review*, 57 (1950), Pages 145–158.
4. ———. "Mathematical Models in Psychological Scaling," *Journal of the American Statistical Association*, 46 (1951), 480–489.
5. Guttman, L. "The Basis for Scalogram Analysis," in S. Stouffer, *et al.*, *Measurement and Prediction: Studies in Social Psychology in World War II*, Volume 4. Princeton, New Jersey: Princeton University Press, 1950. Pages 60–90.
6. Likert, R. "A Technique for the Measurement of Attitudes," *Architecture of Psychology*, No. 140 (1932).
7. Luce, R. D. "Connectivity and Generalized Cliques in Sociometric Group Structure," *Psychometrika*, 15 (1950), 169–190.
8. Stevens, S. S. "On the Theory of Scales of Measurement," *Science*, 103 (1946), 677–680.
9. ———. "Mathematics, Measurement, and Psychophysics," in S. S. Stevens (ed.), *Handbook of Experimental Psychology*. New York: John Wiley and Sons, 1951. Chapter 1.
10. Stouffer, S., Guttman, L., Suchman, E. A., Lazarsfeld, P. F., Star, S. A., and Clausen, J. A. *Measurement and Prediction: Studies in Social Psychology in World War II*, Volume 4. Princeton, New Jersey: Princeton University Press, 1950.
11. Torgerson, Warren. *Theory and Methods of Scaling*. New York: John Wiley and Sons, 1958.

MEASURES
OF CHANGE
AND STABILITY

IV

Convergent Functions

In Chapters 9 through 11, two fundamental notions of mathematics, the notions of number and of function, were combined into what is possibly the greatest single contribution of mathematics to the realm of ideas—that of numerical functions. In this chapter and in the two final chapters, real functions will be considered in an entirely new light. A fundamental scientific concept, that of change, will be constructed from this new perspective. In order to accomplish this, we must establish some new functional categories.

In this chapter we shall consider the way in which some functions grow into a stable pattern, at least in restricted intervals, and then, in the following chapters, we shall use this added knowledge to construct the ideas of change and of mass. The class of functions on integers will be considered first in these terms, and these new ideas about stability or, as it is called, *convergence*, will then be applied to the entire class of real functions.

12.1 Convergent Sequences

Thanks to the order that is built into the domain of sequences, we can observe their varied and sometimes staggering growth patterns as k is allowed to become large. Some sequences never cease growing, whether in a positive or negative direction, and the later elements eventually become colossal. A second growth pattern consists of an endless oscillation in the size of the elements, with gains at one point and losses at the next, but never a final settling down. A third pattern, such as that represented by the reported ages of certain matrons, consists of increase at an ever more sluggish pace, giving promise of an eventual cessation of detectable growth. This third pattern yields what is called the *class of convergent sequences*.

Consider as a (possible) member of the class of convergent sequences the sequence $s_k = \dfrac{k}{k+1}$. An examination of a few terms, such as $s_{20} = 20/21$, $s_{100} = 100/101$, $s_{20,000} = 20,000/20,001$, should convince the reader that the sequence moves progressively closer to the number 1 as k becomes larger. Call this number the *limiting value*, or

12

simply the limit, of s. Several things should be noticed here. First, there is no number k such that $s_k = 1$, since this would require that $k = k + 1$. On the other hand, one can bring s_k just as *close* to the limiting value as he might wish simply by choosing an appropriately large value of k. Suppose that one were required to locate a value of k such that $(1 - s_k) \leq .001$. This is not a large order once the problem is set up properly. The problem requires that:

$$(12.1.1) \qquad \left(1 - \frac{k}{k + 1}\right) \leq .001,$$

from which it should be evident, after a bit of minor algebraic juggling, that $(1 - s_k) \leq .001$ for any value of $k \geq 999$. (This should *not* be taken on faith.) In fact, the value on the right side of the inequality could be made arbitrarily small (although necessarily positive), and an appropriately large value of k could be found to satisfy it. Thus, the elements of the sequence move progressively, inexorably closer to what will be called the limiting value of the sequence, the number one.

If the preceding example was understood, the following definition should offer no added problems; it is merely a formal summary of what was evidenced in the example:

(12.1.2) A sequence, s, is said to converge to a limit (or **Definition** limiting value), α, if and only if, for each positive number, ϵ, there exists a positive integer **K** such that, for each $k \geq \mathbf{K}$,

$$|s_k - \alpha| \leq \epsilon.$$

Otherwise, s is said to diverge.

The number ϵ represents a maximum admissible difference between s_k and the limiting value, α. This value is chosen in an entirely arbitrary manner. In fact, a specific number usually is not assigned at all, since ϵ may be any positive real number. The trick in proving convergence consists of establishing a functional correspondence between **K** and ϵ such that the inequality of 12.1.2 is satisfied. The absolute value on the left side of the inequality is a necessary result of the fact that the sequence could approach its limit either from above, as in $s_k = \dfrac{1}{k}$, or from below, as in the previous example. In the latter case, the *algebraic* difference, $(s_k - \alpha)$, would always satisfy the inequality of 12.1.2, and the definition would be senseless. This necessary insertion of absolute values means that any exploration of convergent sequences must rely heavily on the algebra of absolute numbers (a review of Section 10.2, and especially of Theorem 10.2.2, might be valuable at this stage).

Before the machinery of 12.1.2 is set in motion, a minor notational convention is needed:

(12.1.3) If s is a sequence that converges to a limit, α, **Notation** then the limiting value is noted:

$$\lim_{k \to \infty} s_k = \alpha,$$

or, when the meaning is clear, simply $\lim s_k = \alpha$.
The symbol ∞ denotes infinity. It refers to no particular number but, rather, embraces the entire range of positive numbers. The shorthand phrase of 12.1.3, then, is read "the limit of the sequence, s_k, as k goes to infinity, is the number α."

Let us now put this equipment to use by proving formally that the illustrative sequence $s_k = \dfrac{k}{k+1}$ converges in the limit of k to the number 1.

(12.1.4) $\qquad \lim_{k \to \infty} \left(\dfrac{k}{k+1} \right) = 1.$ **THEOREM**

Let $\mathbf{K} = \dfrac{1}{\epsilon} - 1.$ *Proof*

(1) $\left| \dfrac{k}{k+1} - 1 \right| = \left| -\dfrac{1}{k+1} \right|,$ (Construct a common denominator and cancel)

(2) $\qquad\qquad = \dfrac{1}{k+1}.$ (By 10.2.1 and since $k > 0$)

(3) $\qquad \dfrac{1}{k+1} \le \dfrac{1}{\mathbf{K}+1},$ for all $k \ge \mathbf{K}$,

(4) but $\dfrac{1}{\mathbf{K}+1} = \dfrac{1}{\left(\dfrac{1}{\epsilon}-1\right)+1}$,   (By hypothesis)

(5) $= \epsilon.$

(6) $\left|\dfrac{k}{k+1}-1\right| \le \epsilon,$ all $k \ge \dfrac{1}{\epsilon}-1$ (Steps 2, 3, and 5 and transitivity)

Note that in this proof a value of ϵ was never specified. The entire proof hinged upon finding a critical number, $\mathbf{K}$, such that, for each value of $k \ge \mathbf{K}$, s_k would be within the distance, ϵ, of its limiting value. At least one question should remain in the reader's mind: Where did the functional relation between $\mathbf{K}$ and ϵ, as expressed in the hypothesis, pop up? Unfortunately, there is no absolutely foolproof mathematical answer. The suggested function, as must always be the case, resulted from informal guesswork and, for lack of a better term, from insight gained through working with a number of selected values of ϵ.

Of course, a good start consists of assuming that there is some $\mathbf{K}$ such that $|s_k - \alpha| \le \epsilon$ for $k \ge \mathbf{K}$, simplifying and obtaining $\mathbf{K}$ as a function of ϵ. The reader should note also that $\mathbf{K}$ is not quite the simple function of ϵ that has been represented; $\mathbf{K}$ necessarily is an integer, but the derived function may not yield an integer. This is a minor point, however, since we can always choose the nearest integer greater than the functional value obtained.

Let us go through the entire process of proving the existence of limits once more before looking into some of their more useful properties. The limit of the sequence $s_k = \dfrac{1}{k}$ clearly is the number 0. If the reader is not so convinced, he should experiment with the sequence. He should take larger and larger values of k, asking himself each time whether a still larger value of k could possibly yield a range-value less near to the apparent limit. This is the intuitive, inductive process in operation. The formal proof now requires only that the magic value, $\mathbf{K}$, be located as a function of ϵ. To make this discovery, choose several values of ϵ. For instance, if $\epsilon = .01$, some manipulation should convince the reader that $\mathbf{K} = 100$ satisfies the inequality

$\left|\dfrac{1}{k} - 0\right| \leq .01$ for all $k \geq \mathbf{K}$. If $\epsilon = .001$, the same sort of exploration should convince one that the sufficient value of $\mathbf{K}$ is 1,000. More such experimentation would indicate that, in general, the necessary inequality is satisfied by letting $\mathbf{K} = \dfrac{1}{\epsilon}$. To put these strictly informal parts together and to garb them in an entirely formal manner, we have:

(12.1.5) $$\lim_{k \to \infty} \left(\frac{1}{k}\right) = 0.$$ **THEOREM**

Let $\mathbf{K} = \dfrac{1}{\epsilon}$.   *Proof*

(1) $\left|\dfrac{1}{k} - 0\right| = \dfrac{1}{k}.$ (Since $k > 0$)

(2) $\dfrac{1}{k} \leq \dfrac{1}{\mathbf{K}} = \epsilon.$ $\left(\text{Since } k \geq \mathbf{K} \text{ and since } \mathbf{K} = \dfrac{1}{\epsilon}\right)$

(3) $\left|\dfrac{1}{k} - 0\right| \leq \epsilon.$ (By steps 1 and 2)

By this point, some readers may be convinced that the concept of convergence is an unfathomable maze of abstractions. A careful reading of the preceding pages, however, indicates that the analysis of convergence rests on just four component parts, none of which, singly, is especially complicated.

(12.1.6)   **Components of the Concept of Convergence**

(1) Sequence: a function whose domain consists of any subset of the positive integers. Since the domain is well ordered, the range can be thought of as an ordered set of numbers.

(2) Limit: a number, α, toward which the range values of a (convergent) sequence move. If there exists no such number, the sequence is said to diverge.

(3) ϵ: an interval or unit of distance (expressed as any positive number), which in operation is usually not specified, but which should be thought of as being arbitrarily chosen and tiny. The ϵ-interval ordinarily is allowed

to vary as the domain of a function whose range is a set of positive integers, **K**.

(4) **K**: a critical integer that is a function of ϵ (in general, the smaller a value of ϵ the larger must be the value of **K**). The **K** integer marks that point in the sequential domain ($[1, 2, \cdots, \mathbf{K} - 1], \mathbf{K}, [\mathbf{K} + 1, \mathbf{K} + 2, \cdots]$), beyond which the range values ($[s_1, s_2, \cdots, s_{K-1}], s_K, [s_{K+1}, a_{K+2}, \cdots]$) are uniformly no more than one ϵ-interval distant from the limit.

In terms of these components, a sequence is said to be convergent, or to converge to a limit, α, only if, for every possible ϵ-interval, no matter how small, a critical integer, **K**, can be located such that all range values "farther out" in the ordered set are no more than one ϵ-interval distant from α. Convergence can be represented graphically, as in Figure 12.1.

Figure 12.1   ILLUSTRATION OF A CONVERGENT SEQUENCE

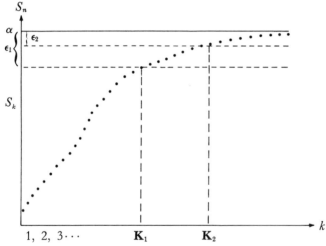

This shows how a value of **K** is determined once an ϵ-interval has been selected. A first choice, ϵ_1, determines **K₁**. The choice of ϵ_2 yields **K₂**. The reader should convince himself that, if the ϵ-interval were allowed to become smaller, the integer **K** would become larger (would move to the right in this figure).

There should be no need to debate the usefulness to social theorists of the mathematician's concept of the limit of a sequence. Let population density, juvenile delinquency rates, interclass movement in a democratic society, or expected years of life be represented as sequences in which the range values, k, represent regular time intervals. Whether sequences such as these converge to limits or whether they diverge (become endlessly larger) are matters of utmost importance for social theory and for social policy. In some cases they are life-and-death issues.

The notion of convergence to a limit clearly merits our examination; but, as the careful reader should have observed, it retains at least one really irksome shortcoming as presented to this point. There exists no routine mathematical system for evaluating the limit of any particular sequence. This is doubly irksome because, in many cases, the issue consists of determining whether or not a limit exists, but not what its specific value happens to be. A mathematician, A. L. Cauchy, remedied this situation by constructing a method of examining sequences for convergence.

(12.1.7) A sequence, s_k, is said to be *Cauchy convergent* if and only if for each positive number, ϵ, there exists a positive integer, **K**, such that, for each pair of integers i and $j \geq \mathbf{K}$,   **Definition**

$$|s_i - s_j| \leq \epsilon.$$

Before going on, the reader would do well to compare this definition with that of 12.1.2. Notice that there are two chief differences. First, at no place in 12.1.7 is the value of the limit, α, involved. Second, rather than comparing the difference between sequential values and the limit, $|s_k - \alpha|$, 12.1.7 compares each possible pair of values $|s_i - s_j|$ that are sufficiently "far out." The Cauchy approach, of course, expresses precisely the same idea as does the classical definition of limit: If a sequence moves closer and closer to a limit (beyond a point **K**, then the differences between pairs of values of the sequence must become progressively smaller. The really important property of the Cauchy criterion is that it tells whether a sequence converges without imposing the burden of discovering the value of the limit.

(12.1.8) A sequence converges to a limit if and only if it is Cauchy convergent.   **THEOREM**

The first part of the proof (the implication) is left as an exercise for the reader. The only trick consists of choosing $\mathbf{K}$ such that $|s_k - \alpha| \leq \frac{\epsilon}{2}$ for all $k \geq \mathbf{K}$. The proof of the second part (the converse of the implication) demands more complicated equipment than has been developed here (see Rudin, *Principles of Mathematical Analysis* [5], page 46).

In order to use the Cauchy criterion, let us prove a theorem on convergence without obtaining the value of the limit. Consider the sequence $s_k = k^{-p}$ for any $p > 0$. Note that this really represents an entire class of sequences, because each different value of p yields a different sequence. Note also that we have considered one member of this class already, namely, that given by $p = 1$.

(12.1.9) If s is any sequence such that $s_k = k^{-p}$, $p > 0$, then s converges to a limit.   **THEOREM**

Let $s_k = k^{-p}$, $p > 0$, and $i, j \geq \mathbf{K} = \left(\dfrac{2}{\epsilon}\right)^{1/p}$.   *Proof*

(1) $s_i, s_j \leq s_{\mathbf{K}}$.   (Since $i^p, j^p \geq \mathbf{K}^p \to i^{-p}$, $j^{-p} \leq \mathbf{K}^{-p}$)

(2) $s_i + s_j \leq 2s_{\mathbf{K}}$.   (By step 1)

(3) $2s_{\mathbf{K}} = \epsilon$. $\left(\text{Since } 2s_{\mathbf{K}} \right.$
$$= 2\left(\frac{1}{\left[\left(\frac{2}{\epsilon}\right)^{1/p}\right]^p}\right) = 2\left(\frac{\epsilon}{2}\right).$$

(4) $|s_i - s_j| \leq |s_i| + |-s_j|$.   (10.2.2.1)
(5) $|s_i| + |-s_j| = s_i + s_j$.   (Since $s_i, s_j > 0$)
(6) $|s_i - s_j| \leq \epsilon$.   (By steps 2, 3, and 5)

As an exercise, the reader ought to guess at the limiting value of this class of sequences and then attempt to re-prove the theorem by the classical definition of convergence to a limit.

The limit of a sequence can be thought of as a property of the sequence, as a way of characterizing it. Thus, one could construct equivalence classes of sequences based on their limit properties. The most general class might be that of all convergent sequences (those not in the class are called *divergent sequences*, according to 12.1.2). Although a limit is a property of a sequence, limits themselves turn out to be intriguing numbers that possess a number of useful properties. Can the reader guess what some of these might be? For instance, does it appear to be a good bet that, if $\lim_{k \to \infty} s_k = \alpha$, then the limit of the related *harmonic* sequence is

$$\lim_{k \to \infty} \frac{1}{s_k} = \frac{1}{\alpha}?$$ This and several similar questions are answered by the following theorem on properties of limits:

THEOREM

(12.1.10) (*Properties of Limits*)
(1) If $s_k = c$, any real number, then $\lim (s_k) = c$.

If s is any convergent sequence such that $\lim (s_k) = \alpha$, then
(2) if β also is a limit of s, $\alpha = \beta$.

(3) $\lim \left(\dfrac{1}{s_k} \right) = \dfrac{1}{\alpha}$ $\left(\text{provided } \alpha \neq 0 \text{ and } \dfrac{1}{s_k} \neq 0, \text{ for all } k \right)$.

(4) $\lim (c s_k) = c\alpha$.
(5) $\lim (c + s_k) = c + \alpha$.

If s' is a second convergent sequence such that $\lim (s'_k) = \alpha'$, then

(6) $\lim (s_k + s'_k) = \alpha + \alpha'$.
(7) $\lim (s_k s'_k) = \alpha\alpha'$.

(8) $\lim \left(\dfrac{s_k}{s'_k} \right) = \dfrac{\alpha}{\alpha'}$,   if α', $s'_k \neq 0$, all k.

Proof

Part 1 should be obvious. *Parts 4* and *5* follow directly from *1*, *6*, and *7*. *Part 8* is an immediate consequence of *Parts 3* and *7*.

Part 2: Let s converge to both α and β. Then, there exists $\mathbf{K}$ such that, for all $k \geq \mathbf{K}$

(1) $|s_k - \alpha| \leq \frac{\epsilon}{2}$ and $|\beta - s_k| \leq \frac{\epsilon}{2}$.   (Since ϵ is arbitrary)

(2) $|(s_k - \alpha) + (\beta - s_k)|$ (By 10.2.2.1 and hy-
$\leq |s_k - \alpha| + |\beta - s_k| \leq \epsilon$.   pothesis)

(3) $|\beta - \alpha| \leq \epsilon$,

(4) hence,* $|\beta - \alpha| = 0 \rightarrow \beta = \alpha$.

Part 3: Let $\lim (s_k) = \alpha \neq 0$. Then there exists **K** such that, for all $k \geq$ **K**,

(1) $|s_k - \alpha| \leq \begin{cases} \dfrac{|\alpha|}{2} \\ \dfrac{|\alpha|^2}{2} \epsilon, \text{ whichever} \\ \qquad \text{is smaller.} \end{cases}$ (Since ϵ is an arbitrary value)

(2) $|s_k - \alpha| \leq \dfrac{|\alpha|}{2} \rightarrow |s_k| \geq \dfrac{|\alpha|}{2}$,

$$k \geq \mathbf{K}. \quad (10.2.2.5)$$

(3) $\dfrac{1}{|s_k\alpha|} \leq \dfrac{2}{|\alpha|^2}.$ $\left(\text{Step 2 and since} \right.$

$$\left. a \geq b \rightarrow \frac{1}{a} \leq \frac{1}{b} \right)$$

(4) $\left| \dfrac{1}{s_k} - \dfrac{1}{\alpha} \right| = \left| \dfrac{\alpha - s_k}{s_k\alpha} \right|$,

(5) $\qquad \leq \dfrac{2}{|\alpha|^2} |s_k - \alpha|$,   (Step 3, 10.2.2.2, and
$$k \geq \mathbf{K}, \qquad 10.2.2.4)$$

(6) $\qquad \leq \left(\dfrac{2}{|\alpha|^2} \right) \left(\dfrac{|\alpha|^2}{2} \epsilon \right) = \epsilon.$ (Steps 1 and 5)

Part 6: Let s converge to α and s' to α'. Then, there exists **K** such that, for all $k >$ **K**:

(1) $|s_k - \alpha| \leq \frac{\epsilon}{2}$ and $|s_k' - \alpha'| \leq \frac{\epsilon}{2}$.   (Since ϵ is arbitrary)

(2) $|s_k - \alpha| + |s_k' - \alpha'| \leq \epsilon$,   (Step 1)

(3) but, $|(s_k + s_k') - (\alpha + \alpha')|$
$\leq |s_k - \alpha| + |s_k' - \alpha'|$,   (10.2.2.1)

(4) thus, $|(s_k + s_k') - (\alpha + \alpha')| \leq \epsilon$.   (Steps 2 and 3 and transitivity)

---

* This assumes the truth of $|\beta - \alpha| \leq \epsilon$, all $\epsilon > 0 \rightarrow |\beta - \alpha| = 0$. The reader should satisfy himself that this is indeed the case. See Exercise 12.13.

Part 7: With the preceding hypothesis, there exists $\mathbf{K}$ such that, for all $k \geq \mathbf{K}$:

(1) $|s_k - \alpha| \leq \sqrt{\epsilon}$ and $|s_k' - \alpha'| \leq \sqrt{\epsilon}$.

(2) The proof follows upon applying step 1 to the identity
$$(s_k s_k' - \alpha\alpha') = (s_k - \alpha)(s_k' - \alpha') + \alpha(s_k' - \alpha')$$
$$+ \alpha'(s_k - \alpha).$$

By virtually any criteria, this theorem contains a large and concentrated amount of information, and parts of its proof are difficult. The really important matter is understanding what the various parts of the theorem say. One can be reasonably certain that he has this understanding if he is able to translate the parts of the theorem correctly into English sentences. For example, 12.1.10.2 is translated into "If a sequence converges, then it converges to a unique number." So far as the proofs are concerned, it should be apparent that the real trick consists of the judicious selection of functions of ϵ, such as $\sqrt{\epsilon}$ or $\epsilon/2$, with which to trap terms of the form $|s_k - \alpha|$.

Exercises

12.1. For each of the following, compute s_{10}, s_{100}, s_{101}, s_{500}, s_{501}:

(a) $s_k = \dfrac{k}{k+3}$.

(b) $s_k = \dfrac{k+3}{k}$.

(c) $s_k = \dfrac{k^2 - 1}{k+1}$.

(d) $s_k = \dfrac{k+1}{k^2 - 1}$, $k > 1$.

(e) $s_k = 4$.

(f) $s_k = \dfrac{2^{2k}}{2^k}$. (Use logs.)

12.2. For each sequence of Exercise 12.1, determine by inspection whether the sequence converges and what its limit appears to be.

12.3. Use Definition 12.1.1 to prove $\lim\limits_{k \to \infty} \dfrac{k-1}{k^2 - 1} = 0$. (HINT: Choose $\mathbf{K} = \dfrac{1}{\epsilon} - 1$. Be sure to show that $k > \mathbf{K} \to 0 < s_k < s_\mathbf{K}$.)

12.4. Let $s_k = \dfrac{k+4}{k+2}$.

(a) Show that $s_k = 1 + \dfrac{2}{k+2}$, that $s_k > 0$, all $k \geq 0$, and that $k_1 > k_2 \to s_{k_1} < s_{k_2}$.

(b) From part (a), what should be $\lim\limits_{k \to \infty} s_k$? Why?

(c) Suppose that a number, $\epsilon > 0$, is chosen and that there exists a number $\mathbf{K}$ such that $s_{\mathbf{K}} - 1 = \epsilon$. What is the number $\mathbf{K}$? (HINT: Set $1 + \dfrac{2}{\mathbf{K}+2} = \epsilon$ and solve for $\mathbf{K}$.)

(d) Verify your answer to (c) by showing that $s_{\mathbf{K}} = \epsilon$.

(e) Using parts (a) through (d), prove that $\lim\limits_{k \to \infty} s_k = 1$.

12.5. Exercise 12.4 represents an informal method of locating the critical integer $\mathbf{K}$ so that the existence of a limit, α, can be proved. Describe what was done in each step and the reason why each step was taken.

12.6. Determine the limit and the critical integer $\mathbf{K}$ required for the limit proof for each of the following sequences:

(a) $s_k = \dfrac{k-1}{k+3}$.

(b) $s_k = 2^{1/k}$.

(c) $s_k = e^{3/k}$.

(d) $s_k = \log(k+1) - \log k$.

(e) $s_k = 2^{-k}$.

(f) $s_k = \left(1 + \dfrac{1}{k}\right)^k$.

12.7. Suppose that a \$20,000 loan is secured at compound interest rate, i, and that *annual* payments of \$1,000 are made. How many years will be required for the debt to be reduced to \$2,000? to \$500?

12.8. Prove that, if a sequence converges, it is Cauchy convergent.

12.9. Suppose that the number of juveniles in a community is n_k in year k, where $n_k = n_1 + 500(k-1)$ and that the number of those who are classed as delinquents is $s_k = s_1 + 20(k-1)$. Let $P_k = \dfrac{s_k}{n_k}$ and $P_1 = .1$. If $n_1 = 1{,}000$,

(a) simplify the expression of P_k. (HINT: First evaluate s_1.)

(b) is the *number* of delinquents increasing?

(c) is delinquency increasing? (HINT: Examine the monotonicity properties of P_k.)

(d) if the sequences s_k and n_k remain unchanged, will delinquency eventually disappear?

(e) Derive $\lim\limits_{k \to \infty} P_k$.

12.10. Construct two sequences that might characterize phenomena of your own field. Examine their limit properties.

12.11. In Exercise 12.6, prove that each sequence converges by the Cauchy criterion.

12.12. Prove 12.1.10.4.

12.13. Prove that $|\beta - \alpha| \leq \epsilon$, all $\epsilon > 0 \to |\beta - \alpha| = 0$. Use a proof by contradiction.

12.2 Series

According to Definition 9.2.1, a partial sum is nothing more than an element of a sequence that is put together by adding the first n values of a second sequence. The preceding discussion of convergence suggested that it can be useful to examine range values of sequences as their domain values, the integers k, are allowed to become quite large. There is nothing to prevent our tacking this idea onto the construct of partial sums. This addition yields an altogether new sort of function, generically labeled *infinite series*.

(12.2.1) If $\mathbf{S}_n = \sum\limits_{k=1}^{n} s_k$ is a partial sum generated by a   **Definition**

sequence, s, then, if it exists,

$$\mathbf{S} = \sum_{k=1}^{\infty} s_k = \lim_{n \to \infty} \mathbf{S}_n$$

is called the sum of the infinite series of s_k. If $\mathbf{S}$ exists, the series is said to converge. Otherwise, it is said to diverge.

The sum of an infinite series, then, is nothing more than the expansion to the limit of a partial sum. One might well ask what sort of nonsense this is. Can one actually add numbers endlessly and come up with a sum that is a sensible number? If the reader will think for a moment, he should be able to come up with an endless string of numbers whose sum is a perfectly sensible number. A sequence defined by $s_k = 0$ certainly is in order. The partial sums generated by this se-

quence, $\mathbf{S}_n = \sum\limits_{k=1}^{n} (0)$, clearly are 0 for each positive integer

n. Intuitively, it should be obvious that the sum of the infinite series generated by this sequence also is 0. Thus, although the notion of infinite series might initially appear to be altogether useless, we have found at least one case in which the sum is a sensible number, even though the case appears to be trivial.

Once it is admitted that an infinite set of numbers can indeed be added to a finite sum, it should be asked whether other sequences might also generate infinite series whose sums are real numbers. What would such a sequence have to look like, if it were to exist at all? Reflection ought to convince one that the range values of such a sequence must become minute as the domain values become larger, for the contribution of each added value should have to become less and less significant to the sum if the sum is to remain within reasonable bounds. What about the limit properties of such a sequence? A good guess, which follows from the preceding idea, would be that the sequential limit would have to be 0 if the sequence of partial sums were to converge to a (finite) limiting value.

Let us examine a particular sequence that meets these criteria. The routine geometric sequence, $s_k = (\frac{1}{2})^{k-1}$ has a limit that should be intuitively obvious. The reader ought to be able to prove that $\lim_{k \to \infty} s_k = 0$. Thus, s_k does have a limiting value such that the series which it generates might possibly converge to some finite number. Before continuing, the reader might try to guess how large a number one would obtain by adding successive values of this sequence together forever. It would seem reasonable to guess that the sum is a huge number. However, the following theorem shows that such a guess would be wildly incorrect:

(12.2.2)
$$\sum_{k=1}^{\infty} (\tfrac{1}{2})^{k-1} = 2.$$
THEOREM

(1) $\displaystyle\sum_{k=1}^{n} (\tfrac{1}{2})^{k-1} = \frac{(\tfrac{1}{2})^n - 1}{(\tfrac{1}{2}) - 1},$ (By 9.2.3)   *Proof*

(2) $\qquad\qquad = 2 - 2(\tfrac{1}{2})^n,$ (By clearing terms in 1)

(3) $\qquad\qquad = 2 - (\tfrac{1}{2})^{n-1}.$ (By 7.2.3.2 and since $2 = (\tfrac{1}{2})^{-1}$)

(4) $\displaystyle\sum_{k=1}^{\infty} (\tfrac{1}{2})^{k-1} = \lim_{n \to \infty}\left[\sum_{k=1}^{n} (\tfrac{1}{2})^{n-1}\right],$ (By 12.2.1)

(5) $\qquad\qquad = \lim_{n \to \infty} (2 - (\tfrac{1}{2})^{n-1}),$ (By step 3)

(6) $\qquad\qquad = 2 - \lim_{n \to \infty} (\tfrac{1}{2})^{n-1},$ (By 12.1.10.1 and 12.1.10.6)

(7) $= 2 - 0 = 2.$ (Since $\lim (\tfrac{1}{2})^{n-1} = 0$)

It is truly remarkable how small the sum of an infinite series can remain. Theorem 12.2.2 can be generalized immensely by substituting for the number $\tfrac{1}{2}$ any number c such that $0 < c < 1$. Why are these particular bounds for c necessary? The reader should convince himself that, in this more general case, we have:

THEOREM

$$(12.2.3) \quad \sum_{k=1}^{\infty} c^{k-1} = \begin{cases} 1/(1-c) & \text{if } 0 < c < 1 \\ \text{diverges} & \text{if } c \geq 1 \end{cases}.$$

It has been suggested that, if a series is to converge, its associated sequence must have the limit zero. This can be demonstrated efficiently by redefining the Cauchy convergence criterion.

Definition

$(12.2.4)$ A series, $\sum\limits_{k=1}^{\infty} s_k$, is Cauchy convergent if and only if, for each real number, $\epsilon > 0$, there exists a positive integer $\mathbf{K}$ such that, for each pair of integers i and $j, j \geq i \geq \mathbf{K}$,

$$\left| \sum_{k=i}^{j} s_k \right| \leq \epsilon.$$

If this definition is compared to that of 12.1.7, it will be apparent that both say essentially the same thing. To show that a convergent series must stem from a sequence whose limit is zero, we have:

THEOREM

$(12.2.5)$ If $\sum\limits_{k=1}^{\infty} s_k$ converges, then $\lim s_k = 0$.

Proof

Let $\sum a_k$ converge so that, for all $j \geq i \geq \mathbf{K}$,

(1) $\left| \sum\limits_{k=i}^{j} s_k \right| \leq \epsilon \quad i, j \geq \mathbf{K}.$ (By 12.2.4)

(2) $\left| \sum\limits_{k=i}^{i} s_k \right| = |s_i| \leq \epsilon.$

(3) $|s_i| \leq \epsilon \rightarrow \lim s_k = 0.$ (Exercise 12.13)

Notice that the theorem says nothing about the converse. That is, the fact that a sequence has a limiting value of zero may not necessarily guarantee that the generated series converges to a finite number. It could be that, although a sequence goes to zero in the limit, it may not move toward the limit rapidly enough to permit the sum to remain within finite bounds. We shall see in just a moment that this is exactly the case for many series, and we shall begin to see how rapidly a sequence must move to zero in order for its partial sums to converge.

Many sequences that converge to zero do so in a regular and undeviating manner. That is, many sequences are monotone decreasing (see Definition 10.3.3). Since the monotone-decreasing characteristic is fairly common to sequences, the following theorem turns out to be quite useful:

(12.2.6) If $s_k \geq s_{k+1} \geq 0$, then: **THEOREM**

$$\sum_{k=1}^{\infty} s_k \text{ converges} \leftrightarrow \sum_{k=1}^{\infty} (2^{k-1})(s_{2^{k-1}}) \text{ converges.}$$

The proof of this seemingly odd theorem can be found in Rudin, *Principles of Mathematical Analysis* [5], page 53. What it says is that $s_1 + s_2 + \cdots$ converges if and only if $s_1 + 2s_2 + 4s_4 + \cdots$ converges. Note how small a subsequence of s_k is sufficient to determine whether or not the entire sequence converges to a limit.

Theorem 12.2.6 is particularly useful in determining just how rapidly a sequence must converge to its limit if its series is also to converge. Zero-convergent sequences are usually geometric or harmonic. By generalizing theorem 12.2.2, the theorem that follows tells us about the convergence of series of harmonic sequences:

(12.2.7) $\displaystyle\sum_{k=1}^{\infty} \frac{1}{k^a}$ converges $\leftrightarrow a > 1$. **THEOREM**

If $a \leq 0$, the sequence clearly does not converge to zero. *Proof*
If $a > 0$, then $s_k > s_{k+1}$, and we can use Theorem 12.2.6.

(1) $\displaystyle\sum_{k=1}^{\infty} 2^{k-1} s_{2^{k-1}} = \sum_{k=1}^{\infty} 2^{k-1} \left(\frac{1}{2^{(k-1)a}} \right),$

(2)
$$= \sum_{k=1}^{\infty} 2^{(k-1)(1-a)},$$

and we are in a position to use Theorem 12.2.3 by setting $c = 2^{1-a}$. Since it follows that

(3) $2^{1-a} < 1 \leftrightarrow a > 1$, the result follows immediately.

Suppose that an economist plotted the changing patterns of the national debt through time and found that the annual increase, say $(D_k - D_{k-1})$ where D_k is the debt at year k, $k = 1, 2, 3, \cdots$, becomes smaller in a regular fashion as a function of time. Suppose, in fact, he found that $(D_k - D_{k-1}) = 1/k$. Now, this discovery might appear comforting, because we know from 12.1.5 that the limit of this sequence is zero, so that, in the long run (in the limit of k), the national debt must stabilize and then stop increasing altogether. This is a less than altogether comforting conclusion, however, for two reasons. First, as Lord Keynes observed, in the long run we shall all be dead. Second, we need be less concerned about the stabilization of the debt than about the total amount of indebtedness that we must shoulder. Since the economist's function tells us that the debt at time k is $D_k = D_{k-1} + 1/k$, it is clear that the total debt at time n is just $D_n = D_0 + \sum_{k=1}^{n} 1/k$. But the limit of the sum in this term is infinitely large, because $\sum_{k=1}^{\infty} 1/k$ fails to converge according to theorem 12.2.7. Our debt, alas, will never stabilize according to our investigator's results. Incidentally, it should be noticed that the series $\sum (1/k)$ fails to converge even though $\lim (1/k) = 0$, which provides a counter-example to the converse of theorem 12.2.5.

Before leaving this topic, it will be worthwhile to consider one especially important infinite series. In Section 7.3, brief reference was made to an irrational number labeled e, which serves as the base of so-called natural logarithms. It turns out that e is the limit of a convergent infinite series.

(12.2.8)
$$e = \sum_{k=0}^{\infty} 1/k!$$
Definition

Recall from Definition 9.4.3 that $k!$ is called k factorial and refers to the serial product of the first k positive integers. It is easy to convince oneself that e is a small number, because it is clear that, for $k \geq 2$, $1/k! \leq \frac{1}{2}^k$. We know by now that the series generated by $\frac{1}{2}^k$ converges to the number two, so that e must be something less than three (the value is $2.71828 \cdots$). It turns out that e is the limiting value of a sequence as well as of this infinite series.

(12.2.9) $$\lim_{k \to \infty} \left(1 + \frac{1}{k} \right)^k = e.$$ **THEOREM**

The proof of this theorem (see Rudin [5], pages 55–56) involves showing that $\left(1 + \frac{1}{k} \right)$ can be no larger than the sum of the reciprocals of the first k factorials and then showing that, at the same time, the latter can be no larger than the former. We shall have occasion to make use of this theorem in a later chapter.

The preceding discussion made implicit use of a property of convergent series that can be quite useful in analysis. This property is as follows: If two sequences of positive terms, say s_k and r_k, are such that $s_k \geq r_k$ for each positive integer k, and if $\sum_{k=1}^{\infty} s_k$ converges, then $\sum_{k=1}^{\infty} r_k$ also converges. Often, an apparently complicated sequence, r_k, can be shown to generate a convergent series if its elements are simply "trapped" between zero and the elements of a simpler sequence, s_k. That is,

(12.2.10) If s_k and r_k are two sequences such that   **THEOREM** $0 \leq r_k \leq s_k$, each $k \; \epsilon \; I^+$, and if $\sum_{k=1}^{\infty} s_k$ converges, then $\sum_{k=1}^{\infty} r_k$ converges. Similarly, if $\sum_{k=1}^{\infty} r_k$ diverges $\left(\text{if } \lim_{n \to \infty} \sum_{k=1}^{n} r_k \neq \alpha, \right.$ for any real number $\alpha \Big)$, then $\sum_{k=1}^{\infty} s_k$ diverges also.

The proof is left as an exercise that requires the Cauchy convergence criterion.

At this point the reader should satisfy himself that he can answer each of the following questions correctly: What is the limit of a sequence? What is meant by the phrase "con-

verge to a limit?" How can one add an infinite set of numbers and still have a finite sum? What is an example of a
sequence in my own field of specialization? of an infinite
series? Might either or both of these be expected to converge? How would the fact of convergence or divergence be
interpreted in terms of social science in these cases?

Exercises

12.14. Prove that $\lim_{k \to \infty} (1/2)^{k-1} = 0$.

12.15. Compute the values $s_k = \dfrac{1}{k!}$ for $k = 1, 2, \cdots, 10$.

(a) Compute $\sum_{k=1}^{4} s_k$.

(b) Compute $\sum_{k=5}^{10} s_k$.

(c) Compute $\sum_{k=1}^{10} s_k$.

12.16. Let $s_k = k^{-1}$ and $r_k = k^{-1.2}$.

(a) Using logs, evaluate s_k and r_k for $k = 1, 2, \cdots, 10$.
(b) Evaluate s_k and r_k for $k = 100, 500, 1,000$.
(c) Compute $\sum_{k=1}^{10} s_k$ and $\sum_{k=1}^{10} r_k$.
(d) Use these data to suggest why $\sum_{k=1}^{\infty} r_k$ converges but $\sum_{k=1}^{\infty} s_k$ does not.

12.3 Limits of Functions and the Notion of Continuity

In this section the notion of a limit will be broadened
from the class of sequences to the much larger class of real
functions. This generalization turns out to be straightforward—with one exception. The exception concerns the
manner in which sequences differ from real functions. This
difference consists of what goes on in the interval between
each pair of successive integers.

In the picture created by a sequence, nothing occurs in
this interval. It is an empty space that need not be consid-

ered in the construction of limits. A real function, on the other hand, crams each such interval with an uncountably large set of numbers. In a real function, it is possible to find that the range correspondents of the integers progress in all serenity while some of or all the numbers between them are dashed about wildly. Consider, for example, the function given by:

$$(12.3.1)\ f(x) = \begin{cases} 1 \text{ if } x \text{ is a rational number} \\ -1 \text{ if } x \text{ is an irrational number} \end{cases}.$$

Notice first that the *sequence* that could be built from this function by pulling the integers (which are rational numbers) would be represented by $s_k = 1$, whose limit is the number 1. (Why?) However, between each two successive integers, the graph of the function would zigzag between 1 and -1 an uncountably large number of times, thus making it impossible to pin down a limit at all.

Because of this difference between a sequence and a real function, we shall have to consider the limit at each *point* in the domain of a real function rather than talking about *the* limit in the singular. Intuitively, the phrase "the limit at a point, x_0, of a function, f" has the following meaning: If a number α is the limit of a domain point, x_0, then the range values of x should smoothly move ever closer to α as values of x are taken closer to x_0. The idea of a smooth, unbroken progression is critical to the notion of a limit.

As a first step in formalizing the notion of limits of functions, consider the assertion that a point, x_0, in the domain of f has a limiting value, α, in the range. If the assertion is true, then the values $f(x)$, where x is reasonably close to x_0, should be close to the number α. Choose a set of numbers that are close to x_0 by constructing an interval with midpoint x_0 and half-length δ.* Symbolically the interval could be represented by $I_{(x_0-\delta,\ x_0+\delta)}$, $\delta > 0$, which contains the set of all domain values, x, such that $|x - x_0| < \delta$. For each x in this set, the f-correspondent should fall within an interval about α, say $I_{(\alpha-\epsilon,\ \alpha+\epsilon)}$, $\epsilon > 0$, which contains the set of all points $f(x)$ such that $|f(x) - \alpha| < \epsilon$. Now squeeze this ϵ-interval so that it closes in on α. No matter how small it

* For the sake of convenience, this is called the δ interval, despite the fact that its length is 2δ. Similarly, the ϵ interval has length of 2ϵ.

becomes, we should be able to locate a corresponding δ-interval about x_0 such that, for each x in the δ-interval, $f(x)$ is in the ϵ-interval. Figure 12.2 contains a picture of these ideas.

Figure 12.2

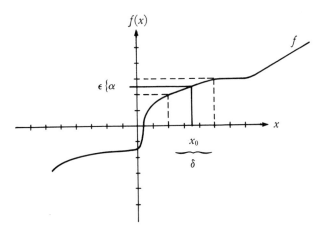

It is a reasonably short jump from these semiformal ideas to a completely formal mathematical definition of the limit at a point of a real function. See if the following does not say exactly what was expressed in the preceding paragraphs, although in much more clipped language.

Definition

(12.3.2) If a function, f, is defined on an interval, $I_{(a, b)}$, that contains a point, x_0, then α is a limit of f at $x_0 \leftrightarrow$ for each positive number, ϵ, there exists a positive number, δ, such that $0 < |x - x_0| < \delta \rightarrow |f(x) - \alpha| < \epsilon$, all $x \in I_{(a, b)}$, and we write:

$$\lim_{x \to x_0} f(x) = \alpha.$$

A frankly cynical thought may have occurred to the careful reader by now. It is at least intuitively clear that each of the major classes of functions that were considered in Chapter 10 had a smoothly moving, continuous graph. If a concept such as that of limit fails to distinguish among any important functions, then why bother with it at all? This cynicism should be reinforced by theorems, to be seen shortly, that demonstrate that virtually all points of power, exponential, and polynomial functions have limits. In order to salvage the whole idea, we must locate functions that contain points with no limiting value.

Although it may appear exotic at first glance, the following function defines a common procedure for reducing a continuous domain to a countable range:

Definition

(12.3.3) A function, f, is said to be a greatest integer function if $f(x) = k$ for $k \leq k < (k + 1)$, k an integer, and f is noted $f(x) = [x]$.

Thus, under this function the domain values 2, 2.5, 2.999 all have a common range value, which is 2. Notice that this function represents one way of expressing age. Instead of saying that someone is $20.677777 \cdots$ years of age, we say that he is 20 years old. The graph of such a function is sketched in Figure 12.3. This sketch should make it clear why such a function is sometimes called a "step function." The reader should recognize that there are points in the function that have no limits and should be able to guess just what those points are.

THEOREM

(12.3.4) If f is a greatest integer function, then the limit of f does not exist at each integral value of x. That is, $\lim_{x \to k} f(x)$ is undefined for each integer k.

Proof

Let f be a greatest integer function, and suppose that there exists a number α such that:

(1) $\lim_{x \to k} f(x) = \alpha$, for k an integer,

that is, suppose that the limit exists at k. Then, for each $\epsilon > 0$ there exists a δ interval, say $\delta_\epsilon(k) = I_{(k-\delta, k+\delta)}$, such that $x \epsilon \delta_\epsilon(k) \rightarrow |f(x) - \alpha| < \epsilon$. Choose two points, x_1 in $\delta_\epsilon(k)$ and x_2 in $\delta_\epsilon(k)$, such that $k - 1 < x_i < h$ and $k L$ $x_2 < k + 1$.

(2) $f(x_1) = k - 1$ and $f(x_2) = k$.   (By hypothesis and 12.3.3)

(3) $|k - 1 - \alpha| < \epsilon$ and $|k - \alpha| < \epsilon$. (By hypothesis)

(4) $|k - 1 - \alpha| + |k - \alpha| < 2\epsilon$. (By step 3)

(5) $\epsilon > \frac{1}{2}$, which contradicts the hypothesis. (By step 4)

Consider the pudding of this proof. It consists simply of demonstrating that there are at least two points in the

Figure 12.3   GRAPH OF $f(x) = [x]$

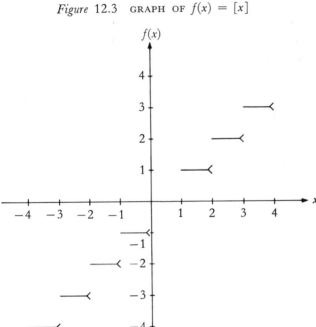

δ-interval whose f-correspondents could not both be placed arbitrarily close to a limit. The ϵ-region about $f(k)$ simply cannot be made arbitrarily small. In fact, it cannot be smaller than one-half. There are one or two odd aspects of this proof that should have raised the eyebrows of the careful reader. For example, how do we know that the points x_1 and x_2 even exist? Although it is perfectly obvious that they *should* exist, we have not proved that they do. A formal proof is beyond the scope of this book (see Rudin [5],

Section 2.22). Also, the jump from step 4 to step 5 was a big one. The reader should convince himself that it is a proper jump. (HINT: Try $\alpha < k - 1$, then $\alpha > k$, then $k - 1 \leq \alpha \leq k$.)

This theorem has shown that some functions exist in which at least some points do not have limits. The proof should have made it clear that, wherever a "jump" occurs in a function, the limit is not defined at that point. A similar but distinct situation occurs whenever the entire graph does not "jump," but a single point is pulled away. In such a case, the limit *does* exist at that point, but turns out to be unequal to the functional value of the point. Consider as an example the function defined by:

$$(12.3.5) \quad f(h) = \frac{(x + h)^2 - x^2}{h}, \qquad h \neq 0,$$

about which much more will be said in the following chapter. As a bit of a switch, note that x remains fixed and that the variable is h. Consider what would happen if h were allowed to become smaller and smaller. Clearly, the decrease in size of the denominator would appear to blow the function sky high. For this reason, $f(0)$ is not even defined. Despite this, the limit of f is defined at $h = 0$. To see this it is necessary only to expand the binomial in the numerator, watch the denominator disappear as though by magic, through cancellation, and come up with:

$$(12.3.6) \quad \lim_{h \to 0} \frac{(x + h)^2 - x^2}{h} = 2x, \qquad h \neq 0.$$

Here, then, we have a single point at which a function is not defined, but its limit does exist.

As a second example, consider the function below, the graph of which is sketched in Figure 12.4.

$$(12.3.7) \quad f(x) = \frac{x^2 - 4}{x - 2}, \qquad x \neq 2.$$

The function is undefined at $x = 2$, since this value would have as its f-correspondent the undefined number $0/0$. Nonetheless, with a little algebraic manipulation, it becomes evident that the limit of this function exists at $x = 2$. To see this clearly, one must recognize that $x^2 - 4 = (x - 2)(x + 2)$, so that:

(12.3.8) $\lim\limits_{x \to 2} \dfrac{x^2 - 4}{x - 2} = \lim\limits_{x \to 2} (x + 2) = 4.$

Thus, although $f(2)$ is no known number, the limit of f as x approaches that number is the perfectly common number 4.

Figure 12.4

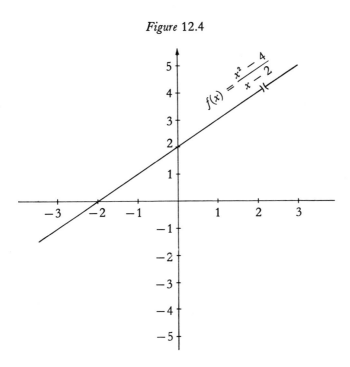

Much has been stated in these few lines that the reader should not allow to pass unchallenged. For one thing, the function defined by 12.3.7 was altered radically in 12.3.8. In this alteration, a fundamental rule must be remembered: A function may be re-expressed by a new defining equation, but it is the same function only so long as *every* ordered pair in the function remains unchanged. The identity expressed in 12.3.8 thus is true only so long as the number 2 is not admitted to the domain of f. But the identity of 12.3.8 does *not* involve $f(2)$ at all. It says instead that, as numbers become arbitrarily near (but do not equal) the number

2, their functional correspondents will be within an ϵ-interval of the limiting number, 4.

There is a second important consideration in these two illustrations. The formal mechanics of proving the existence of limits was sidestepped entirely. Not once did an ϵ or a δ rear its head. The procedure was much less formal, but it was entirely proper. It consisted of reducing the functions to forms that left no doubt about the effect of allowing h to go to 0 or x to go to 2. In both cases, the value of the limit was discovered through substitution of the (formally) inadmissible numbers and solution of their function correspondents. Thus, although $x = 2$ is inadmissible in 12.3.7 and, consequently, in 12.3.8, its informal substitution in the latter makes it perfectly obvious that the limiting value is the number 4.

Theorem 12.1 showed that limits of sequences have several useful properties. Since the limit of a function is similar to the limit of a sequence, it is reasonable to expect that the former has these properties also.

THEOREM

(12.3.9) If two functions, f and g, have limits at a common point, x_0, say $\lim_{x \to x_0} f(x) = \alpha$ and $\lim_{x \to x_0} g(x) = \alpha'$, then:

(1) if $f(x) = c$, any real number, then $\alpha = c$.

(2) if β also is a limit of f at the point x_0, then $\alpha = \beta$.

(3) $\lim_{x \to x_0} \dfrac{1}{f(x)} = \dfrac{1}{\alpha}$, if $f(x)$, $\alpha \neq 0$.

(4) $\lim_{x \to x_0} (cf(x)) = c\alpha$.

(5) $\lim_{x \to x_0} (c + f(x)) = c + \alpha$.

(6) $\lim_{x \to x_0} (f + g)(x) = \alpha + \alpha'$.

(7) $\lim_{x \to x_0} (fg)(x) = \alpha\alpha'$.

(8) $\lim \left(\dfrac{f}{g}\right)(x) = \dfrac{\alpha}{\alpha'}$, if $g(x)$, $\alpha' \neq 0$.

Since the proof here follows exactly the form of that of Theorem 12.1.10, it will not be repeated for 12.3.9. If the reader understands what each part of the theorem says, he should be able to translate each into an English declarative sentence. For example, 12.3.9.4 asserts that the limit at a point of a scalar transformation of a function is just the scalar transformation of the limit at that point.

With this theorem and with the help of a very minor small theorem (or lemma), it becomes possible to show that the primary functions in most social analysis, the power, exponential, and polynomial functions, have limits at nearly every point of R, and it becomes possible to discover what these limits are.

LEMMA

(12.3.10) If a function is defined by the equation $f(x) = x$ (the identity function), then $\lim_{x \to x_0} f(x) = x_0$.

Proof

Let f be an identity function. Then for each $\epsilon > 0$, let $\delta = \epsilon$ and let $\alpha = x_0$.

(1) $|x - x_0| < \delta \to |x - x_0| < \epsilon$, (By hypothesis, $\delta = \epsilon$)

(2) but $|f(x) - \alpha| = |x - x_0|$, (By definition of f and hypothesis about α)

(3) $|f(x) - \alpha| < \epsilon$. (By steps 1, 2 and transitivity)

Thus, at each point of an identity function the limit is defined and is equal to the point itself. Note that this is the first time that the actual value of a limit has been specified in a theorem in this section.

With this it is possible to consider the limits of the three major classes of functions. Since the graphs of these functions flow smoothly along, without erratic jumps, we might expect, as the following theorem asserts, that such functions have limits at each point in their range.

THEOREM

(12.3.11)

(1) If f is a rational polynomial function, say $f(x) = \dfrac{P(x)}{Q(x)}$,

  for all x such that $Q(x) \neq 0$, then

$$\lim_{x \to x_0} f(x) = \frac{P(x_0)}{Q(x_0)}.$$

(2) If g is any power function, say $g(x) = bx^\beta$, $\beta \neq 0$, then

$$\lim_{x \to x_0} g(x) = b(x_0)^\beta.$$

(3) If h is any exponential function, say $h(x) = b\beta^x$, then

$$\lim_{x \to x_0} h(x) = b\beta^{x_0}.$$

Proof

In part 1, $f(x)$ is a ratio of sums of terms of the form $a_k x^k$, where k is an integer. The term x^k is just the product of k identity functions so that $\lim_{x \to x_0} x^k = (x_0)^k$ by 12.3.10 and extension of 12.3.9.7. The rest of the proof follows directly from 12.3.9. In part 2 of the theorem, the result is immediate if β is an integer, since this is a special case of part 1. If β is any real number, then examine the limit of $\log_{x_0}(b(x_0)^\beta)$ to determine that $\log_{x_0} \alpha = \log_{x_0} b + \beta$ so that $\alpha = b(x_0)^\beta$. The proof of part 3 of the theorem is similar.

Exercises

12.17. In 12.1.6 the components of convergence were listed as they applied to sequences. Repeat this list in the case of convergence as applied to real functions.

12.18. The greatest integer function was defined by 12.3.3. Let the least integer function be given as:

$$f(x) = k - 1, \quad k - 1 \leq x < k.$$

Reprove theorem 12.3.4 in the case of the least integer function.

12.19. Prove that:

(a) if $f(x) = [x], f(f(x)) = f(x)$.
(b) if $f(x) = |x|, f(f(x)) = f(x)$.

12.20. Frequently, the proof of a limit theorem requires that the function in question be re-expressed. A device called *rationalizing* the numerator or denominator is sometimes useful. This device involves multiplying the numerator and denominator by the same term, with the effect of simplifying one of the terms. By rationalizing, prove the following:

(a) $\dfrac{2 - x}{2 - \sqrt{2x}} = 1 - \dfrac{\sqrt{2x}}{2}$, $x \neq 2$. (HINT: Multiply numerator and denominator by $2 + \sqrt{2x}$.)

(b) $\dfrac{\sqrt{4 - (x + h)^2} - \sqrt{4 - x^2}}{h} = \dfrac{-(2x + h)}{\sqrt{4 - (x + h)^2} + \sqrt{4 - x^2}}$, $h \neq 0$.

(c) $\dfrac{1 - x^2}{2 - \sqrt{x^2 + 3}} = 2 + \sqrt{x^2 + 3}$, $x \neq 1$.

12.21. Use exercise 12.20 to locate the following:

(a) $\lim\limits_{x \to 2} \dfrac{2 - x}{2 - \sqrt{2x}}$.

(b) $\lim\limits_{h \to 0} \dfrac{\sqrt{4 - (x + h)^2} - \sqrt{4 - x^2}}{h}$.

(c) $\lim\limits_{x \to 1} \dfrac{1 - x^2}{2 - \sqrt{x^2 + 3}}$.

12.22. Find each of the following limits:

(a) $\lim\limits_{x \to 3} \dfrac{x - 3}{x^2 - 9}$.

(b) $\lim\limits_{x \to 4} \dfrac{\sqrt{x^2 - 2}}{x - 4}$. $x > \sqrt{2}$ (HINT: What is $(\sqrt{x} - 2)(\sqrt{x} + 2)$?)

(c) $\lim\limits_{h \to 0} \dfrac{(-4 + h)^2 - 16}{h}$.

(d) $\lim\limits_{h \to 0} \dfrac{(4 - h)^2 - 16}{h}$.

12.23. Use definition 12.3.2 to prove formally the four parts of Exercise 12.22.

12.24. In Theorem 12.3.9, prove:

(a) Part 1
(b) Part 3
(c) Part 6
(d) Part 7
(e) Part 8

12.25. Prove 12.3.11.3.

12.4 Continuity

If a function has a limit at a point, then the limit usually, but not always, turns out to be the functional correspondent at that point. In cases in which the limit exists but is *unequal* to the functional correspondent, a break or minute discontinuity occurs in the graph of the function, as was illustrated in Figure 12.4. Conversely, wherever the limit is equal to the functional correspondent, the graph flows in a smooth, continuous line. It is this property of graphs that gives rise to the notion of continuity of a function at a point.

(12.4.1) If f is a function that has a limit at the point, **Definition** x_0, and if:

$$\lim_{x \to x_0} f(x) = f(x_0),$$

then f is said to be *continuous* at the point x_0.

The important intuitive idea here is that no break can occur in the graph of f at x_0 if it is continuous at that point. Note that Theorem 12.3.11 assures us that polynomial, power, and exponential functions are continuous at each point for which they are defined at all. If a function is continuous at each point in an interval, we can say that it is continuous on that interval.

It should be clear that this definition constitutes nothing more than the addition of a specific value to α in the definition of a limit. Thus, it follows immediately that all the properties true of limits are true of the continuity property as well. Because the connection is so close, it should be unnecessary even to spell out from Theorem 12.3.9 the various basic properties of continuity. For example, by rewriting the continuity property into that theorem, we should see that the sum, product, or ratio of two functions that are continuous at a point is itself continuous at that point.

The notions of continuity and of limit may appear to be far removed from the realm of social analysis. In a sense they are, for by birthright, at least, they belong to the domain of mathematics. However, in two ways they provide useful, indeed necessary, working tools for the social scientist. First, they comprise a means of classifying real functions. Since functions provide an efficient method of representing social facts, a system for classifying functions can be used also as a system for classifying social facts. Second, the notions of continuity and limit provide a basis for analyzing patterns of growth and decay. And these ideas, to be taken up in the next chapter, are at the very heart of any social theory.

Selected References

1. Allendoerfer, C. B., and Oakley, C. O. *Principles of Mathematics*. New York: McGraw-Hill Book Company, Inc., 1955. Chapter 11.
2. Miller, Kenneth S. *Advanced Real Calculus*. New York: Harper & Brothers, 1957. Chapters 1–3.
3. Moore, John T. *Fundamental Principles of Mathematics*. New York: Rinehart and Co., Inc., 1960. Pages 211–226.
4. Richardson, M. *Fundamentals of Mathematics* (Revised Edition). New York: The Macmillan Company, 1958. Chapter 11.
5. Rudin, Walter. *Principles of Mathematical Analysis* (Revised Edition). New York: McGraw-Hill Book Company, Inc., 1964. Chapters 3–4.
6. Tintner, Gerhard. *Mathematics and Statistics for Economists*. New York: Rinehart and Co., Inc., 1953. Chapter 6.
7. Titchmarsh, E. C. *Mathematics for the General Reader*. Garden City, New York: Doubleday & Co., Inc., 1959. Chapters 8–9.

The Calculus of Change

What is a social theory about? If we disregard the broad range of substantive issues, then all social theories have a common concern: that of describing the manner in which one phenomenon operates to effect changes in another. The object of such theories is to describe the way in which social phenomena are interwoven into a dynamic system. The word *dynamic* should here convey the idea that change and motion are central components in any theory, whether explicitly or implicitly. It should not suggest, however, that the dimension of time is the exclusive referent of change.

The term *change* will refer here simply to a number that represents the distance between two points on any dimension of social space, such as age, intelligence, income level, or reproductive rate. Thus, a change of 20 on the scale of age refers to the distance between any given age and one 20 units away. The concern of social science, in these terms, is to determine the nature of the consequences of change in one dimension of social space for the position of an element on another dimension. A psychologist may be concerned with the effect of change in intensity of stimulus on retention of learned material. An economist may study the relation between price changes and change in the demand for a commodity. A sociologist might examine the relation between change in the status structure and aspirations of an individual for formal education. Whatever the discipline, the central concern is with the impact that a change in some dimension of social space has upon a phenomenon under investigation.

In discussing the calculus of change, we must recall from Chapter 11 that measurements do not necessarily have all properties of real numbers. We have seen that much of social measurement consists of nominal or ordinal measurement scales on which addition and multiplication are undefined. It has been suggested that interval and especially ratio scales, for which these arithmetic operations are defined, are more "powerful" than others in that they permit a fuller use of mathematics. The mathematical characterization of change that we are about to consider requires the operations of addition and multiplication and, hence, interval and ratio scales of measurement.

The mathematician's concept of function was presented

13

in earlier pages as being centrally important to any scientific theory. Now, however, that concept will be found grossly unsatisfactory for some purposes. A function, as it stands, has nothing to say about change. We have seen that a function accomplishes nothing more than the establishment of a correspondence between stationery points in a domain and in a range. But this is a static idea, whereas some scientific theory demands dynamics. Although a function provides information about the corresponding value at a point, it seems to say nothing at all about the effect of change, about the correspondent of a *change* in values rather than about the correspondent of a value.

In this chapter we shall modify the idea of function by constructing a system that transforms a static function, say f, into a dynamic one, f'. The new function is *derived* from the original; hence, the mathematical term *derivative* is anticipated. By formalizing the idea of rate of change, we shall be able to convert a function into a second entirely new function whose domain consists of a set of dynamic changes rather than of a set of static points.

13.1 Rate of Change

The translation of a function whose range is points or numerical values into one whose range is units of change is remarkably simple. Intuitively, change was said to be a distance between two points along a dimension of (social) space. A change of distance h from a point x thus could be represented by the *length* $([x + h] - x)$, which is just the number, h. Notice that the measure of change has an algebraic interpretation in that its value is "negative" if $h < 0$ (interpreted as a change of decrease). In this sense, the meaning of change is clear enough, but it is trivial. The scientist is interested in far more than the sheer description of change; he wishes to assess its consequences. It is at this point that the notion of function takes on new life.

Suppose that a domain variable, x (for example, years of education, amount of cigarette consumption, or net income), is related by a function, f, to a range variable, $f(x)$

(which might be bank balance, incidence of disease, or annual taxes), by the identity $f(x) = x^2$. This identity yields the correspondent value for any admissible domain element. But now we have turned our interest to the effects of change, not of static position. What must be assessed, then, is the correspondent of a unit of change, the distance $([x + h] - x)$, and not just the value x or $(x + h)$. Since the number $([x + h] - x)$ clearly is just the number h, it might appear that we need only compute the value of $f(h)$; but life is not so simple as this. In many cases, such as that of the illustrative power function, $f(x) = x^2$, the correspondent of change depends on the point from which the change originates. The effect of a change of magnitude h is not the same if it originates at the point $x = 1$ as it is if it originates at some other point, such as $x = 0$. If the change is measured from 0, then the effect is to move the domain variable from $f(0) = 0$ to $f(0 + h) = h^2$ in magnitude. If a change of size h originates at $x = 1$, then the effect is to move the range variable from $f(1) = 1$ to $f(1 + h) = (1 + h)^2 = h^2 + (1 + 2h)$, which is quite a different change from that effected at 0.

If the point of origin of the change is to be taken into account, that point must be built into the change measure. Clearly, the consequence of a change of magnitude h should be represented by a distance of $(f(x + h) - f(x))$, which involves both the value x and the distance h. Thus, the *rate of change* will mean the change from a point in the range, $f(x)$, *per unit of change* (of magnitude h) in the domain from the point x. All this should suggest what is meant by the rate of change of a function.

(13.1.1) If f is a function for which values are defined at points x and $(x + h)$, then the rate of change in f over the interval $I_{(x,(x+h))}$ is $C(h; f, x) = \dfrac{f(x + h) - f(x)}{h}$, $h \neq 0$.

Definition

The symbol $C(h; f, x)$ represents a number in the range of C, the C-correspondent of h for a given function, f, and a particular number, x, in the domain of f. The idea that underlies the change function is illustrated in Figure 13.1.

Notice carefully that C is an entirely new construct built up from a second function, f. The domain of C consists of numbers, h, that represent intervals of the form $I_{(x,(x+h))}$. This variable is interpreted to be a distance or change value. The range of C consists also of change values, but these are values of change in the range of f for each unit of change in the domain. This distance measure is just $(f(x + h) - f(x)$, which is divided by h, the measure of change, in order to make it relative to that arbitrary number. Notice also that C is a *conditional* function in that it assumes as conditions that a function, f, and a point, x, are given and remain fixed.

Figure 13.1

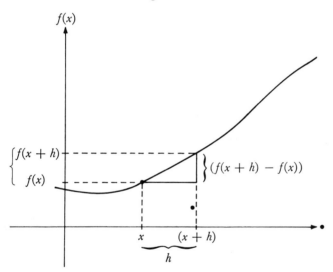

Consider once again the function represented by $f(x) = x^2$. In order to investigate the pattern of change that is associated with this function, let us evaluate $C(h; f, x)$ for selected values of h at one or two points of x.

(13.1.2) If $f(x) = x^2$, then:

(1) $C(1; f, 2) = \dfrac{(2 + 1)^2 - 2^2}{1} = 5.$ (4) $C(1; f, 3) = 7.$

(2) $C(2; f, 2) = 6.$ (5) $C(2; f, 3) = 8.$

(3) $C(3; f, 2) = 7.$ (6) $C(3; f, 3) = 9.$

These trial cases, together with the proper *Gestalt*, should create a spark of recognition in the reader's mind. All the values appear to fit a function given by $C(h; f(x) = x^2, x) = 2x + h$. If true, this would tell us that the change in f is simply a linear function of h for any fixed point, x.

(13.1.3) $C(h; f(x) = x^2, x) = 2x + h$.   **PROPOSITION**

Let $f(x) = x^2$.   *Proof*

(1) $C(h; f, x) = \dfrac{(x + h)^2 - x^2}{h},$ (By 13.1.1 and hypothesis)

(2) $= \dfrac{x^2 + 2xh + h^2 - x^2}{h},$ (By expanding the binomial)

(3) $= 2x + h.$ (By clearing and cancelling)

Then, whenever a function is given by $f(x) = x^2$, it follows that a rate of change of magnitude h at the point x is just twice the value of x plus the value of h. Notice that the proof consisted simply of plugging in the definition of f and then of clearing out terms.

Let us consider one more function and the rate of change that it generates. Consider the function given by $g(x) = x^3$. Does the reader think that the change function generated by g should be the same as that generated by f above? If it is thought to differ, what should the difference be? Should the difference between $C(h; f, x)$ and $C(h; g, x)$ be independent of x? of h? It is important that the reader attempt to locate answers to these questions before he proceeds. Rather than working with the change function for selected values of x, let us look for a more general answer by direct reference to 13.1.1 with regard to another specific function.

(13.1.4) If $g(x) = x^3$, then: **PROPOSITION**
$$C(h; g, x) = 3x(x + h) + h^2.$$

The proof is identical to that of Proposition 13.1.3. Expand the binomial, subtract $-x^3$ from x^3 in the numerator, clear h from the denominator (since each remaining numerator term contains a power of h), and the result follows.   *Proof*

The preceding chapters might suggest that the next appropriate step would consist of examining general properties of the conditional change functions. Such is not the best strategy at this point, however, for we are bearing down rapidly on a weird but remarkably useful idea, that of the rate of change *at a point*. It will be more rewarding to investigate properties of change functions directly in terms of this odd concept, which is usually called the *derivative*.

Exercises

13.1. Propositions 13.1.3 and 13.1.4 together suggest a theorem that would subsume both of them as special cases. Let $f(x) = x^n$ $n \in I^+$, and construct the theorem suggested by these two exercises.

13.2. How would you go about proving the theorem of Exercise 13.1?

13.3. Compute the average rate of change over the intervals $(0, 2)$ and $(10, 12)$ for each of the following functions:

(a) $f(x) = k$.
(b) $f(x) = x$.
(c) $f(x) = \alpha_0 + \alpha_1 x$.
(d) $f(x) = \alpha_0 + \alpha_1 x + \alpha_2 x^2$.
(e) $f(x) = x^4$.

(f) $f(x) = \dfrac{1}{x + 1}$.

13.4. Let $h = 1, .1, .01$, and $.001$. Then find the average rate of change for:

(a) $f(x) = \sqrt{x}$, at $x = 1$ and at $x = 10$.
(b) $f(x) = 3 - 2x^2 + x^3$, at $x = 0$ and at $x = 2$.
(c) $f(x) = \log_{10} x$, at $x = 1$ and at $x = 10$.

13.5. Let p represent the proportion of females in an interacting group, so that $0 \le p \le 1$. Let $f(p)$ represent the proportion of observed interaction between persons of opposite sexes. If f is found to be given by $f(p) = p - p^2$:

(a) Derive $c(h; f, p)$.
(b) Graph $C(h; f, p)$ for $p = .1$.

13.2 The Derivative of a Function

If a function, f, and a particular domain value, x, are selected, then the resultant change function, C, is entirely new. The variable is no longer x; instead, it is h, the unit of change. Our job, then, is to determine the correspondents of the variable h for a fixed value of x. Notice from 13.1.1 that one value of h is never admitted to the domain of C, because the function is undefined at $h = 0$. Nonetheless, it is perfectly proper to examine the consequences of taking smaller and smaller units of change, of allowing h to become arbitrarily close to zero. The result gives an entirely new concept, that of an *instantaneous* rate of change.

It was seen in the preceding chapter that, although a function may not be defined at a particular point, the function can be analyzed at that point if domain values closer and closer to it are taken. The idea of taking a limit at a point was built up in this way. Although a rate of change of zero units is inadmissible, we can examine the limit of C as h goes to zero. Such an examination suggests that a function, f, has built into it the seed of change even though it is a static picture. In fact, a function might be likened to a snapshot that catches and "freezes" action. Although the snapshot does not show the action explicitly, we know that it is occurring. The limit of C as h goes to zero is a means of expressing the amount of action that was going on at the instant at which it was frozen by the functional snapshot at a point, x. With this, we are ready to formalize the idea of a measure of change at a point.

(13.2.1) If f is a function that is defined for a value x, **Definition**
then, *if it is defined*, a second function, f', given by:

$$f'(x) = \lim_{h \to 0} C(h; f, x) = \lim_{h \to 0} \frac{f(x + h) - f(x)}{h},$$

is called the *derivative* of f at the point x.

The derivative is called this because it is a derived function, a new function derived from f by means of two connectors: the change function, C; and the notion of a limit.

Consider once again the two functions $f(x) = x^2$ and $g(x) = x^3$. It was seen above that $C(h; f(x), x) = 2x + h$ and that $C(h; g(x), x) = 3x(x + h) + h^2$. Hefty formal proofs should not be needed to convince the reader that the limits of these two functions, as h goes to zero, are $f'(x) = 2x$ and $g'(x) = 3x^2$, respectively. Thus, at $x = 0$, both functions are "immobile," or motionless, in the sense that the derivatives of both are zero at $x = 0$. At $x = 1$, g experiences a greater rate of change than f, since $f'(1) = 2$ while $g'(1) = 3$. But, as the reader should verify, the situation is just the reverse at $x = \frac{1}{3}$. In fact, for all values of x such that $0 < x < \frac{2}{3}$, f has a faster rate of change. This can be verified by locating solutions of the identity $3x^2 - 2x = 0$, the points at which $f'(x) = g'(x)$.

Economists make liberal use of the derivative in constructing theories about price structures. In the economics of production, for instance, the concept of marginal cost plays an important part. Suppose that a function, f, describes the gross cost of producing x units. Then $f(x + h) - f(x)$ would give the increment in cost that would result from increasing production from x units to $(x + h)$ units. If this difference were divided by h, the resulting quotient would represent the increment in cost *per additional unit*. By taking the limit of this ratio as h moves to zero, the result would be an abstract but most useful number representing the instantaneous increment in cost of production at the production point x. This, of course, is simply f', the derivative of the cost function at the point x. Economists call this the marginal cost function. Suppose that an economist can locate a production figure, x, such that $f'(x) = 0$. Note that x is not a point at which the cost of production is zero, but, rather, is the point at which the *rate of change* in cost is zero. Suppose that f' is monotone decreasing for all values less than x and is monotone increasing for all values greater than x. By doing some very careful thinking, the reader should recognize that x is the most strategic number of units that can be produced. (Why?) This point will be discussed in more detail in Section 13:7.

It is a painful fact of life that different writers adopt different notational systems in dealing with derivatives. The most commonly used of the various systems are the following:

(13.2.2) The derivative of a function f at a point x, if it exists, may be expressed in any of the following ways: **Notation**

(1) $\lim\limits_{h \to 0} \dfrac{f(x+h) - f(x)}{h} = f'(x),$

(2) $\qquad\qquad\qquad\qquad = \dfrac{d}{dx} f(x),$

(3) $\qquad\qquad\qquad\qquad = \dfrac{dy}{dx},$ where $y = f(x),$

(4) $\qquad\qquad\qquad\qquad = \lim\limits_{\Delta x \to 0} \dfrac{\Delta y}{\Delta x},$

(5) $\qquad\qquad\qquad\qquad = D_x f.$

The first expression can be read "f-prime of x," and the second, "the derivative of the function with respect to the value x." Sometimes this form is expressed as $\dfrac{dy}{dx}$, in which it is assumed that y is the same thing as $f(x)$. The latter form is neater, but it is confusing in that it resembles the ratio of two products even though the derivative cannot be interpreted in this way. If Δy were to be thought of as the limit, as h goes to zero, of $f(x + h) - f(x)$, and Δx as the limit of h as h goes to zero, then the quotient $\Delta y / \Delta x$ would necessarily be the undefined number $0/0$. The entire trick in evaluating derivatives consists of re-expressing the ratio of these two numbers in such a way as to locate a number that is defined. The fourth expression in 13.2.2 is somewhat old-fashioned and will be avoided here. In fact, the "f-prime" notation will be used throughout this book, except in one context that makes the second form more convenient. With all this, we are now in a position to explore some of the more elementary and immediately useful properties of derivatives.

Exercises

13.6. In Exercise 13.3, find the derivative of each function. (HINT: In each case, investigate $C(h; f, x)$ as h goes to zero.)

13.7. If f is a production cost function, explain why production level x, given by $f'(x) = 0$, is a strategic level if f' is monotone decreasing to the left of x and is monotone increasing to the right.

13.8. In Exercise 13.7, suppose that f' were monotone increasing to the left of x and monotone decreasing to the right. Interpret the production level, x.

13.9. Suppose that f is a function on $X \times Y$ such that f' is defined for each $x \in X$. Suppose further that there exist points x_1 and x_2 such that, for $x < x_1$, f' is monotone decreasing; that, for $x_1 \leq x \leq x_2$, $f'(x) = 0$; that, for $x > x_2$, f' is monotone increasing. Interpret the results where:

(a) X is a set of man-hours spent in archeological excavation, and Y is a number of artifacts yielded by the excavation.
(b) f is production cost function.
(c) X is a set of stimulus intensities and Y is a set of response intensities.
(d) X is the average number of words per sentence in a set of paragraphs and Y is a set of measures of reading comprehension.

13.3 Some Properties of Derivatives

A disquieting phrase lurked in the background of the preceding section. A derivative was discussed under the condition that it exists, which suggests that there may be cases in which f' is not defined at all. If it is recalled that a derivative is just the limit of the ratio of two functions and that limits sometimes do not exist (as at points of "jump" in a nearest integer function), then it should be clear that cases can be anticipated in which derivatives are undefined. To begin this discussion, let us agree upon the meaning of a common but ostentatious adjective:

(13.3.1) A function, f, is said to be *differentiable* at a point x if $f'(x)$ is defined at the point x. **Definition**

Then the question may be asked: When is a function differentiable and when is it not? Regrettably, it is much simpler to explain when a function is not differentiable than to explain when it is.

The following theorem offers a first lead because it asserts a minimum condition for differentiability—namely, that a function must be continuous at the point under investigation. The reader should convince himself that, to prove this, it is sufficient to show that $|f(x + h) - f(x)| < \epsilon$ for $|h| < \delta$ (here it helps to identify $|h|$ with the interval $|x - x_0|$).

(13.3.2) If $f'(x)$ is defined, then f is continuous at the point x. **THEOREM**

Let f' be defined at the point x. Proof

(1) $\lim\limits_{h \to 0} (f(x + h) - f(x))$

$$= \lim_{h \to 0} \left[\frac{f(x + h) - f(x)}{h} \cdot (h) \right], \qquad \text{(Since } h/h = 1)$$

(2) $\quad = \lim\limits_{h \to 0} \left[\dfrac{f(x + h) - f(x)}{h} \right] \cdot \lim\limits_{h \to 0} (h), \quad \text{(By 12.3.9.7)}$

(3) $\quad = [f'(x)][0],$ $\qquad\qquad$ (By 13.1.1 and 12.3.10)

(4) $\quad = 0.$

Since $\lim\limits_{h \to 0} (f(x + h) - f(x)) = 0 \leftrightarrow \lim\limits (f(x + h)) = f(x)$,

it follows that f is continuous at the point x.

Unfortunately, the theorem by no means states that all continuous functions are differentiable. As a counterexample, consider the following function, whose graph is sketched in Figure 13.2:

$$f(x) = \begin{cases} 1 + 3x & \text{if } x \le 3 \\ 19 - 3x & \text{if } x > 3 \end{cases}.$$

Note that the graph of this function comes to a sharp point at $x = 3$. As the reader might suspect, it is this point that is not differentiable, even though f is continuous at $x = 3$. The proof of the assertion that f is continuous at this point is left as an exercise. (HINT: Choose $\delta = \epsilon/3$ and investigate small values of h, first less than zero and then greater than zero.) To show that $f'(3)$ is undefined, it is necessary to show that the graph of f' jumps (downward, in this case) at $x = 3$. This can be done by proving that $f'(x) = 3$ for all $x \le 3$ and that $f'(x) = -3$ for $x > 3$, which the reader ought to be able to handle by plugging this function into the definition of a derivative in 13.1.1. When all this is done, and when it is recalled from 12.3.4 that a jump function is discontinuous at all points of jump, the result follows.

This adds up to the fact that no such thing as an instantaneous rate of change exists at some points of some functions. The preceding illustration suggests that such points might have to be rather odd in appearance, their graphs taking a sharp zag at the undifferentiable point. Beyond this, we have seen that whenever a function is differentiable at a point it is also continuous at that point. None of this need cause any particular concern, for it will be shown that all of the basic functions with which we are concerned are indeed differentiable at all but a few isolated points.

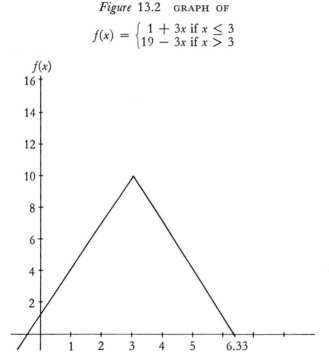

Figure 13.2   GRAPH OF

$$f(x) = \begin{cases} 1 + 3x \text{ if } x \le 3 \\ 19 - 3x \text{ if } x > 3 \end{cases}$$

What properties of derivatives can be anticipated? For instance, if $f'(x)$ is defined, should we expect it to be a unique number—that is, can we imagine two different rates of instantaneous change occurring at a point? What about a constant function of the form $f(x) = c$? Since there is no change in the function, the rate of change function ought to be uniformly zero. These and several other general properties of derivatives are contained in the following:

(13.3.3) If $f'(x)$ is defined, then:

(1) if $f'(x) = \alpha$ and $f'(x) = \beta$, then $\alpha = \beta$.
(2) if $f(x) = c$, then $f'(x) = 0$.
(3) if $f(x) = x$, then $f'(x) = 1$.
(4) if $f'(x) = \alpha$, then $f'(cx) = c\alpha$.

Since f' is a limit, parts 1 and 4 are just restatements of 12.3.9.2 and 12.3.9.4. Proof of part 2 is left as an exercise. To prove part 3, let $f(x) = x$, the identity function. Then:

Proof

$$(1) \quad f'(x) = \lim_{h \to 0} \frac{(x + h) - x}{h}, \qquad \text{(By 13.1.1)}$$

$$(2) \qquad = \lim_{h \to 0} \left(\frac{h}{h}\right),$$

$$(3) \qquad = 1. \qquad \left(\text{Since } \frac{h}{h} = 1, \text{ all } h \neq 0\right)$$

From this it is seen that, if a derivative is defined at a point, then it is a unique number; that the derivative of a constant function is uniformly equal to zero (regardless of x); that the derivative of the identity function is uniformly the number one (again regardless of the value of x); that the derivative of a scalar transformation of a point is the scalar transformation of the derivative at that point.

It was seen in Chapter 10 that it is often useful to combine two or more functions by means of an arithmetic operation. Such an operation yields a new function, whose derivative properties it will be convenient to explore. It might appear that the theorem on limits of combinations of functions (12.3.9, Parts 4–8) would tell us all that we need to know in this regard, since derivatives, after all, are limits of functions. But there is a rub here that stems from the fact that a derivative is the limit of a new *derived* function, so that the investigation must proceed anew.

(13.3.4) If f and g are functions such that f' and g' are defined at a point x, then $(f \pm g)'(x)$ and $(fg)'(x)$ are defined, and if $g(x) \neq 0$, then $(f/g)'(x)$ is defined, and the derivatives are given by the following:

THEOREM

(1) $(f \pm g)'(x) = f'(x) \pm g'(x)$.
(2) $(fg)'(x) = f(x)g'(x) + f'(x)g(x)$.

$$(3)\ (f/g)'(x) = \frac{f'(x)g(x) - f(x)g'(x)}{g^2(x)},\ (g(x) \neq 0)$$

The proof of part 1 is left as an exercise. To prove part 2, we note that: *Proof*

$$(1)\ (fg)'(x) = \lim_{h \to 0} \frac{(fg)(x + h) - (fg)(x)}{h},$$

(2) but $fg(x + h) - (fg)(x),$
$$= f(x + h)g(x + h) - f(x)g(x),$$
$$(3)\quad = f(x + h)[g(x + h) - g(x)] + [f(x + h) - f(x)]g(x).$$

$$(4)\ (fg)'(x) = \lim_{h \to 0} f(x + h) \lim \frac{g(x + h) - g(x)}{h}$$

$$+ \lim_{h \to 0} \frac{f(x + h) - f(x)}{h} \lim_{h \to 0} g(x),$$

$$= f(x)g'(x) + f'(x)g(x).$$

The proof of the third part is similar, but it substitutes for the second and third steps the identity

$$(5)\ \frac{(f/g)(x + h) - (f/g)(x)}{h}$$

$$= \frac{1}{g(x + h)g(x)} \left\{ g(x) \left[\frac{f(x + h) - f(x)}{h} \right] \right.$$

$$\left. - f(x) \left[\frac{g(x + h) - g(x)}{h} \right] \right\}.$$

The minor details of this part of the proof are left as an exercise. The first result is just as we might have anticipated: The derivative of a sum or difference of functions is the sum or difference of their separate derivatives. The second and third results, however, are indeed odd, looking like nothing that has been seen to this point. The reader should consider these results carefully in an attempt to understand exactly what they say. When translated into English, each becomes quite a mouthful, but it will be worth the reader's effort.

The economist makes efficient use of the notion of a derivative and of these properties of derivatives in the construction of theory. Consider the example of the concept of marginal revenue. Let x represent the price of a commodity and $g(x)$, the number of units sold as a function of price. (In most cases, g would be a monotone decreasing function. Why?) Let $G(x)$ represent the gross income or revenue from the sale of $g(x)$ units. Clearly, G is the product of the number of units sold and the price per unit. Define f to be the identity function, $f(x) = x$. Then G is given by $G(x) = f(x)g(x)$. To the economist, *average* revenue over an interval of length h is the increment in revenue over the interval, divided by the length of the interval. But this is nothing more than our change function, so that average revenue can be interpreted as increment in revenue (presumably negative) per unit of increment in price. This in turn suggests that the derivative $G'(x)$ is just the change in revenue at a given price. It is this that the economist calls marginal revenue. That is, if we abbreviate the marginal revenue at price x to $mr(x)$, then we have the following:

(13.3.5) The marginal revenue of a commodity at price x is $mr(x) = xg'(x) + g(x)$. **PROPOSITION**

Let G and g be differentiable at each price, x, and define $G(x) = (fg)(x)$ where $f(x) = x$. *Proof*

(1) $G'(x) = (fg)'(x)$,
$\qquad = f(x)g'(x) + f'(x)g(x)$.   (By 13.3.4.2)
(2) But $f'(x) = 1$.   (Since $f(x) = x$ and
$\qquad\qquad\qquad\qquad\qquad$ by 13.3.3.3)
(3) $G'(x) = xg'(x) + g(x)$.

We have seen repeatedly that a function that consists of the composition of two functions is especially useful in social analysis. Suppose that a composition, call it F, is given by $F(x) = f(g(x))$, where f is a function whose domain is the range of the second function, g. For instance, if g expresses profit in dollars as a function of some domain variable, then $f(g(x))$ expresses profit in cents if $f(g(x)) = 100g(x)$. It will be convenient if we can express the derivative of a composition of two functions as a reasonably simple expression of the derivatives of the two functions involved. That such is the case is seen by the following:

(13.3.6) If g is a function differentiable at a point x and if f is a second function defined on the range of g, such that f is differentiable at the point $g(x)$, and if F is given by $F(x) = f(g(x))$, then the derivative of F is given by $F'(x) = f'(g(x))g'(x)$.

THEOREM:
CHAIN RULE
OF DIFFER-
ENTIATION

A careful proof of this theorem requires some machinery that has not been constructed here (see Miller, *Advanced Real Calculus* [1], page 40). The result is pleasingly straightforward, especially after some of the bizarre results uncovered on earlier pages. The theorem tells us that the derivative of a composition of two functions is just the product of their separate derivatives. Note carefully that the value $g(x)$ is plugged into the derivative of the transformation function, f.

It should have become apparent by now that we need information about the derivatives of specific classes of functions. In the following sections we shall consider those elementary functions that were introduced earlier as being of possibly greatest immediate use in social analysis.

Exercises

13.10. Prove that the function graphed in Figure 13.2 is continuous at $x = 3$.

13.11. Graph the derivative of the function of Figure 13.2.

13.12. Prove 13.3.3.2.

13.13. Prove 13.3.4.1.

13.14. Complete the proof of 13.3.4.3.

13.15. Let $f(x) = x$, $g(x) = \alpha_0 + \alpha_1 x$, $h(x) = x^4$, $u(x) = \dfrac{1}{x+1}$. Evaluate the following:

(a) $(f + g)(x)$
(b) $(fgh)(x)$
(c) $(fg/h)(x)$
(d) $(fu/hg)(x)$
(e) $(f + g/h + u)(x)$

13.16. Note that, for each function, f, g, h, and u, of Exercise 13.15, the derivative was located in Exercise 13.6. Locate the derivative of the compound functions given by parts (a) through (e) of Exercise 13.15.

13.17. Let $g(x)$ represent volume of sales at price x. Suppose that $g(x) = 20e^{-x}$:

(a) Graph $g(x)$ over the interval $[0, 20]$.

(b) Interpret $g(0) = 20$.
(c) Graph the gross income function, $G(x) = f(x)g(x)$ over the interval $[0, 20]$.
(d) Assume that $g'(x) = -20e^{-x}$. Compute $G'(x)$.
(e) Graph $G'(x)$ over the interval $[0, 20]$.

13.18. Using the functions defined in Exercise 13.15, evaluate:

(a) $F'(x)$ where $F(x) = g(h(x))$. (HINT: The answer is $F'(x) = 4\alpha_1 x^3$.)
(b) $G'(x)$ where $G(x) = f(g(x))$.
(c) $H'(x)$ where $H(x) = g(f(x))$.
(d) $U'(x)$ where $U(x) = g(h(u(x)))$. (HINT: Apply the chain rule twice.)

13.4 Derivatives of Power Functions

Three classes of real functions were investigated in Chapter 10—the power, exponential, and polynomial functions. Familiarity with these functions is assumed here. Our job in the remaining sections of this chapter will consist of locating the derivatives that correspond to each of these classes of functions.

Consider first functions of the form $f(x) = x^n$, where n is any positive integer. This is a subtype of the class of power functions and also comprises an important general term of the class of polynomial functions. In Section 13.2 it was discovered $\Big($here using the more convenient notation $f'(x) = \dfrac{d}{dx} f(x)\Big)$ that $\dfrac{d}{dx} x^2 = 2x$ and that $\dfrac{d}{dx} x^3 = 3x^2$. Before proceeding, the reader should verify as an exercise that $\dfrac{d}{dx} x^4 = 4x^3$ and that $\dfrac{d}{dx} x^5 = 5x^4$. When these results are put together, it is not difficult to anticipate the general result of considering the derivative $\dfrac{d}{dx} x^n$. The proof of the obvious result, however, is rather a tricky thing. Finite induction will be put to work here (See Section 5.6), so that we shall have to prove the result for the case of $n = 1$ and then show that the (assumed) truth for the case of $n - 1$ implies the truth of the theorem for the case of n. The real secret here consists of breaking f into the product of two functions. (This theorem and its proof were anticipated in Exercises 13.1 and 13.2.)

(13.4.1) If $f(x) = x^n$, for n any positive integer, then $f'(x) = nx^{n-1}$.

Let $f(x) = x^n$, $n \in I^+$.

(1) If $n = 1$, then $f(x) = x$ and
$$f'(x) = 1 = 1x^0, \qquad \text{(By 13.3.3.3)}$$

so that the theorem is true for the case $n = 1$. Now let $u(x) = x$ and $v(x) = x^{n-1}$, so that $f(x) = (uv)(x)$.

(2) Assume that $v'(x)$
$$= (n - 1)x^{n-2}. \quad \text{(The inductive assumption)}$$

(3) $f'(x)$
$$= u(x)v'(x) + u'(x)v(x), \qquad \text{(13.3.4.2)}$$
(4) $\quad = x(n - 1)x^{n-2} + (1)x^{n-1}$, (By step 2, hypothesis about u and v, and the fact that $u'(x) = 1$ from 13.3.3.3)

(5) $\quad = (n - 1)x^{n-1} + x^{n-1}$. (Since $(x)(x)^{n-2} = x^{n-1}$)

(6) $f'(x) = nx^{n-1}$.

Thus, with no further limit proofs, we can determine immediately that the derivative of $f(x) = x^{16}$ is $f'(x) = 16x^{15}$, that the derivative of $f(x) = x^{258}$ is $f'(x) = 258x^{257}$, and that the derivative of any function given by $f(x) = x^n$, $n \in I^+$ is just $f'(x) = nx^{n-1}$.

Theorem 13.4.1 is all well and good, especially since many functions in social analysis are power functions. Unfortunately, however, many of these have exponents that are not positive integers. More often, the exponent is a real number and, in particular, one that is less than zero. Thus, this theorem needs yet more generalization. To accomplish this, let us consider first functions of the form $f(x) = x^{1/n}$ again, for n a positive integer. The proof that Theorem 13.4.1 is true also for functions of this form deserves careful study, for it illustrates one way in which the chain rule can be used to great advantage.

(13.4.2) If $g(x) = x^{1/n}$, $n \in I^+$, then $g'(x) = \dfrac{1}{n} x^{\left(\frac{1}{n} - 1\right)}$.

Let $g(x) = x^{1/n}$, and let $f(x) = x^n$, $h(x) = f(g(x)) = (x^{1/n})^n = x$.

(1) $f'(x) = nx^{n-1}$ and $h'(x) = 1$.   (By 13.3.3.3 and 13.4.1)

(2) $h'(x) = f'(g(x))g'(x)$.   (By 13.3.6, the chain rule)

(3) $f'(g(x)) = n(x^{1/n})^{n-1}$.   (13.4.1)

(4) $1 = n(x^{1/n})^{n-1}g'(x)$.   (Steps 1, 2, and 3)

(5) $g'(x) = \dfrac{1}{n} x^{-\left(\frac{1}{n}[n-1]\right)}$,   (Step 4)

(6) $= \dfrac{1}{n} x^{\left(\frac{1}{n}-1\right)}$.

When it is recognized that any rational-valued power function can be expressed as a composition of the functions investigated in 13.4.1 and 13.4.2, when the chain rule is reapplied, when a constant coefficient is added, making use of 13.3.3.2 and 13.3.4.2, and when all this is put together, we have:

(13.4.3) If f is any power function given by $f(x) = ax^\alpha$, **THEOREM**
α any rational number, then $f'(x) = a\alpha x^{\alpha-1}$.

The details of the proof are left as an exercise. $\left(\text{Note that}\right.$

$\alpha = \dfrac{m}{n}$, m and n integers. $\left.\right)$ Of course, the case of $\alpha < 0$ must be considered in the proof. The theorem can be extended to the case of irrational exponents by using Theorem 13.5.1. below.

By using the chain rule of 13.3.6, this theorem can be generalized to cover a much broader class of functions. Consider a function of the form $f(x) = ag(x)^\alpha$, where g is any function such that $g'(x)$ is defined. Then 13.3.6 and 13.4.3 together give the following:

(13.4.4) If g is any function such that $g'(x)$ is defined, **PROPOSITION**
and if $f(x) = ag(x)^\alpha$, then $f'(x) = a\alpha[g(x)]^{\alpha-1}g'(x)$.

Psychologists who are interested in problems of learning have examined the relation between learning time and the complexity of the material to be learned. A common experiment in this field consists of measuring the length of time that it takes for subjects to learn a set of nonsense syllables. As would be expected, the length of time increases in rough proportion to the number of syllables on the list. Some evidence suggests that the relation is summarized by the following:

(13.4.5) Let n represent the number of nonsense syllables in a list and $f(n)$ the length of time required to memorize the the list. Then $f(n) = an\sqrt{n - b}$, where a and b are empirically derived constants such that $b < n$.

Of course, f is not a continuous function, since the domain contains only integers. It is sometimes convenient, however, to disregard a fact such as this and to assume continuity. In order to find out whether learning time increases *uniformly* with n, we must examine the derivative of f. This examination requires the use of several of the results from the preceding section.

PROPOSITION

(13.4.6) If $f(n) = an\sqrt{n - b}$, $n > 0$, $n > b$, $a > 0$, then

$$f'(n) = a(n - b)^{1/2}\left[1 + \frac{n}{2(n - b)}\right].$$

Proof

Let $g(n) = an$, $h(n) = n - b$, $v(x) = x^{1/2}$, $u(n) = v(h(n))$, so that $f(n) = g(n)u(n)$. To locate the necessary derivatives, we have

(1) $g'(n) = a$, $h'(n) = 1$.   (13.3.3.3 and 13.3.3.4)

(2) $v'(h(n)) = \frac{1}{2}(h(n))^{-1/2} = \frac{1}{2}(n - b)^{-1/2}$.   (13.4.3)

(3) $u'(n) = v'(h(n))h'(n) = \frac{1}{2}(n - b)^{-1/2}$.   (13.3.6 and steps 1 and 2)

(4) $f'(n) = g'(n)u(n) + g(n)u'(n)$,   (13.3.4.2)

(5) $= a(n - b)^{1/2} + \frac{an}{2}(n - b)^{-1/2}$,   (Steps 1, 3, and 4)

(6) $= a(n - b)^{1/2}\left[1 + \frac{n}{2(n - b)}\right]$.   (By factoring $a(n - b)^{1/2}$ in step 5)

Thus, increase in learning time, f', is itself monotonically increasing and roughly proportional to the square root of the number of syllables in the list. Contrast this with the second learning function given by $g(n) = an$, $a > 0$. In both these functions, the length of time required to memorize a list of nonsense syllables increases as the number of syllables in the list is increased. But here the similarity ends. Under learning conditions given by the function f, the addition of some number of syllables, h, will require a longer added memorization time if the list is long than if it is short. Since $g'(n) = a$ (Does the reader concur?), it follows that an addition of h syllables will require an added learning time that has nothing to do with the length of the original list. In the first situation, that given by f, the instantaneous increase in learning time itself increases with increments in n. In the second case, that given by g, the instantaneous increase remains constant.

Exercises

13.19. Prove Theorem 13.4.3.

13.20. Complete the proof of Proposition 13.4.4.

13.21. Construct the graph over the interval $[-1, 3]$ of f and f' where f is given by each of the following:

(a) $f(x) = 2[x + x^2]^{1/2}$.

(b) $f(x) = 3(g(x))^4$, where $g(x) = \dfrac{1}{x + 1}$.

(c) $f(x) = [3 + 6x + 9x^2]^2$.

13.5 Derivatives of Log and Exponential Functions

Recall from Section 10.4 that if a function is given by $f(x) = \log_\alpha(x)$, $x > 0$ and $1 \neq \alpha > 0$, then we know that $\alpha^{f(x)} = x$. Thus, if $f(x) = \log_{10} x$, we know that $f(10) = 1$, $f(100) = 2$, $f(1,000) = 3$. In Definition 12.2.8 the reader was introduced quite casually to a special number called e. We saw that e was the limit of the binomial expansion $\left(1 + \dfrac{1}{n}\right)^n$ as n becomes large. It turns out that e is an irrational number that is roughly $2.718281 \cdots$, or about 2.7.

It turns out also that the differential calculus sometimes is simplified if we choose $\alpha = e$. A glance at Figure 10.3 should convince the reader that the graph of the logarithmic function changes at an ever more sluggish pace as x becomes larger. This would suggest that the derivative of a log function ought to bear some sort of inverse relation to x. This is precisely the case.

THEOREM

(13.5.1) If $f(x) = \log_\alpha (x)$, $x > 0$ and $1 \neq \alpha > 0$, then $f'(x) = \dfrac{1}{x} \log_e (\alpha)$, and, in particular, if $f(x) = \log_e (x)$, then

$$f'(x) = \frac{1}{x}.$$

Proof

Let $f(x) = \log_\alpha (x)$, $x > 0$, and $1 \neq \alpha > 0$. Then:

(1) $f'(x) = \lim\limits_{h \to 0} \dfrac{\log_\alpha (x + h) - \log_\alpha (x)}{h}$,   (13.2.1)

(2) but $\log_\alpha (x + h) - \log_\alpha (x)$

$$= \log_\alpha \left(\frac{x + h}{x}\right) = \log_\alpha \left(1 + \frac{h}{x}\right). \quad (7.3.4.2)$$

(3) $f'(x) = \dfrac{1}{x} \lim\limits_{h \to 0} \dfrac{x}{h} \log_\alpha \left(1 + \dfrac{h}{x}\right).$ $\left(\begin{array}{l}\text{By steps 1 and} \\ \quad \text{2 and multi-} \\ \text{plying by } \frac{x}{x}\end{array}\right)$

(4) Let $k = \dfrac{x}{h}$, so that for $x > 0$,

$$(h \to 0) \to (k \to \infty).$$

(5) $f'(x) = \dfrac{1}{x} \lim\limits_{h \to 0} \log_\alpha \left(1 + \dfrac{1}{k}\right)^k,$ (Steps 3 and 4)

(6) $\quad = \dfrac{1}{x} \log_\alpha \lim\limits_{k \to \infty} \left(1 + \dfrac{1}{k}\right)^k,$ (Extension of 12.3.11.3)

(7) $\quad = \dfrac{1}{x} \log_\alpha (e).$ (Step 6 and 12.2.9)

The "in particular" part of the theorem is immediately obvious once it is recalled that $\log_e (e) = 1$.

Unfortunately, the log function often becomes more complicated than this in social analysis. More often than not, a model of social behavior contains the log of some *function* of x. For instance, a function may be given by $f(x) = \log_e (2x^2)$. To examine the derivative of this more complicated function, we may call again on the chain rule.* The function $f(x) = \log_e (2x^2)$ can be rewritten as $f(x) = g(h(x))$, where $g(x) = \log_e (x)$ and $h(x) = 2x^2$. The chain rule tells us in this case that $f'(x) = g'(h(x))h'(x)$. But we know that $g'(h(x)) = \dfrac{1}{h(x)} = \dfrac{1}{2x^2}$, according to the preceding theorem. Theorem 13.4.3 told us that $h'(x) = 4x$. Thus, $f'(x) = \dfrac{4x}{2x^2} = \dfrac{2}{x}$. This suggests both a generalization of Theorem 13.5.1 and the method of its proof.

(13.5.2) If $f(x) = \log_\alpha (g(x))$, where $x > 0$ and $1 \neq \alpha > 0$, and if $g'(x)$ exists, then: **THEOREM**

$$f'(x) = \frac{g'(x)}{g(x)} \log_e (\alpha).$$

The proof, which requires reference to 13.5.1 and to the chain rule, is left as an exercise.

In Section 6.6 it was learned that logarithmic functions are the inverses of a second class, called the exponential functions. That is, an exponential function is any function f given by $f(x) = \alpha^x$, $1 \neq \alpha > 0$ (constant coefficients are ignored). The preceding theorem about the derivative of a logarithmic function makes the location of the derivative of an exponential function a simple matter. First, however, the reader ought to guess how the derivative of an exponential function varies as x varies. Notice that, as x increases, α^x increases at a much more rapid rate if $\alpha > 1$ and decreases at an increasing rate if $0 < \alpha < 1$. Thus, it is not surprising to learn that the derivative increases monotonically in x. What is surprising, however, is the discovery that the derivative of an exponential function is no more than the function itself with a constant coefficient appended.

* Appeal to the chain rule is not the only means of solution in this case. See Exercise 13.22.

(13.5.3) If $f(x) = \alpha^x$, $1 \neq \alpha > 0$, then $f'(x) = \alpha^x \log_e \alpha$.   **THEOREM**
In particular, if $\alpha = e$, then $f'(x) = e^x$.

Let $f(x) = \alpha^x$, $1 \neq \alpha > 0$. Also, let $h(x) = \log_e f(x)$, and   *Proof*
let $g(x) = x \log_e \alpha$.

(1) $\log_e f(x) = x \log_e \alpha \rightarrow h(x) = g(x)$.   (By taking logs in identity of hypothesis and by definition of h and g)

(2) $h'(x) = g'(x)$.   (Step 1 and 13.2.1)

(3) But, $h'(x) = \dfrac{f'(x)}{f(x)}$,   (13.5.2)

(4) and $g'(x) = \log_e \alpha$.   (13.3.3.3 and 13.3.3.4)

(5) $f'(x) = f(x) \log_e \alpha = \alpha^x \log_e \alpha$.   (Steps 2–4)

Statisticians frequently encounter a function that looks approximately like $f(x) = ke^{-x^2}$, where k is a positive constant. Because the derivatives of this expression have theoretical importance, it would be handy to evaluate them. Unfortunately, Theorem 13.5.3 fails to provide us with a solution, because the expression involves e raised to a function of x rather than simply to x. To remedy this, we can proceed as in the case of logs, by appealing to the chain rule. Together with 13.5.3, this rule immediately gives us the following:

(13.5.4) If $f(x) = \alpha^{g(x)}$, and if $g'(x)$ exists, then $f'(x) = \alpha^{g(x)} g'(x) \log_e \alpha$.   **THEOREM**

The proof, which is left an exercise, proceeds exactly as did that of 13.5.2. By means of a careful application of this theorem, the reader ought to be able to convince himself that, if $f(x)$ is as defined earlier in this paragraph, then $f'(x) = -2kxe^{-x^2}$, a number that is less than zero for all $x > 0$ and that is greater than zero for all $x < 0$. Thus, at each point in the domain, $x > 0$, the instantaneous rate of increase is actually a decrease.

Exercises

13.22. Prove that, if $f(x) = \log_e 2x^2$, $f'(x) = 2/x$ without using the chain rule. (HINT: $\log_e 2x^2 = \log_e 2 + 2\log_e x$.)

13.23. Prove Theorem 13.5.2.

13.24. Evaluate the derivative of each of the following for $x > 0$:

(a) $f(x) = \log_2 (x)$.
(b) $f(x) = 4\log_{10} (x^2)$.
(c) $f(x) = \log_e (\log_e x)$.
(d) $f(x) = \log_a (\log_e x)$.
(e) $f(x) = \log_e (2x^2) - \log_e (2x^5)$.

13.25. Evaluate the derivatives of each of the following:

(a) $f(x) = 2^x$.
(b) $f(x) = 2^{x^2}$.
(c) $f(x) = x^x$.
(d) $f(x) = 4(1 - 2x^2)^{-2x}$.

13.26. Prove Theorem 13.5.4.

13.27. Construct an exponential function with negative exponent on the positive numbers—that is, a decay function—that might represent a relation in your field of specialization. Investigate and interpret its derivative properties.

13.6 Derivatives of Polynomial Functions

The polynomial, it should be recalled from Section 10.5, is just a sum of power functions with positive integral exponents. That is, any function, f, given by $f(x) = \sum\limits_{i=0}^{n} \alpha_i x^i$ $(= \alpha_0 + \alpha_1 x + \cdots + \alpha_n x^n)$ is called a polynomial function of a degree n (assuming $\alpha_n \neq 0$). With the equipment that has been developed, the location of the derivative of any polynomial is simplicity itself. All that is needed is a theorem about the derivative of a power function and another about the derivatives of a sum of functions, both of which we have. When they are put together, the immediate result is the following:

(13.6.1) If f is a polynomial function given by $f(x) = \sum\limits_{i=0}^{n} \alpha_i x^i$, $\alpha_n \neq 0$, then the derivative of f is given by $f'(x) = \sum\limits_{i=1}^{n} (i)\alpha_i x^{i-1}$.   **THEOREM**

Thus, the derivative of a polynomial is itself a polynomial of degree $n - 1$. Note that the index, i, begins with zero in f but begins with one in f'. The reason for this is that the first term of f is $a_0 x^0 = a_0$, a constant. Since the derivative of any constant term is zero, according to 13.3.3.2, this term drops out in the derivative of a polynomial.

Figure 13.3   SKETCH OF THE GRAPH OF

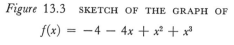

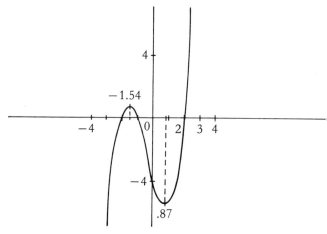

Consider the polynomial function given by $f(x) = -4 - 4x + x^2 + x^3$, whose graph is sketched in Figure 13.3. The graph indicates that the function has solutions at the points -2, -1, and 2. This can be verified if it is recognized that the function can be factored into the alternate form $f(x) = (x - 2)(x + 2)(x + 1)$. Notice that a peak occurs at $x = -1.54$ and that a low point occurs at $x = .87$. Theorem 11.6.1 can be applied to locate the derivative of f at any point x, which turns out to be $f'(x) = -4 + 2x + 3x^2$. Thus, the derivative is itself a polynomial function of second degree. Solutions of this polynomial are most informative. The two points $x = -1.54$ and $x = .87$ satisfy $f'(x) = 0$. The reader ought to verify this by using 10.5.6. The two numbers that satisfy the equality $f'(x) = 0$ are the numbers that yield the "peak" and "trough" points on the graph of the function. All this leads to a new use and interpretation of derivatives, which will be explored in the next section.

Exercises

13.28. Prove Theorem 13.6.1.

13.29. In Exercise 13.5, a function, $f(p) = p - p^2$, was constructed on a set of proportions, $0 \le p \le 1$:

(a) Evaluate $f'(p)$.
(b) Locate a number p such that $f'(p) = 0$.
(c) Interpret this number in terms of the function $f(p)$ described in Exercise 13.5.

13.30. Find the derivative of each of the following:

(a) $f(x) = \sum_{i=0}^{4} a_i x^i$.

(b) $f(x) = \sum_{i=0}^{4} i x^i$.

(c) $f(x) = \left(\sum_{i=0}^{5} 2i x^i \right)^3$.

(d) $f(x) = 5 + 2x^2 + 6x^4$.

13.7 Maxima and Minima of Functions

The derivative of a function at a point is nothing more than a measure of the rate at which the function is changing at that point. Thus, for example, in the case of a linear function, $f(x) = a_0 + a_1 x$, the derivative is $f'(x) = a_1$, a constant. The rate of change of a linear function is a constant number, one that does not depend upon the value of x. But this is precisely what makes a linear function linear. Its graph moves along at a constant rate of change, thus forming a straight line. Of course, many derivatives are not constants but depend on the value of x, as in the case of the cubic polynomial investigated in the preceding section.

Just as the magnitude of $f'(x)$ tells how rapidly the function is changing at a point, the algebraic *sign* of $f'(x)$ also yields important information. What must be the case if

$f'(x) < 0$? The answer is to be found in 13.2.1, the definition of a derivative. As the limit of a change function, the derivative can be less than zero only if the value of the change function itself is less than zero. This in turn can occur only if the numerator, $f(x + h) - f(x)$, and the denominator, h, have unlike signs.

If $h > 0$ and $f(x + h) - f(x) < 0$, for each point, x, in an interval, then the function must be monotone decreasing in that interval and the graph of f must slope downward to the right in the interval. All this merely states the following:

(13.7.1) Let f be a function defined on an interval of real numbers, $X = I_{(a,\,b)}$, such that $f'(x)$ is defined for each $x \in X$. Then:

THEOREM

(1) f is monotone decreasing over $X \leftrightarrow f'(x) < 0$, each $x \in X$.

(2) f is monotone increasing over $X \leftrightarrow f'(x) > 0$, each $x \in X$.

(*Part 1, converse.*) Let $f'(x) < 0$, each $x \in X$, and let $h > 0$. For each $(x + h) \in X$,

Proof

(1) $f(x + h) < f(x)$.   (Since $f'(x) < 0$
                                                      and $h > 0$)

(2) f is monotone decreasing on X.   (By 10.3.3)

Now, let $h < 0$ so that $(x + h) < x$. Then:

(3) $f(x + h) > f(x)$, each $(x + h) \in X$.   (Since $f'(x) < 0$)
(4) f is monotone decreasing on X.   (10.3.3 and since
                                                          $x + h < x$)

The proofs of the implication of Part 1 and of Part 2 of the theorem are similar. Thus, a function is monotone decreasing at a point, and its graph slopes downward at that point only if the derivative is less than zero. If the derivative is greater than zero at a point, it is monotone increasing there and its graph slopes upward.

Finally, consider the singularly important case, $f'(x) = 0$. Since the derivative is the instantaneous rate of change at the point x, it must be that, if $f'(x) = 0$, the function is undergoing no change at all at the point x. Thus,

(13.7.2) If a function f is differentiable at a point x, and if $f'(x) = 0$, then x is called a *stationary point* of f.

At each stationary point, then, the function "stands still," if for no more than an instant.

To get a better idea of what goes on at a stationary point, consider what is happening to the left (that is, at points with smaller values) and to the right (or at points with larger values) of such a point. If the derivatives of points immediately to the left of a stationary point have the same sign as those immediately to the right, then the function is monotone in that region and the point represents a momentary "jog" at which the function neither increases nor decreases. On the other hand, suppose that the signs of derivatives to the immediate left of a stationary point are the opposite of those to the immediate right. Suppose first that derivatives of points to the left are negative and that those to the right are positive. By Theorem 13.7.1, the function is monotone decreasing to to the left and monotone increasing to the right. The stationary point, then, is the point at which the graph of the function ceases to drop, levels off, and begins to climb. Thus, the stationary point represents a (relative) minimum value of the function f. The term relative pops up in parentheses to remind the reader that this need not be the only such minimum point in the interval. Next consider the reverse situation, that in which the derivatives just to the left are positive and those to the immediate right are negative. Then, by similar reasoning, the stationary point must be a (relative) maximum of f. All this is illustrated in Figure 13.4 and is summarized by the next theorem.

(13.7.3) Let a function, f, be defined and differentiable on an interval, $X = I_{(a, b)}$. If there is a point $x_0 \in X$ such that $f'(x_0) = 0$, then for any subinterval, Y, such that $x_0 \in Y \subset X$, with x_0 the only stationary point in Y,

(1) $f(x_0) < f(x)$, all $x \in Y$ (that is, $f(x_0)$ is a *minimum* value of f) $\leftrightarrow f'(x) < 0$, each $x < x_0$, and $f'(x) > 0$, each $x > x_0$.

(2) $f(x_0) > f(x)$, all $x \in Y$ (that is, $f(x_0)$ is a *maximum* value of f) $\leftrightarrow f'(x) > 0$, each $x < x_0$, and $f'(x) < 0$, each $x > x_0$.

The proof of this extremely important theorem should be apparent from the preceding discussion.

Figure 13.4

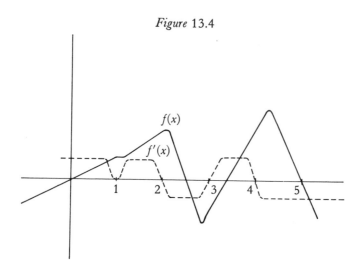

Figure 13.4 contains sketches of the graph of a function, $f(x)$, and of its derivative, $f'(x)$. Notice that a stationary point occurs at $x = 1$, since $f'(1) = 0$. The values of $f'(x)$ for x in the immediate region of 1, both above and below, are positive. Thus, the value $x = 1$ provides neither a maximum nor a minimum point of f according to 13.7.3, but it does give a point of stationarity by 13.7.2. On the open interval $(1, 3)$ there is just one value of x such that $f'(x) = 0$. This is given by $x = 2$. The reader should verify the fact that this value provides a maximum of f on this interval according to 13.7.3. On the interval $(0, 5)$ there occur two relative maxima, at $x = 2$ and $x = 4$ (note that $f'(2) = f'(4) = 0$), but no maximum according to 13.7.3. There is a minimum on this interval, however, at $x = 3$.

Theorem 13.7.3 suggests that maximum and minimum values of functions, if they exist at all, can be located by examining the derivatives for stationary points and then testing the derivatives on either side of such points. In order to get the feel of minima and maxima, the reader should go over the theorem carefully and then apply it to the function that is graphed in Figure 13.3.

Statisticians make frequent use of this theorem. As an illustration, let p represent the proportion of a population possessing such an attribute as being a male or being married. That is, p is the number of people in the population, with the attribute divided by the total number of people in the population, so that $0 \leq p \leq 1$. The "variance" of a measure such as p is itself a statistical measure, one that shows how heterogeneous or homogeneous the population is with respect to the trait at hand. The variance of the statistic p turns out to be a function of p given by $f(p) = p(1 - p)$. This function makes quite good sense in one respect: It is obvious that $f(p)$ is a minimum either when $p = 0$ or when $p = 1$. That is, the population is said to be least heterogeneous whenever either no members or all members possess the attribute. To locate a point of maximum heterogeneity, we can use Theorem 13.7.3. Since $f(p) = p(1 - p) = p - p^2$, a second degree polynomial, $f'(p) = 1 - 2p$. (Does the reader agree?) To locate a maximum, set $f'(p) = 0$ so that $1 - 2p = 0$, from which it follows that $p = \frac{1}{2}$. To make certain that this is a maximum, simply plug $p < \frac{1}{2}$ into $f'(p)$ and observe that $f'(p) > 0$ whenever $p < \frac{1}{2}$, and then repeat for $p > \frac{1}{2}$. All this should satisfy one that $p = \frac{1}{2}$ is the maximum value of $f(p)$. Again, this makes sense if it is agreed that maximum heterogeneity requires that half the population possesses the attribute while the other half does not.

Exercises

13.31. Complete the proof of Theorem 13.7.1.

13.32. Consider Theorem 13.7.3:

(a) Why was the derivative of f examined in a particular sub-interval, $Y \subset X$? How does this pertain to the phrase "*relative* maximum" or minimum?

(b) Complete the proof of this theorem.

13.33. Locate all points of stationarity of the following functions (if any exist), and determine whether each is a relative minimum or maximum, or neither:

(a) $f(x) = e^x, x \geq 0.$

(b) $f(x) = xe^{-x}, x \geq 0.$

(c) $f(x) = 1 + 4x + 4x^2.$

(d) $f(x) = 2 + 9x + 12x^2 + 4x^3.$ (HINT: Multiply $f(x)$ in part (c) by $(2 + x)$.)

(e) $f(x) = 4 + 16x + 15x^2 - 4x^3 - 4x^4.$ (HINT: Multiply $f(x)$ in part (d) by $(2 - x)$.)

13.8 Higher Derivatives

The derivative of a function is itself a function. It was seen, for instance, that the derivative of a polynomial function of degree n is a new polynomial function of degree $n - 1$. Since a derivative can be constructed from any (differentiable) function, nothing prevents us from taking the derivative of a function that is itself a derivative. And, given the derivative of a derivative, nothing prevents the construction of *its* derivative. Let us first define a so-called second derivative and then see whether it can be used profitably.

(13.8.1) If f is a function such that $f'(x)$ is defined at a point x, then, if it exists, the second derivative is written $f''(x)$, and is given by: **Definition**

$$f''(x) = \lim_{h \to 0} \frac{f'(x + h) - f'(x)}{h}.$$

Thus, $f''(x)$, the second derivative, of f at x is the derivative of the (first) derivative. Nothing really new need be said about the second derivative since, being a derivative itself, it is subject to all the rules and regulations regarding derivatives that were established in earlier sections of this chapter.

What might the derivative of a derivative represent? The answer comes immediately from the interpretation of the first derivative. If a derivative is the (instantaneous) rate of change of a function at a point, then the second derivative must be the *rate of change of the rate of change* at that point. The derivative indicates the extent to which a function increases or decreases as it reaches a point. The second derivative tells whether this rate of change is itself changing. The first derivative of a linear function $\alpha_0 + \alpha_1 x$, as was seen, is

$f'(x) = \alpha_1$, so that the function increases or decreases at the constant rate α_1. According to 13.3.3.2, the derivative of any constant function is zero. Hence, in this case $f''(x) = 0$, which says that the rate of change is itself unchanging.

The function whose graph was plotted in Figure 13.3, $f(x) = -4 - 4x + x^2 + x^3$, was seen to have derivative $f'(x) = -4 + 2x + 3x^2$. By another application of 13.6.1, the second derivative is seen to be $f''(x) = 2 + 6x$. The derivative of $f''(x)$, or third derivative, call it $f'''(x)$, must by the same reasoning be $f'''(x) = 6$. Finally, the fourth and all higher derivatives must equal zero. (Why?) One can find a zero solution of the second derivative of this function by using Theorem 10.5.5. The reader should verify that $f''(-\frac{1}{3}) = 0$, that $f''(x) < 0$ for all $x < -\frac{1}{3}$, and that $f''(x) > 0$, for all $x > -\frac{1}{3}$. Thus, to the left of this critical point, the rate of change decreases in an ever more rapid fashion, while to the right of it, the function's rate of change increases in an accelerating fashion.

In mechanics, we can represent the speed of a moving object as a function by letting t represent elapsed time in some standard unit such as seconds and $f(t)$ represent the *distance* that the object has traveled from its starting point at time $t = 0$. It has been established that the distance traveled by a free-falling object in a vacuum at sea level is given approximately by the function $f(t) = 16t^2$ where length is measured in feet and time is measured in seconds. Then the *velocity*, or rate of speed at an instant in time, is $f'(t) = 32t$. Thus, at the end of 10 seconds, a free-falling object has traveled $f(10) = 1600$ feet, and its rate of speed at that point is $f'(10) = 320$ feet per second. The second derivative tells us the rate of *acceleration* of the object—that is, the rate of increase in the velocity. In this case $f''(x) = 32$, so that at each point in time, the velocity accelerates at a rate of 32 feet per second.

The second derivative of a function is useful in yet another respect. In the last section it was seen that maxima and minima of functions can be located if the first derivative is subjected to a rather complicated analysis. By looking at both the first and second derivatives, we can sometimes make the location of such points simpler. Suppose that x_0 is a point in the domain of a differentiable function such that $f'(x_0) = 0$ and that $f''(x) < 0$. Then it must be that, for a small $h > 0, f'(x_0 + h) < f'(x_0)$, which implies that $f'(x + h) < 0$. If h is sufficiently small and is less than zero, then $f'(x_0 + h) > f'(x_0)$. But these conditions imply that the graph of f slopes up to the point x_0, where it becomes stationary, and then slopes downward to the right. All this indicates that x_0 is a maximum point of f. Now consider a second point in the domain of f, say x_1, such that $f'(x_1) = 0$ and $f''(x_1) > 0$. By carefully retracing this argument, the reader should be able to convince himself that these conditions of the first and second derivatives are sufficient to show that the point x_1 is a minimum point of f. The foregoing provides an informal proof of the following:

(13.8.2) If f is a function whose first and second derivatives are defined at a point x, then: **THEOREM**

(1) x is a maximum point of $f \leftrightarrow f'(x) = 0$ and $f''(x) < 0$.
(2) x is a minimum point of $f \leftrightarrow f'(x) = 0$ and $f''(x) > 0$.

As an exercise, the reader should determine what the graph of a function would look like at a point for which both $f'(x) = 0$ and $f''(x) = 0$.

Exercises

13.34. Construct a third degree polynomial function such that, for some number x, $f'(x) = f''(x) = 0$. Graph this function in an interval about x and interpret the meaning of this function. (HINT: Choose arbitrary numbers, α_2 and α_3. Then, if $f''(x) = 0$, it must be that $x = -\alpha_2/\alpha_3$. Use this identity to locate α_1.)

13.35. Investigate f'' and f''' for each function of Exercise 13.24.

13.36. Investigate second and third derivatives of the functions of Exercise 13.33.

13.9 Partial Derivatives

In Section 10.6 multivariate functions were explored briefly. Recall that a function of two variables is just a set of ordered pairs, $\{\langle\langle x, y\rangle, f(x, y)\rangle : x \in X, y \in Y\}$ where X and Y are intervals of real numbers. The point $\langle x, y\rangle$ is a point in two-dimensional space and the number $f(x, y)$ is the unique number that corresponds to the point $\langle x, y \rangle$ under the function f. For example, suppose that a psychologist hypothesizes that retention of learned material depends jointly on two variables, strength of stimulus and measured intelligence level, and that the relation is presumed to be given by $f(x, y) = (x + 2y)^2$, where $f(x, y)$ is measured retention, x is stimulus strength, and y is intelligence. By expanding the binomial, we have $f(x, y) = x^2 + 4xy + 4y^2$, so that retention might be said to depend on three factors: stimulus; intelligence; and the *interaction* of these two variables (represented by the term $4xy$).

A function such as this, in the context of this chapter, creates some new problems. What does the derivative of a multivariate function mean? Does it refer to the instantaneous rate of change in x, in y, or in both? It should be fairly obvious that one would want to consider separately the effects of change in each variable of a multivariate function. Thus, a notion of the derivative is needed in which only one variable is considered at a time, the others being treated as constants. In this sense, the illustrative function might be treated as either of two simple polynomial functions, one with variable x and the other with variable y. The definition that follows should begin to pull this idea together.

(13.9.1) If f is any function of two variables, X and Y, that is defined at a point (x, y), then the *partial* derivative of f with respect to x is denoted $\dfrac{\partial f}{\partial x}$ and, if it exists, is given by:

Definition

$$\frac{\partial f}{\partial x} = \lim_{h \to 0} \frac{f((x + h), y) - f(x, y)}{h}.$$

And, if it exists, the partial derivative of f with respect to y is given by:

$$\frac{\partial f}{\partial y} = \lim_{h \to 0} \frac{f(x, (y + h)) - f(x, y)}{h}.$$

Let us use this definition to discover the partial derivatives of the psychologist's retention function.

(13.9.2) If $f(x, y) = x^2 + 4xy + 4y^2$, then:

$$\frac{\partial f}{\partial x} = 2(x + 2y), \quad \text{and} \quad \frac{\partial f}{\partial y} = 4(x + 2y).$$

(1) $\dfrac{\partial f}{\partial x}$

$$= \lim_{h \to 0} \frac{(x + h)^2 + 4(x + h)y + 4y^2 - x^2 - 4xy - 4y^2}{h},$$

(13.9.1)

(2) $= \lim_{h \to 0} \dfrac{2xh + h^2 + 4hy}{h}$, (By expanding and cancelling in step 1)

(3) $= \lim_{h \to 0} (2x + h + 4y) = 2(x + 2y)$. (By cancelling h in step 3)

The proof with respect to $\dfrac{\partial f}{\partial y}$ is similar.

Thus, even if y is considered to be "held constant," the instantaneous rate of change in f depends on the value of y as well as on x.

Higher partial derivatives can be considered just as were higher simple derivatives. However, matters become a bit more complicated by the fact that a partial derivative, say with respect to x, may turn out to be a function of two or more variables, such as in 13.9.2. In that case, a second partial derivative could be considered either with respect to x or with respect to y. Higher partial derivatives will not be used in this volume, but the reader should be able to understand what they are from the following:

(13.9.3) Let $f(x, y)$ be a function with partial derivatives with respect to x and with respect to y defined at each point, (x, y), in the domain. Let $q(x, y) = \dfrac{\partial f}{\partial x}$ and $r(x, y) = \dfrac{\partial f}{\partial y}$. Then, if they exist,

(1) $\dfrac{\partial^2 f}{\partial x^2} = \lim_{h \to 0} \dfrac{q((x + h), y) - q(x, y)}{h}$.

(2) $\dfrac{\partial^2 f}{\partial y^2} = \lim_{h \to 0} \dfrac{r(x, (y + h)) - r(x, y)}{h}$.

$$(3) \quad \frac{\partial^2 f}{\partial x \partial y} = \lim_{h \to 0} \frac{r((x + h), y) - r(x, y)}{h}.$$

$$(4) \quad \frac{\partial^2 f}{\partial y \partial x} = \lim_{h \to 0} \frac{q(x, (y + h)) - q(x, y)}{h}.$$

Part 1 is called the *second partial derivative* of f with respect to x; Part 2 is called the second partial with respect to y; Part 3 is called the mixed partial, first with respect to y, then with respect to x; and Part 4 is called the mixed partial, first with respect to x and then with respect to y.

It turns out to be quite generally, but not entirely, true that the two mixed partial derivatives are equal to one another (see Miller, *Advanced Real Calculus* [1], pages 130–134).

And that, in a rather large nutshell, is the concept of change as viewed through the elegant lenses of mathematics. Certainly, the reader must recognize that what has been said here is little more than an introduction to the mathematics of change. On the other hand, the ideas that have been discussed in this chapter are sufficiently advanced to permit the reader to digest much of the more formalized literature in the fields of social science. When carefully and critically translated from purely abstract notions into analogues of social behavior, into mathematical models, these elements of the calculus of change have worked a sometimes profound change on the fabric of social theory.

In addition to this substantive usefulness, the materials considered in this chapter lend themselves to the construction of yet newer mathematical systems that, in turn, also prove to be highly useful in social analysis. In the next chapter the tools of the derivative calculus will be put to work in the construction of what is known as the *integral calculus*, which provides a formal analogue of the notion of physical or social mass.

Exercises

13.37. In 13.9.2, prove that $\frac{\partial f}{\partial y} = 4(x + 2y)$.

13.38. Investigate $\frac{\partial f}{\partial x}$ and $\frac{\partial f}{\partial y}$ of each of the functions below:

(a) $f(x, y) = \sum_{i=1}^{n} \alpha_i(xy)^i$.

(b) $f(x, y) = \alpha^{(x+y)}$.

(c) $f(x, y) = (x + y)^\alpha$.

(d) $f(x, y) = (xy)^\alpha$.

13.39. Investigate $\dfrac{\partial^2 f}{\partial x^2}$, $\dfrac{\partial^2 f}{\partial y^2}$, $\dfrac{\partial^2 f}{\partial x \partial y}$ and $\dfrac{\partial^2 f}{\partial y \partial x}$ of each function in Exercise 13.38.

Selected References

1. Miller, Kenneth S. *Advanced Real Calculus.* New York: Harper & Brothers, 1957. Chapters 2–3.
2. Moore, John T. *Fundamental Principles of Mathematics.* New York: Rinehart and Co., Inc., 1960. Chapter 8.
3. Nielsen, Kaj L. *College Mathematics.* New York: Barnes and Noble, Inc., 1958. Pages 212–225.
4. Peters, Charles C., and Van Voorhis, Walter R. *Statistical Procedures and Their Mathematical Bases.* New York: McGraw-Hill Book Company, Inc., 1940. Chapter 1.
5. Rudin, Walter. *Principles of Mathematical Analysis* (Revised Edition). New York: McGraw-Hill Book Company, Inc., 1964. Chapter 5.
6. Tintner, Gerhard. *Mathematics and Statistics for Economists.* New York: Rinehart and Co., Inc., 1953. Chapters 9–18.
7. Titchmarsh, E. C. *Mathematics for the General Reader.* Garden City, New York: Doubleday & Co., Inc., 1959. Chapter 13.

The Calculus of Mass

Two new topics are taken up in this chapter. The first concerns antiderivative systems. Such systems represent an operation rather like the inverse of that of constructing derivatives. The second topic concerns a method for evaluating the area or volume in a space bounded by the graph of a function and its horizontal axis between any two points. At first glance these topics may appear entirely unrelated and, hence, to be odd bedfellows. With some patience the reader will discover that this impression is mistaken. Antiderivatives and areal measurements represent two facets of a single mathematical device called *integration*.

A question of applicability might be appropriate at this point: Why should a social scientist be particularly concerned about such a directly physical notion as that of area or mass? The answer is twofold. In the first place, the integral is an exceedingly useful tool in the construction of social theory. The reader who mastered the preceding chapter certainly should recognize that the derivative is useful in this respect. As an inverse derivative, the integral shares much of this utility. In the second place, the integral, as a measure of area or volume, is indispensable to the statistician in that his continuous probability distributions act essentially like an area or a volume. Probability theory, in turn, is used by the social investigator in the evaluation of research data and in the construction of substantive theories.

14

14.1 Antiderivatives and the Indefinite Integral

A derivative is a function that gives the instantaneous rate of change at a point in the domain of a second function. The derivative function ordinarily is thought of as being a by-product of an original function. A second distinct view is possible, however. Given the rich interpretative value of the derivative, it is not surprising to discover that social theory sometimes focuses directly on derivative functions, showing only secondary interest in what might be called the parent function. As an example, the economist's concept of marginality was introduced in Section 13.3.

To an economist, the marginal demand for a commodity at a given price, x, is the instantaneous rate of change in the demand for the commodity, $f(x)$, given a change in price. It was seen that marginal demand is just the derivative of a demand function. Now, since the concept of marginal demand is invested with substance and meaning of its own, it is reasonable to expect that a theory of marginal demand might be developed more or less independent of a theory of demand. Consider the following miniature theory of marginal demand:

(14.1.1) Let a differentiable function, g, be defined on a domain of real numbers $X \subset I_{(0,\infty]}$. Then g is a *marginal* demand function $\leftrightarrow$.

A THEORY OF MARGINAL DEMAND

(1) $g(0) = 0$.
(2) $g(x) < 0, x > 0$.
(3) $g'(x) \leq 0, x \geq 0$.

Although extremely oversimplified, this theory manages to get across some of the more obvious substance of marginal demand functions. Note that the domain of g is a subset of the set of nonnegative numbers that is taken to represent the possible prices of a commodity. The range variable, $g(x)$, represents the rate of change in demand at a particular price level, given a change from that price. More properly, $g(x)$ is the limit of the rate of change in demand as the amount of change in price approaches zero. The substantive meaning of "demand" is ignored here, but it might be interpreted as the number of units that a market would be willing to purchase at a particular price level.

The first axiom of the theory, 14.1.1.1, says that the marginal demand system is stationary at the price $x = 0$. Axiom 2 asserts that marginal demand is negative for all prices greater than zero. This says only that, at each price level, a price increase would yield a decrement in demand. Axiom 3 states that the rate of change of marginal demand itself declines. Some thought should convince the reader that this means only that the market is less sensitive to price increases if the price originally is high than if it is low.

Suppose that an economist investigates actual fluctuations in the demand for a commodity by a specified market given fluctuations about various price levels, uses a statistical device to fit a function to the data, and concludes:

EMPIRICAL
PROPOSITION

(14.1.2) The marginal demand for a specified commodity is approximately:

$$f(x) = -x^2, 0 \leq x \leq 6.$$

The term *approximately* refers to the closeness of the statistical "fit" of the function to the data and can be ignored for the present. The reader should convince himself that a function defined by 14.1.2 does indeed satisfy the three axioms of our marginal demand theory. That is, $f(0) = 0$, $-x^2 < 0$ and $f'(x) = -2x$, which is negative for all positive values of x.

Recall once again that a marginal demand function gives the rate of change in demand at a price, x, but that it emphatically does *not* give the actual demand at that price. On the other hand, a marginal demand function is the derivative of another function that gives precisely this information. A situation such as this rather naturally suggests a question: Given a derivative function, can the function of which it is the derivative be recovered? Before proceeding, the reader should consider this question carefully, understand precisely what it asks, and then attempt to answer it. As a start, what about the function defined above? Can a function, call it F, be discovered such that $F'(x) = -x^2$?

As a first step toward an answer, some nomenclature might help:

Definition

(14.1.3) If any two functions, F and f, satisfy the identity

$$F'(x) = f(x), a < x < b,$$

then F is called an *antiderivative* (or a *primitive*) of F on the interval $I_{(a,b)}$.

In the event that $F'(x) = f(x)$ for all values of x, the restriction on x can be ignored. Before we can explore general properties of antiderivatives, it is important to discover whether or not it is proper to speak about *the* antiderivative of a function, f. The following shows that a function that has an associated antiderivative has an entire *class* of such associated functions as well.

(14.1.4) Given two functions F and f, such that F is an   **THEOREM**
antiderivative of f on an interval $I_{(a,b)}$, then any function of
the form $G(x) = F(x) + c$, for c any real number, also is
an antiderivative of f.

Let $F'(x) = f(x)$ and $G(x) = F(x) + g(x)$, where $g(x) = c$.   *Proof*

(1) $G'(x) = F'(x) + g'(x)$,   (By 13.3.4.1)
(2) $= f(x) + 0$,   (By hypothesis and
                                    13.3.3.2)

(3) $= f(x)$.
(4) G also is an antiderivative of f.   (By 14.1.3)

Thus, if a single antiderivative of a function can be located, an entire class can be located, any member of the class differing from any other by no more than a constant. For this reason we often write the antiderivative as $F(x) + c$, rather than as $F(x)$.

The following definition will later be seen to provide a first connection between the two seemingly disparate views of integration mentioned earlier:

(14.1.5) If a function $F = F_1(x) + c$ is an antiderivative   **Definition**
of a second function, f on an interval $I_{(a,b)}$, then we write:

$$F(x) = F_1(x) + c = \int f(x)\,dx, \quad a < x < b,$$

in which the symbol $\int$ is called the *indefinite integral sign*, $f(x)$ is called the *integrand*, and c is called the *constant of integration*. The term $\int f(x)\,dx$ is called an *indefinite integral* of f.

For the present the term dx tacked onto the integrand can be ignored.

Now let us return to the economist's marginal demand function, $f(x) = -x^2$. By this point the insightful reader should have recognized that the original demand function, call it F, of which f is the derivative, is given by the following:

(14.1.6) If $F'(x) = f(x) = -x^2$, then,   **PROPOSITION**

$$F(x) = F_1(x) + c = \int f(x)\, dx = -\frac{x^3}{3} + c.$$

Let $F'(x) = f(x) = -x^2$. Assume $F(x) \neq -\frac{x^3}{3} + c$.   *Proof*

(1) $F'(x) \neq -\frac{1}{3} 3x^2 + 0,$ (13.3.3, parts 1 and 2;
                                                  13.3.4.1 and 13.4.1)

(2) $\neq -x^2 = f(x),$ a contradiction.

(3) Hence, $F(x) = -\frac{x^3}{3} + c.$

Proposition 14.1.6 provides information about the demand function, but the information is insufficient to evaluate the function. However, only one additional piece of information would permit the evaluation of the demand function for each admissible value, x. This information consists of the range correspondent of F for any admissible value of x. Suppose, for example, that our economist has discovered with respect to the demand function, F, that $F(3) = 63$. Then, since $-\frac{3^3}{3} + c = 63$, it follows that $c = 72$. Thus, $F(0) = 72$, which could be interpreted to mean that 72 units is the market "saturation point," that is, the maximum demand for the commodity even if it should be offered free. In addition, this information tells us that $F(6) = 0$, which says that any price equal to or greater than 6 money units (whether pennies, dollars, or millions of dollars, whatever the unit selected initially by the investigator) would price the commodity out of the market.

The foregoing should suggest that two pieces of information are sufficient to characterize fully any differentiable function, F. These are, first, an identity for F' and, second, the value of $F(x)$ for some number x. These two pieces of information together make up what is sometimes called an *antiderivative system*.

If the reader understands clearly that Definition 14.1.5 stipulates that $\int f(x)\, dx = F(x) \leftrightarrow F'(x) = f(x)$, then a review of the properties of derivatives should provide him with a formidable collection of information about indefinite integrals. In particular, the following should be apparent:

(14.1.7) If f and g, functions defined on an interval of numbers, are such that $\int f(x)\,dx$ and $\int g(x)\,dx$ are defined on the interval, then,   **THEOREM**

(1) $\int 0\,dx = c.$ (13.3.3.2)

(2) $\int \alpha\,dx = \alpha x + c.$ (13.3.3.3 and
                                            13.3.3.4)

(3) $\int \alpha f(x)\,dx = \alpha \int f(x)\,dx.$ (13.3.3.4)

(4) $\int (f \pm g)(x)\,dx = \int f(x)\,dx \pm \int g(x)\,dx.$ (13.3.4.1)

Only the appropriate theorems on derivatives were appealed to here, but of course the definition of an indefinite integral also was assumed.

Exercises

14.1. Use the axioms of 14.1.1.

(a) Prove that there are no points of stationarity in G, the original demand function.
(b) Interpret this theorem in terms of consumer demand.
(c) Suppose there exists a point x such that $g'(x) = 0$. Interpret this point.
(d) Suppose that Axiom 3 were changed to say that $g'(x) > 0$, all $x \in X$. How would this contradict substantive economic theory and/or common sense?
(e) What sociological effect might make the substitute axiom of part (d) at least partially sensible? (HINT: Consult Thorstein Veblen.)

14.2. Use the empirical demand function of 14.1.2 in the following.

(a) Compute and interpret $g'(0)$.
(b) Prove that there exists no point $x > 0$ such that $g'(x) = 0$.
(c) Interpret the result of (b).
(d) Evaluate g'' and g''' and interpret these in the sense of the marginal demand theory, 14.1.1.

14.3. In 14.1.2, substitute each of the following and determine whether they satisfy the axioms of 14.1.1:

(a) $g(x) = e^{-2x} - 1.$
(b) $g(x) = x - x^2.$
(c) $g(x) = -x^{-\alpha}$, α any rational number greater than zero.

(d) $g(x) = -2(x^\alpha)$.

(e) $g(x) = -e^{2x} + 1$.

14.4. Locate an antiderivative for each function of Exercise 14.3.

14.5. Give detailed proofs of the four parts of Theorem 14.1.7.

14.2 Integrals of a Few Functions

In Chapter 13 the derivatives of certain major functions were examined. In Sections 13.4 through 13.6 it was found that the derivatives of power, logarithmic, exponential, and polynomial functions were defined and could be evaluated. It was asserted also that these classes of functions and their compositions comprise probably the most important of all relational sets for social analysts today. Thus, if indefinite integrals can be established for these few functional classes, an added segment of mathematical theory will have been made available to social analysis.

Let us begin with the class of power functions. Recall from Section 13.4 that power functions appear to represent certain forms of social relations relatively closely. In 13.4.3 we found that the derivative of any power function of the form $f(x) = ax^\alpha$ was a new function given by $f'(x) = a\alpha x^{\alpha-1}$. Now think about this in reverse. Begin with a function such as f and try to imagine what sort of function might have this form as a derivative. The form of f', of course, gives the answer.

(14.2.1) If $f(x) = ax^\alpha$, then: **THEOREM**

$$\int f(x)\, dx = \frac{ax^{\alpha+1}}{\alpha + 1} + c, \quad \alpha \neq -1.$$

Let $F(x) = \dfrac{ax^{\alpha+1}}{\alpha + 1}, \; \alpha \neq -1$.   *Proof*

(1) $F'(x) = \dfrac{a}{\alpha + 1}(\alpha + 1)x^{(\alpha+1)-1}$,   (By 13.4.3)

(2) $= ax^\alpha$,   (By cancelling and clearing in the exponent)

(3) $= f(x)$.

Thus, f is the derivative of F, so that F is an antiderivative of f, and $F(x) + c$ is the indefinite integral of f, so long as $\alpha \neq -1$.

This theorem remains a bit clay-footed until we can take care of that one disturbing parameter $\alpha = -1$. Notice first why this is problematic in the statement of this theorem. In the case of $\alpha = -1$, the antiderivative is not defined at all. To take care of this case, it is necessary to cast about for a function whose derivative is x^{-1}. A glance at 13.5.1, which states that $f'(x) = x^{-1}$ so long as $f(x) = \log_e x$, provides the answer. By putting this theorem about a derivative into reverse and adding 14.2.1, we formulate a perfectly general proposition:

(14.2.2) If $f(x) = ax^{\alpha}$,   **THEOREM**

$$\int f(x)\, dx = \begin{cases} \dfrac{ax^{\alpha+1}}{\alpha+1} + c & \alpha \neq -1 \\ a \log_e x + c & \alpha = -1 \end{cases}, \quad \text{(By 14.2.1 and 13.5.1)}$$

which disposes quite completely of the indefinite integrals of power functions. The reader may well be disquieted at the odd-appearing result of this theorem in the case $\alpha = -1$. This outcome is representative of the treachery that this sort of mathematics can play on the student who anticipates uniformly neat "symmetric" results from building such exotic concepts as the indefinite integral. If 14.2.2 makes sense, it should be clear that, if $f(x) = x^3$, $\int f(x)\, dx = \dfrac{x^4}{4} + c$; if $g(x) = 5x^4$, $\int g(x)\, dx = x^5 + c$; if $u(x) = \dfrac{3}{x}$, $\int u(x)\, dx = 3 \log_e (x) + c$.

The chain rule of differentiation, 13.3.6, offers a powerful mechanism for evaluating the derivatives of functions of functions. Recall that the chain rule said that, for any three differentiable functions, say f, g, and h, such that $f(x) = g(h(x))$, then $f'(x) = g'(h(x))h'(x)$. In light of this theorem it might be asked whether the integrals of more complicated power functions can be evaluated. For example, let $f(x) = (2x + 1)^{4.2}$. To locate the integral of f, the process of differentiation must be reversed in that a function must be found whose derivative is f. Consider the function $F(x) = \dfrac{(2x+1)^{5.2}}{5.2}$. A careful application of the chain rule should convince the reader that $F'(x) = 2(2x+1)^{4.2}$ in which the coefficient 2 is the derivative of the term $(2x+1)$. To get rid of this term, it is necessary to divide F by 2. From all this, we have:

PROPOSITION

(14.2.3) $\displaystyle\int (2x+1)^{4.2}\,dx = \dfrac{(2x+1)^{5.2}}{(2)(5.2)} + c.$

In order to generalize this result to any composition of a power function, we have the following:

THEOREM

(14.2.4) If u is any differentiable function, then:

$$\int [u(x)]^{\alpha} u'(x)\,dx = \begin{cases} \dfrac{[u(x)]^{\alpha+1}}{\alpha+1} + c, & \alpha \neq -1 \\[2mm] \log_e u(x) + c, & \alpha = -1 \end{cases}.$$

Proof

Let $u(x)$ be any differentiable function, and let $F(x) = g(u(x)) + c$, in which $g(x) = \dfrac{x^{\alpha+1}}{\alpha+1}$, $\alpha \neq -1$. Thus, g is differentiable by 13.4.4, $F(x) = \dfrac{[u(x)]^{\alpha+1}}{\alpha+1}$, and:

(1) $F'(x) = g'(u(x))u'(x)$, (By 13.3.6)

(2) but $g'(u(x)) = \dfrac{(\alpha+1)(u(x))^{\alpha}}{\alpha+1}$. (By 13.4.4)

(3) $F'(x) = u(x)^{\alpha} u'(x)$. (Steps 1 and 2)

(4) $\displaystyle\int u(x)^{\alpha} u'(x)\,dx = \dfrac{[u(x)]^{\alpha+1}}{\alpha+1} + c,$

$$\alpha \neq -1.$$

The proof for the case $\alpha = -1$ proceeds in a similar manner.

Thus, if $f(x) = 3(2+3x)^4$ it follows from this theorem that $\displaystyle\int f(x)\,dx = \dfrac{(2+3x)^5}{5} + c.$ This can be seen clearly by letting $u(x) = 2 + 3x$ so that $u'(x) = 3$, from which we see that $[u(x)]^4 u'(x) = 3(2+3x)^4$. If $f(x) = 3(2+3x)^{-1}$, then the theorem tells us that $\int f(x)\ dx = \log_e (2 + 3x) + c$.

The two illustrative cases contain an oversimplification that must be eliminated. Both were carefully chosen so as to represent the product of two functions, $u'(x)$ and $[u(x)]^\alpha$. This does not tell us what is the integral of, say, $h(x) = (2 + 3x)^4$. Since $u'(x) = 3$ if $u(x) = 2 + 3x$, the judicious use of 14.1.7.3 should convince the reader that $\int (2 + 3x)^4\ dx = \dfrac{(2 + 3x)^5}{(3)(5)}$. That is, since $u'(x)$ is just a constant, it can be factored and eliminated. More generally,

(14.2.5) If u is any differentiable function such that $u'(x) = k$, any constant other than zero, then:

PROPOSITION

$$\int [u(x)]^\alpha\ dx = \frac{[u(x)]^{\alpha+1}}{u'(x)(\alpha + 1)} + c, \quad \alpha \neq -1.$$

The proof of this is left as an exercise. The theorem does us no good, of course, if $u'(x)$ is anything other than a constant. Some tricks will be presented in the remaining parts of this chapter that will simplify this problem, if not eliminate it altogether.

Consider next the class of polynomial functions. In 13.6.1 it was seen that the derivative of a polynomial function of degree n was a second polynomial function of degree $(n - 1)$. If this conclusion is turned about, it should be clear that, for any polynomial of degree n, the integral is a polynomial of degree $(n + 1)$, and that the relation is given by the following:

(14.2.6) If a polynomial function of degree n is given by:

THEOREM

$$f(x) = \sum_{i=0}^{n} \alpha_i x^i,$$

then the integral of f is given by:

$$\int f(x)\ dx = \sum_{i=0}^{n} \frac{\alpha_i x^{i+1}}{i + 1} + c.$$

Once again, the proof is left as an exercise (which, in this case, requires Theorem 13.6.1). If the procedure of 14.2.5 is followed, it should be clear that, if u is any function such that $u'(x) = k$, any constant unequal to zero, then the proposition below is true:

(14.2.7) If u is a differentiable function such that $u'(x) = k \neq 0$, for all x, and if $f(x) = \sum_{i=0}^{n} \alpha_i [u(x)]^i$, then:

PROPOSITION

$$\int f(x)\, dx = \sum_{i=0}^{n} \frac{\alpha_i [u(x)]^{i+1}}{u'(x)(i+1)} + c.$$

In earlier chapters the exponential function was seen to play a particularly important part in social analysis as a model of growth or of decay. In a rather different context, it will become apparent that the exponential function also plays an important role in statistical theory, as a model of certain events in probability theory. In the latter context, antiderivatives take a central role; therefore, it will be useful to investigate properties of the antiderivative of the exponential function. In one sense, Theorem 13.5.3 makes this inquiry the essence of simplicity. In another, however, the situation becomes complicated. Recall from 13.5.3 that the exponential function, to the base, e, is unique in that it is its own derivative. Using this fact in reverse, it follows immediately that any function that is its own derivative must also be its own integral. That is,

(14.2.8) If $f(x) = \alpha^{ax}$ ($\alpha \neq 1$, $a \neq 0$), then:

THEOREM

$$\int f(x)\, dx = \frac{\alpha^{ax}}{a \log_e \alpha} + c.$$

In particular, if $f(x) = e^{ax}$ ($a \neq 0$), then:

$$\int f(x)\, dx = \frac{e^{ax}}{a} + c.$$

Thus, if $f(x) = e^{-x}$, then $\int f(x)\, dx = -e^{-x}$, which is an important special case in statistics.

Now, Theorem 14.2.8 provides a certain flexibility in that it allows x to be transformed by any *scalar* function. But this is not to say that it permits the exponent to appear with *any* function of x. It turns out, most unhappily, that the integral of e to any power that is an even moderately complicated function of x is incalculable by direct mathematical procedures. It also is the case, yet more unhappily, that an exponential function of e, of the general form $f(x) = e^{-x^2}$, is particularly important in statistical research. To evaluate functions of this sort, we must resort to procedures other than clean mathematical solutions. These are usually called *numerical integration procedures*. They require such steps as taking approximating functions of a simpler form or evaluating at a few convenient values of x and then playing largely by ear. Aside from recognizing that they exist, this book will ignore such numerical procedures as these.

Exercises

14.6. Evaluate $F(x)$ for each of the antiderivative systems below, given that $F'(x) = f(x)$:

(a) $f(x) = 2 - 3x^2$, $F(0) = 0$.
(b) $f(x) = 2 - 3x^2$, $F(0) = 10$.
(c) $f(x) = 4(2^x)$, $F(2) = 5$.

(d) $f(x) = \dfrac{1}{x}$, $F(e) = 1$.

(e) $f(x) = \dfrac{5}{x}$, $F(5) = 2$.

(f) $f(x) = e^x$, $F(0) = 0$.

14.7. Prove 14.2.2.

14.8. Prove 14.2.4 for $\alpha = -1$.

14.9. Prove 14.2.5.

14.10. Prove 14.2.7, using 13.6.1.

14.11. Suppose that a psychologist determines by experiment that galvanic reaction to electric shock increases with an increment in voltage by a function given by $f(x) = (2x)^{1/2}$, where x is voltage of shock and $f(x)$ is galvanic measure:

(a) If $F'(x) = f(x)$ and $F(0) = 0$, evaluate $F(x)$.
(b) Interpret F and contrast it with f.
(c) Is F monotone? Explain your answer.

14.3 Functions and the Measurement of Area

For no very obvious reason, let us consider a rectangle. Everyone knows that a rectangle is nothing more than a flat "thing" with base of length b and height, altitude, or tallness of size a. If $a = b$, the "thing" is called a *square*. Moreover, it has been drilled into all of us from early years that the area of a rectangle of base b and altitude a is exactly the number ab. All this may be quite obvious, but it is also too vague and logically imprecise for our purposes. In order to investigate the notion of area in relation to functions, a new and perhaps peculiar definition is in order.

(14.3.1) If f is any constant function given by $f(x) = \alpha$, **Definition** then the area generated by f and an interval, $I_{[a,b]}$ of real numbers such that $a < b$, is a new function, $A(f, [a, b])$, given by:

$$A(f, [a, b]) = \alpha(b - a).$$

The number $\alpha(b - a)$ corresponds intuitively to the area of a rectangle in the xy-plane bounded by the x axis, the line $y = \alpha$, and the pair of lines $x = a$ and $x = b$. Thus, the

Figure 14.1   AREA GENERATED BY CONSTANT FUNCTIONS

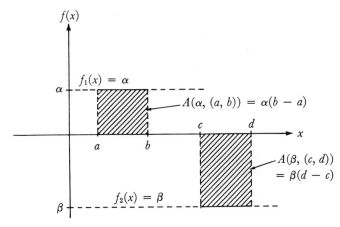

number might be thought of as a measure of square units in a rectangle. Clearly, if $\alpha < 0$, then $A(f, [a, b]) < 0$, which should be interpreted only as indicating whether the area occurs above or below the x axis. The sense of this definition as it incorporates the ideas of area and of function is represented in Figure 14.1. The areas represented by the two functions f_1 and f_2 are represented by the shaded portions of the figure. Definition 14.3.1 generates one or two properties that ought to be immediately obvious but that are nonetheless useful.

(14.3.2) If f is any constant function given by $f(x) = \alpha$,   **PROPOSITION**
then if $a \leq x \leq b$,

(1) $A(f, [a, a]) = 0$.
(2) $A(f, [a, b]) = A(f, [a, x]) + A(f, [x, b])$.

The proofs are left as exercises. Part 1 of the proposition gives a familiar axiom of geometry—"a line has no area." Part 2 says that areas are additive.

All this amounts to nothing more than making up a fancy definition for a common notion. Moreover, it is so restricted as to be almost entirely useless, because the only sort of area that it defines is that of a rectangle. Our task for the remainder of this chapter will be to develop tools by which we can measure the area generated by a large class of functions, such as polynomials and exponentials. Because of its restricted nature, 14.3.1 certainly will not do the job for us, but it does provide the necessary basis, in conjunction with the materials of Chapter 12, for the construction of these tools.

To get a first purchase on the problem and to get a preview of things to come, consider the problem of measuring the area under the graph of a simple function, but of a function that is not a constant. Consider the identity function, $f(x) = x$, on the interval $[0, 1]$. If instead this were the constant function, $f(x) = 1$, then 14.3.1 would tell us that $A(1, [0, 1]) = 1$. Since $f(x) = x$, the definition gives no information at all. Intuition and a glance at Figure 14.2 should make it clear, however, that the area $A(x, [0, 1])$ is the number $\frac{1}{2}$, since the identity function simply divides the square with unit side into two equal parts. But we cannot rely on intuition, especially with respect to more complicated functions than this.

Let us impose a series of rectangles on Figure 14.2 in such a way as to trap the area under f within their union. To do this, divide the interval $[0, 1]$ into n subintervals of equal width. Since the n subintervals are to be of equal width, each must be of width $1/n$. (Why?) This procedure, in turn, generates a set of $n + 1$ numbers, $x_i = i/n$, which

Figure 14.2   GRAPH OF

$A(x, (0, 1))$

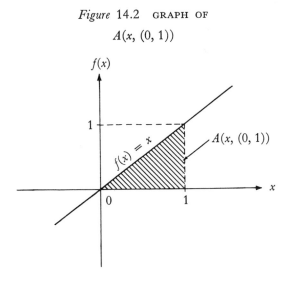

form the boundaries of the n subintervals. The ith subinterval is just $I(x_{i-1}, x_i)$. (The two preceding sentences should now be reread, *slowly*.) The altitude of the rectangle on this interval is $f(x_i) = i/n$. In Figure 14.3, ten such rectangles are imposed on the identity function over the interval $[0, 1]$. Notice that the altitude of the seventh rectangle, on the interval $[.6, .7]$, is $f(.7) = .7$, so that the area of this particular rectangle is $.7(.7 - .6) = .07$. It follows from 14.3.2.2 that the area of the total "step" construction is just the sum of the areas of the ten rectangles. To give this sum a label and, at the same time, to approximate the more general case, we have:

Definition

(14.3.3) Let S_n, an approximating sum of $A(f, [a, b])$, be

$$S_n = \sum_{i=1}^{n} f(x_i) \frac{(b - a)}{n}, \; x_i = a + \frac{i(b - a)}{n}, \; i = 0, 1, \cdots, n.$$

In the special case represented by Figure 14.3, the reader should convince himself that $n = 10$, $a = 0$, $b = 1$, and $f(x_i) = x_i = \dfrac{i}{n}$. Then, by computing and adding the ten rectangular areas, he should verify that $S_{10} = \frac{11}{20}$. (Note that $\frac{11}{20} = \frac{1}{2} + \frac{1}{20}$. The reason for this parenthetic remark will become clear in a moment.)

Figure 14.3   A FIRST MEASUREMENT OF

$$A(x, [0, 1]) \; (n = 10)$$

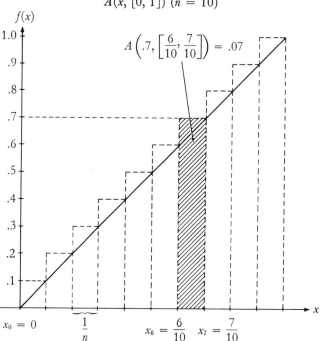

Before we explore this sum in greater detail, the reader ought to consider what would be the effect of increasing the number of intervals—that is, of allowing n to become larger. It should be clear that the larger the number of intervals into which a fixed length is divided, the smaller any subinterval must become. With this in mind, look again at Figure 14.3. The area of S_{10} was found to be $\frac{11}{20}$, which is just $\frac{1}{20}$ greater than our intuitive guess as to the area under the function f. Now, this value of $\frac{1}{20}$ ought to represent the area of the ten little triangles that jut out above the graph of f. As the number of rectangles is allowed to become larger, the area of any one of these should become smaller. (Why?) On the other hand, there would be correspondingly more such triangular areas, so that it is a moot question whether the "error area" of the approximating sum would be reduced. The question is answered, of course, by investigating the limit of S_n as n becomes large.

(14.3.4) If $S_n = \sum_{i=1}^{n} \left(\frac{i}{n}\right)\left(\frac{1}{n}\right)$, then $\lim_{n\to\infty} S_n = \frac{1}{2}$.   **PROPOSITION**

Let $S_n = \sum_{i=1}^{n} \left(\frac{i}{n}\right)\left(\frac{1}{n}\right)$.   *Proof*

(1) $S_n = \sum_{i=1}^{n} \frac{i}{n^2}$,   (By hypothesis and 6.2.1.3)

(2) $\quad = \frac{1}{n^2} \sum_{i=1}^{n} i$,   (By 7.1.2.3)

(3) $\quad = \frac{1}{n^2}\left(\frac{n(n+1)}{2}\right)$,   (By 5.6.4)

(4) $\quad = \frac{1}{2} + \frac{1}{2n}$, $\left(\text{By distributing } \frac{1}{n^2} \text{ and cancelling}\right)$

(5) $\lim S_n = \lim \left(\frac{1}{2}\right) + \dfrac{\lim}{n\to\infty}\left(\frac{1}{2n}\right)$ (By 12.1.10.6)

(6) $\quad = \frac{1}{2}$.   (By 12.1.10.1 and 12.1.5)

And this limit is just our intuitive value of the area under the graph of f in Figure 14.3. This proof should suggest that the error of the approximating sum is itself a monotone decreasing function of n.

For reasons that will eventually become apparent the limit of S_n as n goes to infinity is called the *definite integral* of $f(x) = x$ over the interval $[0, 1]$.

Look once again at (14.3.3) and consider the strategy in setting $x_i = a + (b - a)i/n$. The reader should convince himself that this identity divides the interval into n equal subintervals, each of length $(b - a)/n$ such that $x_i = a$, for $i = 0$, and $x_i = b$, for $i = n$. That is,

(14.3.5) On an interval $I_{[a,b]}$, if $x_i = a + (b - a)i/n$, **PROPOSITION**

$i = 1, 2, \cdots, n$, then $x_i - x_{i-1} = x_j - x_{j-1} = \dfrac{b - a}{n}, j = 1,$

$2, \cdots, n.$

Notice that the truth of this minor assertion depends in no way on the location of the origin of the interval, a, nor on its length, $b - a$. This subdivision of $I_{[a,b]}$ into equal subintervals imposes a certain loss of generality in advanced analysis but will create no problems in the topics considered here.

In order to see how the approximating sum of 14.3.3 works on something other than the simple interval $[0, 1]$, let us investigate it on the interval $[-1, 2]$ with respect to the more complicated function, $f(x) = x^2$.

(14.3.6) If S_n is as defined in 14.3.3, then the approx- **PROPOSITION**
imating sum of $f(x) = x^2$ on $I_{[-1,2]}$ is:

$$S_n = 3 + \frac{9(n + 1)}{2n^2}.$$

Let S_n be as defined in 14.3.3 and $f(x) = x^2$ on the in- *Proof*
terval $[-1, 2]$. Then:

(1) $x_i = -1 + \dfrac{3i}{n}$ and $\dfrac{b - a}{n} = \dfrac{3}{n}.$ (14.3.3)

(2) $S_n = \displaystyle\sum_{i=1}^{n} \left(-1 + \frac{3i}{n}\right)^2 \frac{3}{n},$ (Step 1 and 14.3.3)

(3) $= \displaystyle\sum_{i=1}^{n} \left(\frac{3}{n} - \frac{18i}{n^2} + \frac{27i^2}{n^3}\right),$ (By expanding the binomial and distributing $3/n$)

(4) $= 3 - \dfrac{18}{n^2} \displaystyle\sum_{i=1}^{n} i + \frac{27}{n^3} \sum_{i=1}^{n} i^2.$ (7.1.2)

(5) But $\displaystyle\sum_{i=1}^{n} i = \frac{n(n+1)}{2}$,

and $\displaystyle\sum_{i=1}^{n} i^2 = \frac{n(n+1)(2n+1)}{6}$.

(6) $S_n = 3 + \dfrac{9(n+1)}{2n^2}$.

The curious reader should satisfy himself that, in this case, $\lim\limits_{n\to\infty} S_n = 3$. This limit is the definite integral of $f(x) = x^2$ over the interval $[-1, 2]$.

This section has contributed little to our knowledge about areas generated by functions, but then it was not meant to. It was intended simply to introduce the reader to the idea that real functions can be used in order to build up the notion of area and to provide an initial suggestion about the way in which such areas will be measured. None of this manages to tie the idea of area back to the concept of the indefinite integral, but this will be done in the next section, where the idea of definite integral is given formal existence.

Exercises

14.12. Prove the two parts of Proposition 14.3.2.

14.13. Show by means of a graph the sense of the two parts of 14.3.2.

14.14. Construct the approximating sum, S_n, for each of the following of 14.3.3:

(a) $f(x) = x$ on $I_{[5,7]}$.

(b) $f(x) = x$ on $I_{[a,b]}$, $a < b$. $\left(\text{HINT: Recall that } \displaystyle\sum_{i=1}^{n} i = \frac{n(n+1)}{2}.\right)$

(c) $f(x) = x^2$ on $I_{[a,b]}$, $a < b$. $\left(\text{HINT: Recall that } \displaystyle\sum_{i=1}^{n} i^2 = \frac{n(n+1)(2n+1)}{6}.\right)$

(d) $f(x) = 4/3 + 2x - 4x^2$ on $I_{[0,1]}$.

14.15. Investigate $\lim S_n$ for each approximating sum of Exercise 14.14.

14.16. Another way of defining the approximating sum of 14.3.3 is to let:

$$S_n^* = \sum_{i=1}^{n} f(x_{i-1}) \frac{b-a}{n}, \text{ where } x_i \text{ is as in 14.3.3:}$$

(a) In the case of $f(x) = x$, $a = 0$, $b = 1$, $n = 10$, graph $f(x)$ and impose the approximating sum S_{10}^* on the graph.

(b) Contrast S_n and S_n^*.

(c) Investigate $S_n - S_n^*$.

(d) Prove that, under the conditions of part (a), $\lim_{n \to \infty} (S_n - S_n^*) = 0$. Interpret this result.

14.17. Proposition 14.3.4 can be approached in a different manner.

Let $R_n = \dfrac{1}{2n} \sum_{i=1}^{n} (f(x_i) - f(x_{i-1}))$. Let $f(x) = x$ on $I_{[0,1]}$, so that $f(x_i) = \left(\dfrac{i}{n}\right)$:

(a) Simplify the expression of R_n.
(b) Prove that $\lim_{n \to \infty} R_n = 0$.

(c) On a graph, show what $\dfrac{1}{2n}(f(x_i) - f(x_{i-1}))$ represents. (Hint: It is an area.)

(d) Interpret part (b) in terms of part (c).

14.18. Suppose that the marginal revenue of a commodity is given by $f(x) = 25 - 2x$, where $f(x)$ can be interpreted to mean the rate of change in demand (measured by, say, volume of sales) for the commodity given a change from the price x:

(a) Let $F(x)$ be such that $F'(x) = f(x)$. Interpret F.
(b) If $F(0) = 0$, evaluate $F(x)$. Is it reasonable that $F(0) = 0$?
(c) State a general relation between marginal and "absolute" concepts in economics—for example, between marginal profit and profit, between marginal cost and cost.

14.19. Export the economist's marginal and "absolute" concepts into your own field of specialization and relate them to antiderivative systems.

14.4 The Definite Integral

This section consists of little more than a formalization of the ideas that were developed in the preceding one. In this section only the class of continuous functions will be considered. From a mathematician's viewpoint, this restriction involves an intolerable loss of generality. In fact, the class of what are called *integrable functions* contains the continuous functions, as we shall see; but it also contains a much larger set. From the point of view of social analysis, however, this restriction is not especially confining, because relatively few of the functions involved in this kind of analysis are integrable but discontinuous.

The order of business in this section will consist, first, of developing a few minor new tools with which to work. Then, a formal definition of an integrable function will be constructed. The reader should anticipate the appearance of limit theory and notation, of ϵ's and δ's in the definition, since a definite integral is just the limit of the area of a set of rectangles as their bases become uniformly smaller. With these tools and with this definition, some properties of integrals will be investigated. In particular, the seemingly disparate ideas of antiderivative or indefinite integral and area or definite integral will be tied together by means of a most important theorem. This connection not only clears the air intellectually, it turns out to make the evaluation of many definite integrals a considerably simpler job.

Since the definite integral turns out to be the limit of a partial sum of numbers—that is, since it is the sum of an infinite series—the reader would do well to review quickly Section 12.2. One or two additional properties of sums and series will prove to be useful in our exploration of integrals. These are given by:

LEMMA

(14.4.1) Let $n + 1$ points, x_i, $(i = 0, 1, \cdots, n)$ be selected from an interval, $[a, b]$, such that $x_0 = a$, $x_n = b$, and $x_i > x_{i-1}$. Let $S_n = \sum_{i=1}^{n} f(x_i)\Delta$ and $S_n^* = \sum_{i=1}^{n} f(x_{i-1})\Delta$, Δ any real number greater than zero, f any real function.

(1) $|S_n - S_n^*| = |f(b) - f(a)|\Delta$.

(2) $|S_n - S_n^*| = \left| \sum_{i=1}^{n} [f(x_i) - f(x_{i-1})] \right|\Delta$.

The proofs are to be done as exercises. In Section 12.2 we learned something of the nature of infinite series. The next proposition is especially useful in working with infinite series that are integrals and comprises nothing more than the definition of Cauchy convergent series given in 12.2.4.

LEMMA

(14.4.2) If S_n and S_n^* are any two series such that $\lim S_n = \lim S_n^*$, then for each positive number, ϵ, there exists an integer, N, such that, for all $n > N$,

$$|S_n - S_n^*| < \epsilon.$$

Proof

Let S_n and S_n both converge to the limit α. Then there exists a positive integer, N, such that, for all $n > N$,

(1) $|S_n - \alpha| < \dfrac{\epsilon}{2}$ and $|\alpha - S_n^*| < \dfrac{\epsilon}{2}$.   (Hypothesis, 12.1.2, and 10.2.2.4)

(2) $|\mathbf{S}_n - \alpha| + |\alpha - \mathbf{S}_n^*| < \epsilon.$ (Step 1)

(3) $|\mathbf{S}_n - \alpha + \alpha - \mathbf{S}_n^*| < \epsilon.$ (Step 2 and 10.2.2.1)

(4) $|\mathbf{S}_n - \mathbf{S}_n^*| < \epsilon.$ (Cancelling on left in step 3)

One final lemma consists of little more than substituting notation in the definition of a continuous function, 12.4.1.

(14.4.3) If f is any function that is continuous on an in-   **LEMMA**
terval $[a, b]$, if $\Delta = (x_i - x_{i-1}) = \dfrac{b - a}{n}$, then for each number $\gamma > 0$ there exists a number $\delta > 0$ such that $\Delta < \delta \rightarrow |f(x_i) - f(x_{i-1})| < \gamma$.

The proof follows directly from 12.4.1 and 12.3.2. With these tools the notion of the definite integral of a function between any two points can be established.

(14.4.4) A function, f, is said to be integrable on an in-   **Definition**
terval, $[a, b]$, if and only if there exists a number A such that to each positive number ϵ there corresponds a positive integer, N, such that, for all $n > N$,

$$|A - \mathbf{S}_n| < \epsilon \quad \text{and} \quad |A - \mathbf{S}_n^*| < \epsilon,$$

where $\mathbf{S}_n$ and $\mathbf{S}_n^*$ are as defined in 14.4.1 with $\Delta = \dfrac{b - a}{n}$.

This definition requires that one be able to choose as the altitude of the rectangle with base $[x_{i-1}, x_i]$ either the number $f(x_i)$ or $f(x_{i-1})$. This precludes the possibility of the number A taking on more than one value. It is now time to introduce this number, which we can clearly interpret as the area under the graph of f between the points a and b, by its more familiar mathematical notation.

(14.4.5) If f is integrable on the interval $[a, b]$, then the   **Definition**
limit of $\mathbf{S}_n$, the number A, is defined and is noted by:

$$A = \int_a^b f(x)\, dx,$$

where A is called the *definite integral* of f between a and b, a and b are called the *lower* and *upper bounds* or limits of integration respectively, $f(x)$ is called the *integrand*, and dx is called the *index of integration*.

The reason for using the same symbol, $\int$, as in the indefinite integral will be made clear when the two are tied together by 14.4.10 below.

One fact should be clearly understood about this notation: The numbers x really have nothing at all to do with the definite integral. In Section 14.3 area was labeled $A(f, [a, b])$, and it should be clear that this means exactly the same thing as does the more conventional notation, $\int_a^b f(x)\ dx$. But the number x does not appear at all in $A(f, [a, b])$ because it is not a necessary part in the determination of area. For the same reason, one could substitute any letter that he pleased for x—that is, $\int_a^b f(x)\ dx = \int_a^b f(t)\ dt = \int_a^b f(u)\ du$, and so on. On the other hand, the expression $\int_a^x f(t)\ dt$ does definitely depend on the value of x since, in this case, x stands as a limit of integration.

Now, rather than attempting to prove integrability separately for each of the major classes of functions, let us investigate the entire class of continuous functions in a single frontal attack.

(14.4.6) If a function f is continuous on an interval $[a, b]$, then it is integrable on that interval.   **THEOREM**

Let f be continuous on $[a, b]$, let $0 < \Delta = \dfrac{b - a}{n}$, and   *Proof*
let S_n and S_n^* be as defined as in 14.4.1. For each positive number, ϵ, select a number $\gamma > 0$, such that:

(1) $\gamma < \dfrac{\epsilon}{b - a}$.

By the continuity of f, to each number γ there corresponds a number, δ, such that:

(2) $\Delta < \delta \rightarrow |f(x_i) - f(x_{i-1})| < \gamma.$ (By 14.4.3)

Let n be large enough that $\Delta < \delta$. Then:

(3) $|S_n - S_n^*| = \left| \sum\limits_{i=1}^{n} [f(x_i) - f(x_{i-1})]|\Delta \right|.$ (By 14.4.1.2)

(4) $\left| \sum\limits_{i=1}^{n} [f(x_i) - f(x_{i-1})]|\Delta < \sum\limits_{i=1}^{n} \gamma\Delta. \right.$ (By step 2 and 10.2.2)

(5) $\sum\limits_{i=1}^{n} \gamma\Delta = n\gamma\Delta,$ (By 7.1.2.2)

(6) $= (b - a)\gamma < \epsilon.$ $\left(\text{Since } \Delta = \dfrac{b - a}{n} \right.$
and by step 1)

(7) $|S_n - S_n^*| < \epsilon$, and f is integrable.   (By steps 3–6 and 14.4.4 and 14.4.2)

We know now that continuous functions are integrable, but the theorem provides no hint about what the integral would look like for any specified continuous function. Moreover, it should be clear that, while 14.4.5 provides a working definition of the integral, its use in evaluation would frequently be difficult. These considerations are eliminated, however, by the so-called *fundamental theorem of the calculus*. This theorem can be proved easily enough if we first investigate some properties of integrals, all of which are immediate consequences of 14.4.5.

(14.4.7) (*Elementary Properties of Integrals*). Let f and g **THEOREM**
be any integrable functions on an interval $[a, b]$.

(1) $\int_a^a f(x) \, dx = 0.$

(2) $\int_a^b f(x) \, dx = \int_a^k f(x) \, dx + \int_k^b f(x) \, dx$, for $a \le k \le b$.

(3) $\int_a^b (f + g)(x) \, dx = \int_a^b f(x) \, dx + \int_a^b g(x) \, dx.$

(4) $\int_a^b kf(x) \, dx = k \int_a^b f(x) \, dx.$

(5) If $f(x) \le g(x)$, each $x \, \epsilon \, T \, [a, \wedge b]$,

then $\int_a^b f(x) \, dx \le \int_a^b g(x) \, dx.$

(6) $\left| \int_a^b f(x) \, dx \right| \le \int_a^b |f(x)| \, dx.$

(7) The product fg is integrable.

The proofs are left as exercises. The unusual statement of Part 7 ought to suggest that the integral of the product of two integrable functions sometimes turns out to be a cantankerous affair with no simple representation, as in the case of the sum of two integrable functions, given in Part 3.

With one more preliminary statement, we shall be able to take on the fundamental theorem.

(14.4.8) Let $G(x) = \int_a^x f(t)\, dt$, for f any integrable function on an interval $[a, b]$. Then G is continuous and differentiable on $[a, b]$, and for each $c \, \epsilon \, [a, b]$, $G'(c) = f(c)$. **THEOREM**

The proof requires only the materials of Chapter 12 but will be bypassed here (see Rudin, *Principles of Mathematical Analysis* [5], pages 98–99). The reader should recognize clearly that, as G is defined, x is no longer a dummy variable but instead, is *the* critical variable for any selected function, f, and fixed lower bound, a. Moreover, an immediate consequence of this theorem in conjunction with 14.4.7.2 is the following:

(14.4.9) If G is as defined in 14.4.8, then for $a \leq x_1 < x_2 \leq b$, **PROPOSITION**

$$\int_{x_1}^{x_2} f(t)\, dt = G(x_2) - G(x_1).$$

With this we have finally arrived.

(14.4.10) (*The Fundamental Theorem of the Calculus*). If f is any integrable function on $[a, b]$ such that $F'(x) = f(x)$ for each $x \, \epsilon \, [a, b]$, then: **THEOREM**

$$\int_a^b f(x)\, dx = F(b) - F(a).$$

Let f be integrable and $F'(x) = f(x)$ on $[a, b]$. Let $G(x)$ be as defined in 14.4.8. Then, for each $x \, \epsilon \, [a, b]$, *Proof*

(1) $\dfrac{d}{dx}[F(x) - G(x)] = 0.$ (By hypothesis, $F'(x) = f(x)$, 13.3.4.1, and since $G'(x) = f(x)$ by 14.4.8)

Thus, F and G differ by at most a constant. That is, there exists a point c such that:

(2) $G(x) = F(x) + c.$ (14.1.4)

(3) $G(a) = \int_a^a f(x)\,dx = 0.$ (14.4.7.1 and 14.4.8)

(4) $F(a) + c = 0.$ (Steps 2 and 3)

(5) $c = -F(a).$ (Step 4)

(6) $\int_a^b f(x)\,dx = G(b),$ (14.4.8)

(7) $= F(b) - F(a).$ (Steps 2 $[G(b) = F(b) + c]$ and 5)

And the tie between indefinite and definite integrals is complete. The definite integral, that is, the area under the graph of a function, f, between any two points, a and b, is just the value of the indefinite integral of f evaluated at b minus its evaluation at a. This is sometimes indicated by the following:

(14.4.11) If f is integrable on $[a, b]$ and $F'(x) = f(x)$, each $x \in [a, b]$, then we write:

$$\int_a^b f(x)\,dx = F(x)\Big]_a^b \;(= F(b) - F(a)).$$

                                                   Notation

Thus, for example, if $f(x) = 2x^3$, the integral on the interval $[0, 1]$ would be evaluated simply by locating the antiderivative of f, disregarding the additive constant, evaluating the antiderivative at the points $x = 1$ and $x = 0$, and subtracting the latter from the former.

(14.4.12) Evaluate $\int_0^1 (2x^3)\,dx$:   **Illustration**

(1) $f(x) = 2x^3 \rightarrow F(x) = \dfrac{x^4}{2}.$ (14.2.1)

(2) $\int_0^1 (2x^3) = \dfrac{x^4}{2}\Big]_0^1.$ (14.4.11)

(3) $\dfrac{x^4}{2}\Big]_0^1 = \dfrac{1^4}{2} - \dfrac{0^4}{2} = \dfrac{1}{2}.$

Thus, the area under the graph of $f(x) = 2x^3$ between the points 0 and 1 is just $\int_0^1 (2x^3)\,dx = \frac{1}{2}.$

All this makes the evaluation of integrals a vastly simpler business. Even with the fundamental theorem at our disposal, however, the evaluation of definite integrals can be extremely difficult. It was learned in Section 14.3 that some functions that are compounded from two or more simpler functions simply cannot be integrated by straightforward procedures. Nonetheless, this theorem does make the evaluation of area a possibility for many classes of relatively complicated functions.

One added trick can often lead to the solution of integral problems that defy more straightforward approaches. This is called *integration by parts* and is derived from the product rule of differentiation. Recall from 13.3.4.2 that $(fg)'(x) = f(x)g'(x) + f'(x)g(x)$. The trick in turning this identity inside out and using it in integration consists of identifying the function to be integrated as the product of one function and the derivative of a second. If this can be done, then the following theorem sometimes can be used to advantage:

(14.4.13) (*Integration by Parts*).　　　　　　　　　　　　**THEOREM**

$$\int f(x)g'(x)\, dx = f(x)g(x) - \int f'(x)g(x)\, dx.$$

Let f and g be integrable functions.　　　　　　　　　　*Proof*

(1) $(fg)'(x) = f(x)g'(x) + f'(x)g(x).$　　　　(13.3.4.2)

(2) $\int (fg)'(x)\, dx = \int f(x)g'(x)\, dx$　　　(Step 1 and
　　　　　　　　　$+ \int f'(x)g(x)\, dx,$　　　14.4.7.2)

(3) but $\int (fg)'(x)\, dx = (fg)(x) + c.$　　　(14.4.10)

(4) $f(x)g(x) = \int f(x)g'(x)\, dx + \int f'(x)g(x)\, dx.$ (Steps 2 and
　　　　　　　　　　　　　　　　　　3)

(5) $\int f(x)g'(x)\, dx = f(x)g(x) - \int f'(x)g(x)\, dx.$

We may disregard the c that appears in step 3, as it will be taken care of by the constant of integration for the unevaluated integrals. To return to the illustration of 14.4.12 for a moment, let $u(x) = 2x^3$, $f(x) = x^3$, and $g'(x) = 2$, so that $g(x) = 2x$, and $u(x) = f(x)g'(x)$. The theorem on integration by parts then tells us that:

(14.4.14) $\int u(x)\, dx = f(x)g(x) - \int f'(x)g(x)\, dx,$ **Illustration**

(1) $\qquad\qquad = (x^3)(2x) - \int (3x^2)(2x)\, dx,$

(2) $\qquad\qquad = 2x^4 - \int 6x^3\, dx,$

(3) $\qquad\qquad = 2x^4 - \dfrac{6x^4}{4} + c,$

(4) $\qquad\qquad = \dfrac{x^4}{2} + c,$

which, in indefinite form, is the same result that was obtained in 14.4.12. A comparison of these two illustrations should certainly convince one that, although the end results are identical, the labor involved in the application of this theorem actually made the job more difficult. There is simply no good rule to determine when the application of the theorem on integration by parts would simplify matters. In a very rough way it may be correct to say that, the more complicated the function to be integrated, the greater is the likelihood that integration by parts will pay off.

As a second illustration, consider the following:

(14.4.15) Evaluate $\int_0^2 xe^x\, dx$. Let $f(x) = x$ and $g'(x) = e^x$,   **Illustration**
so that $(fg')(x) = xe^x$.

(1) $f'(x) = 1$ and $\int g'(x)\, dx = e^x + c.$ (By 13.3.3.3
                                                                                                and
                                                                                                14.2.8)

(2) $\int xe^x\, dx = xe^x - \int e^x\, dx + c$

(3) $\qquad\qquad = e^x(x - 1) + c,$

(4) $\int_0^2 xe^x\, dx = e^x(x - 1)\Big]_0^2 = e^2(1) - e^0(-1)$

(5) $\qquad\qquad = e^2 + 1.$

To see how important the choice of f and g in 14.4.13 can be, the reader should try to complete this evaluation by letting $f(x) = e^x$ and $g'(x) = x$, the reverse of the choice made above. If this is done it will be seen that the result is an end-less maze.

Exercises

14.20. Prove the two parts of 14.4.1.

14.21. Prove 14.4.7, parts 1 and 2.

14.22. Use Exercise 14.21 to prove that:

(a) $\int_a^b -f(x)\ dx = -\int_a^b f(x)\ dx.$

(b) $\int_a^b \sum_{i=1}^n f_i(x)\ dx = \sum_{i=1}^n \int_a^b f_i(x)\ dx.$

(c) $\int_a^b (f - g)(x)\ dx = \int_a^b f(x)\ dx - \int_a^b g(x)\ dx.$

14.23. Prove 14.4.9.

14.24. Use 14.4.10 to provide an explicit function for each of the following:

(a) $\int_a^b a\alpha^x\ dx$

(b) $\int_a^b e^x\ dx$

(c) $\int_a^b ae^{-x}\ dx$

(d) $\int_a^b \sum_{i=1}^n \alpha_i x^i\ dx$

14.25. In statistics a function, $p(x)$, on a set of numbers $\{x\}$ to the interval $[0, 1]$, is called a density function if:

(1) $p(x) \geq 0$, all $x \in X$.

(2) $\int_{\{x\}} p(x)\ dx = 1.$

Determine whether each of the following is a density function on the interval specified. If it is not, attempt to make a transformation of the function that would convert it into a density:

(a) $p(x) = \dfrac{1}{b - a}$ on $I_{[a,b]}$.

(b) $p(x) = \dfrac{1}{4} - \dfrac{x}{3} + \dfrac{x^2}{4}$ on $I_{[3,5]}$.

(c) $p(x) = \alpha e^{-\alpha x}$ on $I_{[0,\infty]}$.

(d) $p(x) = e^{-x}$ on $I_{[0,1]}$.

(e) $p(x) = x^3$ on $I_{[0,1]}$.

14.26. To the statistician, the *average value*, μ, of a density function is given by:

$$\int_{\{x\}} xp(x) \, dx, \text{ where } \{x\} \text{ is the domain set.}$$

For each of the functions of Exercise 14.25 (or for its density equivalent), compute μ.

14.5 Multiple Integration

In Section 13.9 the topic of differentiation of multivariate functions was introduced. Now that we have available the tools with which to integrate functions, it will be useful in certain problems to investigate *integrals* of multivariate functions. Consider a function of two variables, say $f(x, y) = (x + 2y)^2$. If y were a constant rather than a variable, then the integral would make perfectly good sense and could be interpreted as the area under the graph of a function between any two specified points. But this is a multivariate function in which both x and y are variables. The graph of such a function, to be represented properly, should appear in three-dimensional space, one axis representing the set of numbers containing x, a second axis representing y and the third representing $f(x, y)$.

Rather than speaking of the area under the graph of a multivariate function, one should have to speak about its *volume*. Intuitively, then, the integral of a function of two variables can be taken to represent a measure of volume in three-dimensional space. Of course, there is nothing to prevent our considering integrals of functions of more than two variables. In a case such as this, the integral would have to represent a volume in space of more than three dimensions, called *n-dimensional Euclidian space*.

To be consistent, the integral of a multivariate function should be so defined that the integral of a function of one variable can be treated as a special case. See if the following does not accomplish this:

(14.5.1) Let R^2 be a set of ordered pairs, $\langle x, y \rangle$, such **Definition**
that $x \in I_{[a,b]}$ and $y \in I_{[c,d]}$, and let $f(x, y)$ be defined and continuous on R^2. Then let (x_i), $i = 0, 1, 2, \cdots, n$, and

(y_j), $j = 0, 1, 2, \cdots, m$, be two sequences of numbers from $I_{[a,b]}$ and $I_{[c,d]}$, respectively, such that $x_0 = a$, $x_n = b$, $x_i > x_{i-1}$, $y_0 = c$, $y_m = d$, and $y_j > y_{j-1}$. Let:

$$S_{m,n} = \sum_{i=1}^{n} \sum_{j=1}^{m} f(x_i y_j) \, \Delta x \Delta y, \quad \Delta x = \frac{b-a}{n}, \quad \Delta y = \frac{d-c}{m}.$$

$$S_{m,n}^* = \sum_{i=1}^{n} \sum_{j=1}^{m} f(x_{i-1}, y_{j-1}) \, \Delta x \Delta y.$$

Then, if there exists a number V and, corresponding to each positive number, ϵ, there exists a positive integer N, such that for $m, n > N$:

$$|V - S_{m,n}| < \epsilon \quad \text{and} \quad |V - S_{m,n}^*| < \epsilon,$$

then V is called the integral of f on R^2 and is noted:

$$V = \iint_{R^2} f(x, y) \, dy dx \text{ or, equivalently,}$$

$$V = \int_{x=a}^{b} \int_{y=c}^{d} f(x, y) \, dy dx.$$

This is indeed a complicated definition, but a careful reading should convince one that it is a perfectly straightforward outgrowth of the definition of the integral of a function of a single variable. In it, two sets of three-dimensional solids are constructed, with dimensions Δx, Δy, and $f(x_i, y_j)$ in the first and Δx, Δy, and $f(x_{i-1}, y_{j-1})$ in the second. The volume of each solid is considered to be given by the product of these dimensions: $f(x_i, y_i) \, \Delta x \Delta y$ or $f(x_{i-1}, y_{j-1}) \, \Delta x \Delta y$. The sums of these approximating volumes are examined as the base dimensions are squeezed arbitrarily close to zero by increasing the number of points x_i and y_j.

In order to evaluate multiple integrals, one must exploit antiderivative systems, as we learned in the preceding section. But since the concern here is with functions of several variables, it should not come as a shock that the antiderivatives must be with respect to *partial* derivatives. As an illustration, consider $\int_{x=0}^{1} \int_{y=1}^{2} (2x + y) \, dy dx$. This is a shorthand symbol for the phrase "the integral of the function $f(x, y) = (2x + y)$ over the values of x from 0 to 1 and over the values of y from 1 to 2." Matters are made a good deal clearer by the judicious use of brackets in the following manner:

(14.5.2)

$$\int_{x=0}^{1} \int_{y=1}^{2} (2x + y) \, dy dx = \int_{x=0}^{1} \left[\int_{y=1}^{2} (2x + y) \, dy \right] dx.$$

Now, the term in the brackets is just a function of y, with x taking on the status of a constant (note that the index of integration is dy within the brackets). Once this integral is evaluated, the variable y disappears, and what remains is a function with terms x, which now becomes a variable, and perhaps some constants. This function then is evaluated as a simple integral of a function of x. Let us see how the evaluation proceeds.

(14.5.3) Let $f(x, y) = 2x + y$.   **Illustration**

(1) $\dfrac{\partial}{\partial y} \left(2xy + \dfrac{y^2}{2} \right) = 2x + y.$ (13.9.1)

(2) $\displaystyle\int_{y=1}^{2} (2x + y) \, dy = 2xy + \dfrac{y^2}{2} \Big]_{1}^{2},$ (Step 1)

(3) $= 4x + 2 - 2x - \frac{1}{2},$
                       $= 2x + 1.5.$

(4) $\displaystyle\int_{x=0}^{1} \int_{y=1}^{2} (2x + y) \, dy dx$

                       $= \displaystyle\int_{0}^{1} \left[\int_{1}^{2} (2x + y) \, dy \right] dx,$ (14.5.2)

(5) $= \displaystyle\int_{0}^{1} (2x + 1.5) \, dx,$ (Step 3)

(6) $= x^2 + 1.5x \Big]_{0}^{1},$

(7) $= 1 + 1.5 = 2.5.$

This procedure involved the following sequence of steps: (1) locate the (partial with respect to y) antiderivative of $f(x, y)$. Call this $F_y(x, y)$; (2)–(3) Integrate $f(x, y)$ over the y region only. In this case, this means to evaluate $F_y(x, 2) - F_y(x, 1)$, which gives a function of x that can be noted $f_x(x, y)$; (4)–(7) Integrate over the X region $f_x(x, y)$.

What if the procedure of 14.5.3 were reversed? That is, what would be the result if, in the first step, the partial antiderivative with respect to x rather than y had been evaluated, and if the resulting function of y, $f_y(x, y)$, had then been integrated over the y region? Would the result have been different? In order to get a first purchase on answers to these questions, the reader ought to do exactly what has been suggested. (HINT: $f_y(x, y) = 1 + y$.) The outcome should be identical to that of the first procedure. A careful reconsideration of the definition of a multiple integral should further convince one that the results really have to be identical.

(14.5.4) $$\iint_{xy} f(x, y) \, dydx = \iint_{xy} f(x, y) \, dxdy.$$ **PROPOSITION**

Exercises

14.27. In Exercise 14.25, the statistician's density function was introduced. A joint density function is just a function, $p(x, y)$, that satisfies the same axioms as those of Exercise 14.25. Evaluate each of the following in order to determine which is a density function:

(a) $p(x, y) = \dfrac{4x + 2y}{3}$ on $X = [0, 1]$, $Y = [0, 1]$.

(b) $p(x, y) = 4x + 2y$ on $X = [0, 1]$, $Y = [0, 1]$.
(c) $p(x, y) = x^2 + y^2$ on $X = [0, 5]$, $Y = [1, 10]$.

(d) $p(x, y) = \dfrac{xy}{2,500}$ on $X = [0, 10]$, $Y = [0, 20]$.

14.28. Convert the first function that is not a density in Exercise 14.27 into a density by adjusting the function itself.

14.29. Convert the second function that is not a density in Exercise 14.27, into one that is by adjusting the upper limit of integration of X or Y.

14.30. Extend 14.5.1 into a definition of triple integration using $f(x, y, z)$.

Selected References

1. Allendoerfer, C. B., and Oakley, C. O. *Principles of Mathematics.* New York: McGraw-Hill Book Company, Inc., 1955. Chapter 12.
2. Courant, Richard. *Differential and Integral Calculus.* New York: Interscience, 1936.
3. Miller, Kenneth S. *Advanced Real Calculus.* New York: Harper & Brothers, 1957. Chapter 4.
4. Moore, John T. *Fundamental Principles of Mathematics.* New York: Rinehart and Co., 1960. Chapter 9.
5. Nielsen, Kaj L. *College Mathematics.* New York: Barnes and Noble, Inc., 1958. Pages 225–231.

6. Rudin, Walter. *Principles of Mathematical Analysis* (Revised Edition). New York: McGraw-Hill Book Company, Inc., 1964. Chapter 6.

7. Titchmarsh, E. C. *Mathematics for the General Reader.* New York: Doubleday & Co., Inc., 1959. Chapter 14.

Subject Index

Name Index